SAILBOAT BUYERS' GUIDE

Compiled and Edited by
Alan Chappell

Sea Shore Publications
Long Beach, Mississipppi

Sailboat Buyers' Guide

published by
Sea Shore Publications
211 S. Sea Shore Ave.
Long Beach, MS 39560
U.S.A.
(601) 864-4573

ISBN 0-9611342-0-8

Second Printing

Printed in U.S.A.

CONTENTS

FOREWORD

The Sailboat Buyers' Guide is a valuable reference whether you are buying a new sailboat or just dreaming. This guide is the only complete source of information on all sailboats currently in production. Photos, line drawings, specifications, and prices are presented on over 1000 sailboats. This book shows you what new sailboats are available and helps you evaluate how well each boat meets your needs.

Dreaming about your next sailboat is a very pleasant pastime, and nothing makes that fantasy more tantalizing than the Sailboat Buyers' Guide. So whether you're buying soon, or "someday", enjoy your Sailboat Buyers' Guide.

Alan Chappell

INTRODUCTION

The purpose of the Sailboat Buyers' Guide is to show you, the sailboat buyer, all the new sailboats sold in the U.S. and to provide as much information as possible about each boat to help you choose the one right for you. It is important for the consumer to be as educated as possible before making any purchase especially one as crucial as a boat. Prior to this book, there was no single source for detailed information on all sailboats in production. Sea Shore Publications has contacted hundreds of sailboat manufacturers, both large and small, to obtain information on the boats they produce. This information took months to obtain and correlate. A buyer doesn't have the time or money to devote to such extensive research. The Sailboat Buyers' Guide is a "Boat Show in a Book". It will aid you in the search for your new boat and enhance your enjoyment of sailing.

This edition includes information on 1019 sailboats of all types. The book is divided into three sections: Sailboards, Multihulls, and Monohulls. Within each section, boats are arranged by length on deck from smallest to largest. Notes and abbreviations are explained at the beginning of each section. Two indices, one by boat name and one by manufacturer, are provided to make locating any specific boat easier.

All the information presented has been provided by the manufacturers except the performance prediction ratios which were computed from the information supplied. One-third page was given to each boat at no charge to the manufacturer. Full page displays were purchased by some to allow them to describe their boats in greater detail. The comments expressed on these pages are those of the manufacturer. Under each boat listed is the manufacturer's name, address and phone number so you can contact him for brochures and names of dealers in your area.

The prices listed are subject to change without notice. Prices are for a completed boat unless kit price is stipulated. All prices are base prices and include no options. When reviewing prices, keep in mind that they can be hard to compare. What some manufacturers consider standard equipment, others treat as optional. The price listed is the lowest price available. Some optional rigs and interior layouts may be more expensive. Kit prices are especially hard to compare. Some kits include only a hull and deck, while others may represent a more complete boat. Contact the manufacturer for a list of standard equipment and options price list.

SAILBOARDS

Paul Kennedy photo

S A I L B O A R D S

Abbreviations:

cu ft	Cubic Feet
lbs	Pounds
na	Not Available
No.	Number
oz	Ounces
sq ft	Square Feet

Prices:

Prices are subject to change without notice.

Price listed includes mast and sail unless labeled otherwise.

Photos and drawings may show optional equipment.

The base price is listed. Optional rigs may be higher priced.

Windsurfer Rocket 83

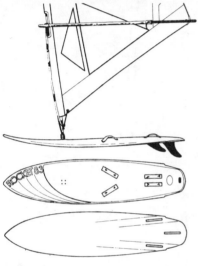

Length	8'1"
Beam	1'10"
Draft	8"
Daggerboard	none
Skeg	one 8" - two 5"
Weight	45 lbs
Bottom	4 Channel
Sail Area	50 sq ft
Sail Material	Dura-Lam
Mast Length	14'8"
Boom Length	6'6" - 7'6"
Hull Shell	Polyethylene
Core	Polyurethane Foam
Mast	Fiberglass
Boom	Aluminum/Rubber
Foot Straps	Standard
Designer	Hoyle Schweitzer
First Built	1983
Price	$1,095

WINDSURFING INTERNATIONAL INC.
1955 West 190th St.
P. O. Box 2950
Torrance, CA 90509
(213) 515-4900

Wave Rider

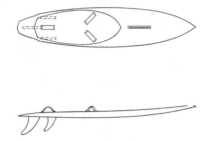

Length	8'2"
Beam	1'9"
Draft	10"
Daggerboard	none
Skeg	three
Weight	15 lbs
Sail Area	35 sq ft
Sail Material	Mylar
Mast Length	15'
Hull Shell	Fiberglass
Mast	Fiberglass
Foot Straps	Standard
Designer	Doug Haut
First Built	1982
No. Built	35
Price	$550

FLEETWOOD SAILBOARDS INTERNATIONAL
P. O. Box 1385
Santa Cruz, CA 95061
(408) 427-1235

Windsurfer Rocket 88

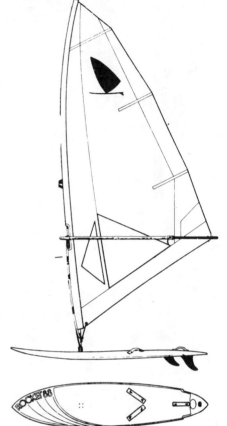

Length	8'11"
Beam	1'11"
Draft	8"
Daggerboard	none
Skeg	one 8" - two 5"
Weight	45 lbs
Bottom	Drop Winger
Sail Area	50 sq ft
Sail Material	Dura-Lam
Mast Length	14'2"
Boom Length	6'6" - 7'6"
Hull Shell	Polyethylene
Core	Polyurethane Foam
Mast	Fiberglass
Foot Straps	Standard
Designer	Hoyle Schweitzer
First Built	1982
Price	$1,075

WINDSURFING INTERNATIONAL INC.
1955 West 190th St.
P. O. Box 2950
Torrance, CA 90509
(213) 515-4900

Sky Hawk

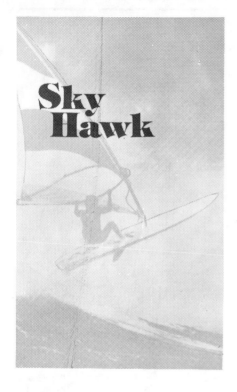

Length	9'
Daggerboard	Pivoting
No. Mast Steps	1
Surface	Non-skid
Hull Shell	ABS
Core	Foam
Foot Straps	Adjustable
First Built	1982
Price	$1,295

FUNSURF
3773 South Van Dyke
Marlette, MI 48453

Con Sailsurfer

Length	9'6"
Beam	2'1"
Hull Shell	Fiberglass
Core	Polyurethane Foam
Designer	Con Colburn
Price	$715

CON SURFBOARDS
553 Venezia Avenue
Venice, CA 90291
(213) 823-9208

Windsurfer Rocket 99

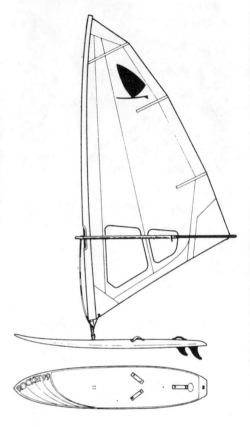

Length	9'6"
Beam	2'
Daggerboard	none
Skeg	one 8" - two 5"
Weight	40 lbs
Bottom	Flat
Sail Area	58 sq ft
Sail Material	Dura-Lam
Mast Length	14'8"
Boom Length	6'6"-7'6"
Hull Shell	Polyethylene
Core	Polyurethane Foam
Mast	Fiberglass
Boom	Aluminum/Rubber
Foot Straps	Standard
Designer	Hoyle Schweitzer
First Built	1982
Price	$1,125

WINDSURFING INTERNATIONAL, INC.
1955 W. 190th St.
P. O. Box 2950
Torrance, CA 90509
(213) 515-4900

Bic 200 S

Length	10'2"
Beam	2'1"
Skeg	Adjustable
Weight	34 lbs
Volume	7 cu ft
Sail Area	59 sq ft
Mast Length	14'9"
Hull Shell	ABS
Core	Foam
Mast	Polyester
Price	$899

BIC LEISURE PRODUCTS INC.
1070 Sherman Ave.
Hamden, CT 06514
(800) 243-6699

Windsurfer Rocket 103

Length	10'3"
Beam	2'2"
Draft	11"
Daggerboard	none
Weight	37 lbs
Bottom	Tri-fin
Sail Area	58 sq ft
Mast Length	14'8"
Boom Length	6'6"-7'6"
Hull Shell	Polyethylene
Core	Polyurethane Foam
Mast	Fiberglass
Boom	Aluminum/Rubber
Foot Straps	Standard
Designer	Hoyle Schweitzer
First Built	1982
Price	$1,165

WINDSURFER INTERNATIONAL, INC.
1955 W. 190th St.
P. O. Box 2950
Torrance, CA 90509
(213) 515-4900

Bic 180

Length	10'4"
Beam	2'2"
Daggerboard	Pivoting
Weight	34 lbs
Volume	6.3 cu ft
Sail Area	43 sq ft
Mast Length	12'6"
Hull Shell	ABS
Core	Foam
Mast	Polyester
Price	$599

BIC LEISURE PRODUCTS INC.
1070 Sherman Ave.
Hamden, CT 06514
(800) 243-6699

Highwind I Fiberglass

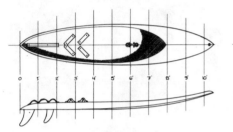

Length	10'6"
Beam	2'2"
Draft	2'1"
Daggerboard	Non-pivoting/Fiberglass
Skeg	Three
Weight	27 lbs
Sail Area	
Standard	40 sq ft
Regatta	60 sq ft
Sail Material	Dacron
Mast Length	15'
Hull Shell	Fiberglass/Kevlar
Core	Foam
Mast	Fiberglass
Boom	Aluminum/Rubber
Foot Straps	Standard
Designer	Bob Ergan
First Built	1982
No. Built	225
Price	$750

FLEETWOOD SAILBOARDS INTERNATIONAL
P. O. Box 1385
Santa Cruz, CA 95061
(408) 427-1235

Highwind Wood

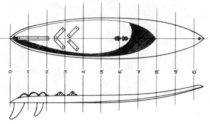

Length	10'6"
Beam	2'2"
Draft	2'1"
Daggerboard	Nonpivoting/Fiberglass
Skeg	three
Weight	30 lbs
Sail Area	
Standard	40 sq ft
Regatta	60 sq ft
Sail Material	Mylar
Mast Length	15'
Hull Shell	FRP/Wood-Veneer
Core	Foam
Mast	Fiberglass
Boom	Aluminum/Rubber
Foot Straps	Standard
Designer	Bob Ergan
First Built	1982
No. Built	289
Price	$995

FLEETWOOD SAILBOARDS INTERNATIONAL
P. O. Box 1385
Santa Cruz, CA 95061
(408) 427-1235

Speed Board

Length	10'9"
Beam	2'2"
Daggerboard	Pivoting
Skeg	3-Retracting
Weight	37 lbs
Volume	6.7 cu ft
Thickness	6"
Sail Area	65 sq ft
Mast Step	Adjustable
No. Mast Steps	2
Surface	High-Traction
Hull Shell	ABS
Core	Polyurethane
Mast	Epoxy
Boom	Aluminum
Foot Straps	Adjustable
Designer	Larry Stanley
Price	$940
	without rig

ALPHA INTERNATIONAL INC.
2832 Westin Building
2001 Sixth Avenue
Seattle, WA 98121
(206) 621-9914

Pintail Chi Chi

Snark Windjammer

Fencer

The World's First Soft Sailboard

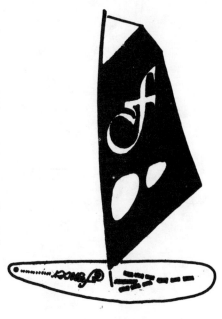

Length	10'10''
Beam	2'2''
Daggerboard	Pivoting
Weight	35 lbs
Volume	5.6 cu ft
Thickness	5''
Sail Area	65 sq ft
Mast Step	Adjustable
Surface	Traction
Hull Shell	Lupolen
Core	Foam
Mast	Epoxy
Boom	Aluminum
Foot Straps	Adjustable
Designer	Larry Stanley
Price	$970
	without rig

Length	11'
Beam	2'4''
Daggerboard	Retractable
Skeg	Variable
Weight	28 lbs
Bottom	Flat
Sail Area	45 sq ft
Mast Step	Locking
No. Mast Steps	3
Surface	Soft
Hull Shell	Foam
Core	Polyethylene
Mast	Fiberglass
Boom	Aluminum
Price	$695

Length	11'2''
Beam	2'3''
Daggerboard	Pivoting/Lexan
Skeg	Adjustable/Lexan
Volume	7.8 cu ft
Sail Area	68 sq ft
Mast Length	14'9''
Boom Length	8'
Hull Shell	Polyethylene
Core	Foam
Mast	Epoxy
Foot Straps	Standard
Designer	van der Harst
Price	$1,195

Windsurfer Star

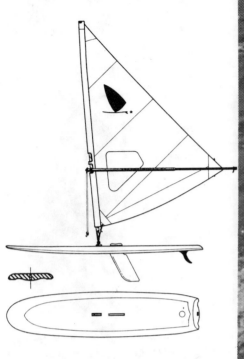

Length	11'5"
Beam	2'7"
Draft	2'
Daggerboard	yes
Weight	65 lbs
Bottom	Double Tunnel
Sail Area	51 sq ft
Sail Material	3.8 oz
Mast Length	11'5"
Boom Length	9'
Hull Shell	Polyethylene
Core	Polyurethane Foam
Mast	Aluminum
Boom	Aluminum/Rubber
Foot Straps	none
Designer	Hoyle Schweitzer
First Built	1976
Price	$895

WINDSURFING INTERNATIONAL, INC.
1955 W. 190th St.
P. O. Box 2950
Torrance, CA 90509
(213) 515-4900

Hifly 700

MUNICH/HAWAII

Length	11'8"
Beam	2'3"
Daggerboard	Pivoting
Skeg	Lexan
Weight	39 lbs
Volume	6.7 cu ft
Thickness	5"
Sail Area	64 sq ft
Sail Material	Nijlam
No. Mast Steps	2
Surface	Non-slip
Hull Shell	Polyethylene
Foot Straps	Standard
Price	$1,100

HIFLY
Robin Hill Corporate Park
Route 22
Patterson, NY 12563
(914) 878-3303

Cyclone Compact

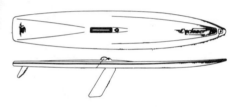

Length	11'10"
Beam	2'3"
Daggerboard	Pivoting
Skeg	Removeable
Weight	42 lb
Volume	8.3 cu ft
Sail Area	61 sq ft
Mast Length	14'9"
Mast Step	Adjustable
No. Mast Steps	1
Surface	Non-skid
Hull Shell	ABS
Core	Polyurethane
Mast	Fiberglass
Boom	Aluminum
Builder	Sainval, France
Price	$695

AMERICAN SAILBOARD CORP.
7715 Chevy Chase Dr.
Austin, TX 78752

MK 1000

The MK 1000 was directed toward the largest segment of the American market . . . the recreational user. This board is unusually light, fast and extremely bouyant. The stable hull is easy to learn on, yet its 35 lb. weight and flangeless hull make it ideal for racing and freestyle. These important features enhance the resale value. The first company to manufacture ABS sailboard hulls in the U.S., MK Engineering feels the market demands trouble-free components and therefore uses International Singer Corporation in France to supply daggerboards, cassettes, skegs and booms.

The MK-1000 has an adjustable daggerboard, drop-in skeg, toe eye, two mast step positions, non-skid across the entire deck, snap-in universal, epoxy fiberglass tapered mast, Gaastra/Horizon sails and Hawaiian type uphaul.

MK Engineering

16 REASONS TO BUY THE MK 1000

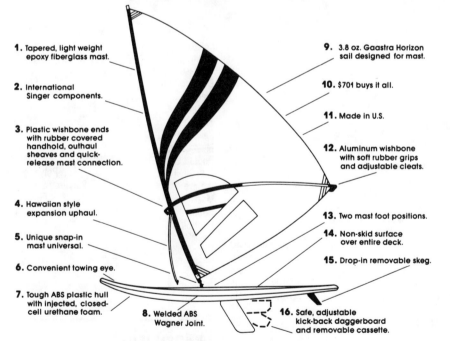

1. Tapered, light weight epoxy fiberglass mast.

2. International Singer components.

3. Plastic wishbone ends with rubber covered handhold, outhaul sheaves and quick-release mast connection.

4. Hawaiian style expansion uphaul.

5. Unique snap-in mast universal.

6. Convenient towing eye.

7. Tough ABS plastic hull with injected, closed-cell urethane foam.

8. Welded ABS Wagner Joint.

9. 3.8 oz. Gaastra Horizon sail designed for mast.

10. $701 buys it all.

11. Made in U.S.

12. Aluminum wishbone with soft rubber grips and adjustable cleats.

13. Two mast foot positions.

14. Non-skid surface over entire deck.

15. Drop-in removable skeg.

16. Safe, adjustable kick-back daggerboard and removable cassette.

If you've been boardsailing since the beginning, you've probably already used our boards. We've been making them for some of the biggest and best names in the industry. But the MK 1000 is all new. It's made tough, to last. It's made light (only 35 lbs.) to go like crazy. And it's made affordable, because this isn't a rich man's sport.

Length	11'9"
Beam	2'3"
Draft	2'1"
Daggerboard	Pivoting
Skeg	Removeable
Weight	35 lb
Sail Area	58 sq ft
Mast Length	15'
Mast Step	Quick Release
No. Mast Steps	2
Surface	Non-skid
Hull Shell	ABS
Core	Polyurethane
Mast	Epoxy
Boom	Aluminum
Designer	Heinz Wagner
First Built	1979
No. Built	4,500
Price	$695

MK ENGINEERING
43 Homestead Ave.
Stamford, CT 06902
(800) 243-3350

Freesail 3

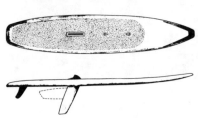

Length	11'10"
Beam	2'2"
Draft	2'4"
Daggerboard	Pivoting
Skeg	Fixed
Weight	40 lbs
Volume	7.2 cu ft
Sail Area	
Standard	60 sq ft
Regatta	68 sq ft
Storm	45 sq ft
Mast Step	Adjustable
No. Mast Steps	2
Surface	Non-slip
Hull Shell	Polyethylene
Core	Polyurethane
Mast	Epoxy
Boom	Aluminum/Rubber
Designer	O'Brien
First Built	1983
Price	$649

O'BRIEN WATER SKI
14615 NE 91st Street
Redmond, WA 98052
(206) 881-5900

Phase II

Length	11'10"
Beam	2'3"
Draft	2'1"
Daggerboard	Pivoting
Sail Area	
Standard	66 sq ft
Storm	40 sq ft
Mast Length	16'
No. Mast Steps	2
Hull Shell	Fiberglass
Core	Foam
Mast	Fiberglass
Designer	Mickey Fremons
Builder	Howmar Boats
First Built	1981
No. Built	2000
Price	$1,027

HOWMAR BOATS
983 New Durham Rd.
Edison, NJ 08817
(201) 287-8882

Windsurfer Sport

Length	11'10"
Beam	2'4"
Draft	2'
Daggerboard	Pivoting
Weight	66 lbs
Bottom	Flat
Sail Area	59 sq ft
Sail Material	3.8 oz
Mast Length	14'2"
Boom Length	9'
Hull Shell	Polyethylene
Core	Polyurethane Foam
Mast	Fiberglass
Boom	Aluminum/Rubber
Foot Straps	none
Designer	Hoyle Schweitzer
First Built	1981
Price	$890

**WINDSURFING
INTERNATIONAL, INC.**
1955 W. 190th St.
P. O. Box 2950
Torrance, CA 90509
(213) 515-4900

Blue Marlin 701

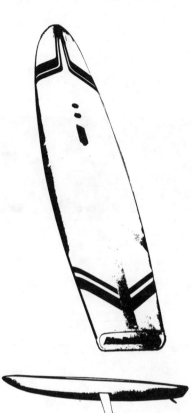

Length . . . . 12'
Beam . . . . 2'1"
Daggerboard . . . . Pivoting
Skeg . . . . Swing/Nylon
Weight . . . . 44 lbs
Thickness . . . . 6"
Sail Area
   Standard . . . . 60 sq ft
   Regatta . . . . 68 sq ft
   Storm . . . . 41 sq ft
Sail Material . . . . Tetoron
Mast Length . . . . 15'
Boom Length . . . . 9'3"
Mast Step . . . . Quick Lock
No. Mast Steps 2
Surface . . . . Non-skid
Hull Shell . . . . Fiberglass
   Core . . . . Polyurethane Foam
Mast . . . . Fiberglass
Boom . . . . Aluminum/Rubber
Foot Straps . . . . none
Builder . . . . Wah Lee, Taiwan
First Built 1981
Price . . . . na

RAY ENTERPRISES
4962 El Camino Real
Suite 206
Los Altos, CA 94022
(800) 227-8218

Curtis Hawk

Length . . . . 12'
Beam . . . . 2'2"
Daggerboard . . . . Multipositional
Skeg . . . . Pop up
Weight . . . . 42 lbs
Sail Area
   Standard . . . . 68 sq ft
   Storm . . . . 44 sq ft
Sail Material . . . . Dacron
Mast Step . . . . Locking
No. Mast Steps 2
Surface . . . . Non-skid
Hull Shell . . . . ABS
   Core . . . . Foam
Mast . . . . Epoxy
Boom . . . . Aluminum
Foot Straps . . . . none
First Built 1980
Price $995

FUNSURF
3773 South Van Dyke
Marlette, MI 48453

Free Style

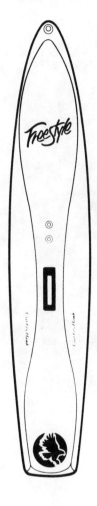

Length . . . . 12'
Daggerboard . . . . Pivoting
Skeg . . . . Retractable
Bottom . . . . Flat
Sail Area . . . . 56 sq ft
Sail Material . . . . Dacron
Mast Step . . . . Locking
No. Mast Steps 2
Surface . . . . Non-skid
Hull Shell . . . . ABS
   Core . . . . Foam
Mast . . . . Epoxy
Boom . . . . Aluminum/Rubber
Foot Straps . . . . none
First Built 1981
Price $795

FUNSURF
3773 South Van Dyke
Marlette, MI 48453

Heron

Length	12'
Beam	2'2"
Draft	2'
Daggerboard	Pivoting
Weight	42 lbs
Bottom	Flat
Sail Area	54 sq ft
Mast Length	14'
Boom Length	9'
No. Mast Steps	2
Hull Shell	Fiberglass
Core	Polyurethane
Mast	Fiberglass
Boom	Aluminum
Builder	Incomex, Israel
First Built	1979
No. Built	3000
Price	$480

Jay Hawk

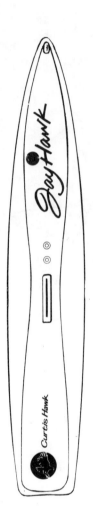

Length	12'
Daggerboard	Pivoting
Sail Area	
Standard	68 sq ft
Storm	44 sq ft
No. Mast Steps	2
Surface	Non-skid
Hull Shell	ABS
Core	Foam
Mast	Epoxy
Foot Straps	none
First Built	1982
Price	$1,075

Meritex C

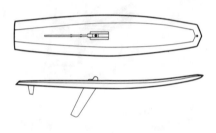

Length	12'
Beam	2'1"
Daggerboard	Fixed
Skeg	Removeable
Weight	48 lbs
Sail Area	
Standard	60 sq ft
Regatta	73 sq ft
Storm	45 sq ft
Mast Length	15'
Mast Step	Quick Connect
No. Mast Steps	1
Hull Shell	Fiberglass
Core	Foam
Mast	Fiberglass
Boom	Aluminum
Foot Straps	Optional
Designer	Stan Onerblad
Builder	JK Camera Eng.
First Built	1979
No. Built	740
Price	$999

INCOMEX
9370 Sunset Dr. A-214
Miami, FL 33173
(305) 596-1687

FUNSURF
3773 South Van Dyke
Marlette, MI 48453

MERITEX SAILBOARDS
5101 San Leandro St.
Oakland, CA 94601
(415) 635-2787

Meritex R

Length	12'
Beam	2'1"
Daggerboard	Fixed
Skeg	Removeable
Sail Area	
Standard	60 sq ft
Regatta	71 sq ft
Storm	45 sq ft
Mast Length	15'
Boom Length	7'4"
No. Mast Steps	2
Hull Shell	Fiberglass
Core	Foam
Mast	Fiberglass
Boom	Aluminum
Foot Straps	optional
Designer	Stan Onerblad
Builder	JK Camera
First Built	1980
No. Built	3800
Price	$599

MERITEX SAILBOARDS
5101 San Leandro St.
Oakland, CA 94601
(415) 635-2787

Pelican

Length	12'
Beam	2'5"
Draft	1'11"
Daggerboard	Pivoting
Weight	42 lbs
Bottom	V
Sail Area	
Standard	59 sq ft
Regatta	70 sq ft
Mast Length	15'1"
Hull Shell	ABS
Core	Foam
Designer	Pelican International
First Built	1980
Price	$905

ESKAY PLASTICS
Box 428 Le Corbusier Stat.
Chomedy Lay PQ Canada H75 129

SR — 1

Length	12'
Beam	2'2"
Daggerboard	Kick-up
Skeg	Fixed
Weight	41 lbs
Sail Area	59 sq ft
Mast Length	15'
Boom Length	9'
No. Mast Steps	2
Hull Shell	ABS
Core	Polyurethane
Mast	Fiberglass
Boom	Aluminum/Rubber
Price	$949

SAILRIDER
92 Narragansett Avenue
P. O. Box 2726
Providence, RI 02907

Waikiki

Length	12'
Beam	2'2"
Daggerboard	Pivoting
Weight	44 lbs
Volume	8.5 cu ft
Thickness	6"
Sail Area	62 sq ft
Mast Length	14'10"
Mast Step	Adjustable
Surface	High-traction
Hull Shell	Lupolen
Core	Polyurethane
Mast	Epoxy
Boom	Aluminum
Price	$950

ALPHA INTERNATIONAL INC.
2832 Westin Building
2001 Sixth Avenue
Seattle, WA 98121
(206) 621-9914

Windsurfer Comp

Windsurfer Offshore

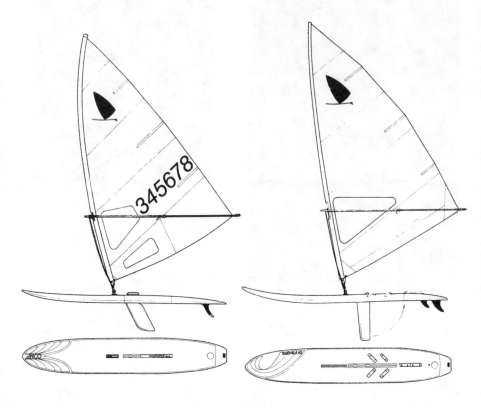

Length	12'
Beam	2'2"
Daggerboard	Pivoting
Weight	65 lbs
Bottom	Flat
Sail Area	61 sq ft
Sail Material	Dura-Lam
Mast Length	14'2"
Boom Length	9'
Hull Shell	Polyethylene
Core	Polyurethane Foam
Mast	Fiberglass
Boom	Aluminum/Rubber
Foot Straps	none
Designer	Hoyle Schweitzer
First Built	1983
Price	$1060

WINDSURFING INTERNATIONAL INC.
1955 W. 190th St.
P. O. Box 2950
Torrance, CA 90509
(213) 515-4900

Length	12'
Beam	2'2"
Daggerboard	Pivoting
Skeg	3
Weight	67 lbs
Bottom	Flat
Sail Area	65 sq ft
Sail Material	Dura-Lam
Mast Length	14'8"
Boom Length	9'
Hull Shell	Polyethylene
Core	Polyurethane Foam
Mast	Fiberglass
Boom	Aluminum/Rubber
Foot Straps	Standard
Designer	Hoyle Schweitzer
First Built	1983
Price	$1145

WINDSURFING INTERNATIONAL, INC.
1955 W. 190th St.
P. O. Box 2950
Torrance, CA 90509
(213) 515-4900

Windsurfer One-Design

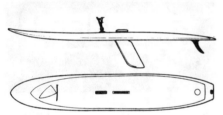

Length	12'
Beam	2'2"
Daggerboard	Non-pivoting
Weight	65 lbs
Bottom	Flat
Sail Area	61 sq ft
Mast Length	14'2"
Boom Length	9'
Hull Shell	Polyethylene
Core	Polyurethane Foam
Mast	Fiberglass
Boom	Aluminum/Rubber
Foot Straps	none
Designer	Hoyle Schweitzer
First Built	1970
No. Built	300,000
Price	$935

WINDSURFING INTERNATIONAL INC.
1955 W. 190th St.
P. O. Box 2950
Torrance, CA 90509
(213) 515-4900

Windsurfer Rocket 12

Length	12'
Beam	2'2"
Daggerboard	yes
Skeg	Twin
Weight	65 lbs
Bottom	Flat
Sail Area	59 sq ft
Sail Material	3.8 oz
Mast Length	14'8"
Boom Length	9'
Hull Shell	Polyethylene
Core	Polyurethane Foam
Mast	Fiberglass
Boom	Aluminum/Rubber
Foot Straps	Standard
Designer	Hoyle Schweitzer
First Built	1978
Price	$1130

WINDSURFING INTERNATIONAL, INC.
1955 W. 190th St.
P. O. Box 2950
Torrance, CA 90509
(213) 515-4900

Competition

Length	12'1"
Beam	2'2"
Daggerboard	Pivoting
Skeg	Retractable
Weight	44 lbs
Volume	8.5 cu ft
Thickness	6"
Bottom	Flat
Sail Area	
Standard	62 sq ft
Regatta	69 sq ft
Mast Length	14'10"
Mast Step	Adjustable
Surface	High-traction
Hull Shell	Polyethylene
Core	Polyurethane
Mast	Epoxy
Boom	Aluminum
Foot Straps	Adjustable
Price	$1095

ALPHA INTERNATIONAL INC.
2832 Westin Building
2001 Sixth Avenue
Seattle, WA 98121
(206) 621-9914

Cyclone Hawaiian

MK 2000

SR – 2

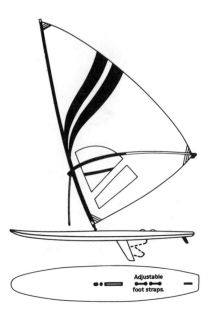

Adjustable
foot straps.

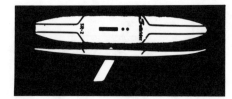

Length . . . . 12'3"
Beam . . . . 2'1"
Draft . . . . 2'1"
Daggerboard . . . . Pivoting
Skeg . . . . Removable
Weight . . . . 39 lbs
Sail Area . . . . 71 sq ft
Mast Length . . . . 15'
Mast Step . . . . Quick Release
No. Mast Steps 2
Surface . . . . Non-skid
  Core . . . . Polyurethane
Hull Shell . . . . ABS
  Core . . . . Polyurethane
Mast . . . . Epoxy
Boom . . . . Aluminum/Rubber
Foot Straps . . . . Standard
Designer . . . . Heinz Wagner
First Built 1979
No. Built 2000
Price $895

Length . . . . 12'1"
Beam . . . . 2'1"
Daggerboard . . . . Pivoting
Weight . . . . 42 lbs
Volume . . . . 8.5 cu ft
Sail Area . . . . 60 sq ft
Hull Shell . . . . ABS
  Core . . . . Polyurethane
Mast . . . . Epoxy
Foot Straps . . . . Standard
Builder . . . . Sainval, France
Price $995

Length . . . . 12'3"
Beam . . . . 2'3"
Daggerboard . . . . Kick-up
Skeg . . . . Fixed
Weight . . . . 42 lbs
Bottom V
Sail Area . . . . 68 sq ft
Mast Length . . . . 15'
Boom Length . . . . 9'
No. Mast Steps 2
Hull Shell . . . . ABS
  Core . . . . Polyurethane
Mast . . . . FRP
Boom . . . . Aluminum/Rubber
Price $1099

AMERICAN SAILBOARD CORP.
7715 Chevy Chase Dr.
Austin, TX 78752

MK ENGINEERING
43 Homestead Ave.
Stamford, CT 06902
(800) 243-3350

SAILRIDER
92 Narragansett Avenue
P. O. Box 2726
Providence, RI 02907

Freesail 1

Freesail 2

YPSI

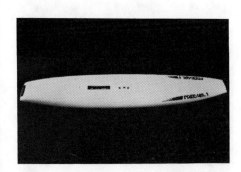

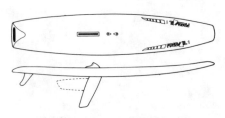

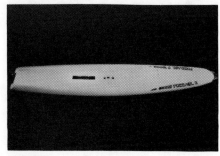

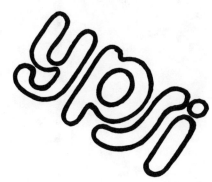

Length	12'4"
Beam	2'3"
Draft	2'4"
Daggerboard	Pivoting
Weight	46 lbs
Volume	7.9 cu ft
Sail Area	
Standard	60 sq ft
Regatta	68 sq ft
Storm	45 sq ft
Mast Step	Adjustable
No. Mast Steps	2
Hull Shell	Polyethylene
Core	Polyurethane
Mast	Epoxy
Boom	Aluminum/Rubber
Designer	O'Brien
First Built	1982
No. Built	1000
Price	$682

Length	12'4"
Beam	2'2"
Draft	2'3"
Daggerboard	Pivoting
Weight	47 lbs
Volume	7.8 cu ft
Bottom	Semi-V
Sail Area	
Standard	60 sq ft
Regatta	68 sq ft
Storm	45 sq ft
Mast Step	Adjustable
No. Mast Steps	2
Hull Shell	Polyethylene
Core	Polyurethane
Mast	Epoxy
Boom	Aluminum
First Built	1982
No. Built	1000
Price	$712

Length	12'4"
Beam	2'3"
Daggerboard	Pivoting
Volume	8.3 cu ft
Sail Area	58 sq ft
Mast Length	14'9"
Boom Length	8'
Hull Shell	Polyethylene
Core	Foam
Mast	Epoxy
Foot Straps	optional
Price	$895

O'BRIEN WATER SKI
14615 NE 91st Street
Redmond, WA 98052
(206) 881-5900

O'BRIEN WATER SKI
14615 NE 91st Street
Redmond, WA 98052
(206) 881-5900

G. S. SPORTS INC.
223 Interstate Rd.
Addison, IL 60101
(312) 543-2310

Hifly 555

Spectre

Bic 250

Length	12'5"
Beam	2'3"
Draft	2'4"
Daggerboard	Variable
Skeg	Fixed
Weight	41 lbs
Volume	7.4 cu ft
Sail Area	78 sq ft
No. Mast Steps	2
Foot Straps	Standard
Price	$1050

Length	12'5"
Beam	2'3"
Daggerboard	Kick-up
Weight	42 lbs
Sail Area	57 sq ft
Sail Material	Dacron
Mast Length	14'2"
Hull Shell	ABS
Core	Foam
Mast	Fiberglass
Boom	Aluminum
Price	$799

Length	12'6"
Beam	2'3"
Daggerboard	Pivoting
Weight	44 lbs
Volume	9 cu ft
Sail Area	
Standard	59 sq ft
Regatta	68 sq ft
Mast Length	14'9"
Hull Shell	Polyethylene
Core	Foam
Mast	Polyester
Price	$699

HIFLY
Robin Hill Corporate Park
Route 22
Patterson, NY 12563
(914) 878-3303

SAILRIDER
92 Narragansett Avenue
P. O. Box 2726
Providence, R.I. 02907

BIC LEISURE PRODUCTS INC.
1070 Sherman Ave.
Hamden, CT 06514
(800) 243-6699

Brise

Crit 600

Dufour Wing

Length	12'6"
Beam	2'3"
Daggerboard	Pivoting
Skeg	Adjustable
Volume	8.8 cu ft
Sail Area	65 sq ft
Sail Material	Mylar
Mast Length	14'9"
Boom Length	8'
Hull Shell	Polyethylene
Core	Foam
Mast	Epoxy
Foot Straps	optional
Price	$1,095

Length	12'6"
Beam	2'5"
Draft	3'4"
Daggerboard	Pivoting
Skeg	Fixed
Weight	46 lbs
Volume	9.5 cu ft
Sail Area	65 sq ft
Mast Length	15'
Mast Step	Adjustable
No. Mast Steps	2
Hull Shell	ABS
Mast	Fiberglass
Designer	Crit, France
Builder	Crit, France
First Built	1979
No. Built	10,000
Price	$849

Length	12'6"
Beam	2'3"
Daggerboard	Pivoting
Weight	41 lbs
Volume	7 cu ft
Sail Area	
Standard	59 sq ft
Regatta	68 sq ft
Mast Length	14'9"
Hull Shell	ABS
Core	Foam
Mast	Polyester
Price	$799

Hifly 500

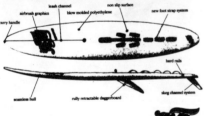

carry handle
leash channel
airbrush graphics
blow molded polyethylene
non slip surface
new foot strap system
hard rails
seamless hull
fully retractable daggerboard
skeg channel system

MUNCH/HAWAII

Length	12'6"
Beam	2'3"
Daggerboard	Pivoting
Weight	41 lbs
Volume	7.9 cu ft
Thickness	5"
Sail Area	72 sq ft
Sail Material	Nijlam
No. Mast Steps	1
Surface	Non-slip
Hull Shell	Polyethylene
Foot Straps	Standard
Price	$1,150

HIFLY
Robin Hill Corporate Park
Route 22
Patterson, NY 12563
(914) 878-3303

Meritex Div II

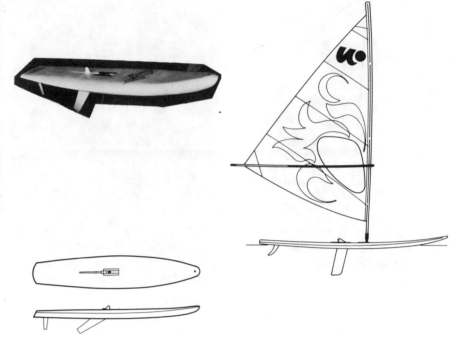

Length	12'6"
Beam	2'
Daggerboard	Pivoting
Skeg	Removeable
Sail Area	
Standard	60 sq ft
Regatta	73 sq ft
Storm	45 sq ft
Mast Length	15'
Mast Step	Quick Connect
No. Mast Steps	1
Hull Shell	Fiberglass
Core	Foam
Mast	Fiberglass
Boom	Aluminum
Designer	J-K Camera Eng.
Builder	J-K Camera Eng.
Price	$1,199

MERITEX SAILBOARDS
5101 San Leandro St.
Oakland, CA 94601
(415) 635-2787

Wayler

Length	12'6"
Beam	2'2"
Daggerboard	Adjustable
Skeg	Adjustable
Volume	8.8 cu ft
Sail Area	
Standard	64 sq ft
Regatta	71 sq ft
Storm	49 sq ft
Mast Length	14'9"
Boom Length	8'6"
Hull Shell	Polyethylene
Mast	Epoxy
Designer	Van
Builder	Wayler, Holland
First Built	1981
No. Built	25,000
Price	$995

G. S. SPORTS INC.
223 Interstate Rd.
Addison, IL 60101
(312) 543-2310

Crit 560

Length	12'8''
Beam	2'5'
Draft	3'
Daggerboard	Pivoting
Skeg	Fixed
Weight	46 lbs
Volume	8.5 cu ft
Sail Area	60 sq ft
Mast Length	15'
Mast Step	Adjustable
No. Mast Steps	2
Hull Shell	Polyethylene
Mast	Fiberglass
Designer	Crit, France
Builder	Crit, France
First Built	1980
No. Built	12,000
Price	$695

THE ROMNEY GROUP, INC.
165-B New Boston St.
Woburn, MA 01801
(617) 935-6802

Crit 630

Length	12'8''
Beam	2'5''
Draft	3'4''
Daggerboard	Pivoting
Skeg	Fixed
Weight	42 lbs
Volume	8.5 cu ft
Bottom	Flat
Sail Area	70 sq ft
Sail Material	Dacron
Mast Length	15'
Mast Step	Adjustable
No. Mast Steps	2
Hull Shell	Fiberglass
Core	Foam
Mast	Fiberglass
Foot Straps	none
Designer	Crit, France
Builder	Crit, France
First Built	1980
No. Built	10,000
Price	$1,195

THE ROMNEY GROUP, INC.
165-B New Boston St.
Woburn, MA 01801
(617) 935-6802

Cyclone
Grand Bahama

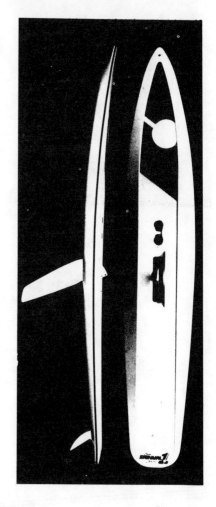

Length	12'8'
Beam	2'3''
Daggerboard	Pivoting
Weight	46 lbs
Volume	9.2 cu ft
Sail Area	60 sq ft
No. Mast Steps	2
Hull	ABS
Core	Polyurethane
Mast	Fiberglass
Builder	Sainval, France
Price	$895

AMERICAN SAILBOARD CORP.
7715 Chevy Chase Dr.
Austin, TX 78752

Cyclone Mark II

Length	12'8"
Beam	2'1"
Daggerboard	Pivoting
Skeg	Removeable
Weight	46 lbs
Sail Area	61 sq ft
Mast Length	14'9"
Mast Step	Adjustable
No. Mast Steps	2
Surface	Non-skid
Hull Shell	ABS
Core	Polyurethane
Mast	Fiberglass
Boom	Aluminum
Builder	Sainval, France
Price	$795

AMERICAN SAILBOARD CORP.
7715 Chevy Chase Dr.
Austin, TX 78752

Hifly 300

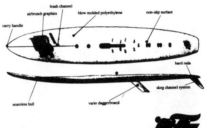

MUNICH/HAWAII

Length	12'8"
Beam	2'4"
Daggerboard	Variable
Weight	41 lbs
Volume	8.5 cu ft
Thickness	6"
Bottom	V
Sail Area	72 sq ft
No. Mast Steps	2
Surface	Non-slip
Hull Shell	Polyethylene
Foot Straps	optional
Price	$850

HIFLY
Robin Hill Corporate Park
Route 22
Patterson, NY 12563
(914) 878-3303

Sea Hawk

Length	12'8"
Beam	2'2"
Daggerboard	Multiposition
Thickness	6"
Sail Area	
Standard	68 sq ft
Storm	44 sq ft
No. Mast Steps	2
Surface	Non-skid
Hull Shell	ABS
Core	Foam
Mast	Epoxy
Boom	Aluminum/Rubber
First Built	1982
Price	$875

FUNSURF
3773 South Van Dyke
Marlette, MI 48453

Bic Ken Winner

Professional

Surfsprint

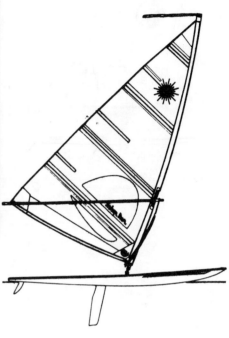

Length	12'9"
Beam	2'1"
Daggerboard	Pivoting
Weight	46 lbs
Volume	8.5 cu ft
Sail Area	68 sq ft
Mast Length	14'9"
Hull Shell	ABS
Core	Foam
Mast	Aluminum
Price	$999

Length	12'9"
Beam	2'2"
Daggerboard	Pivoting
Skeg	Retractable
Weight	46 lbs
Volume	8.8 cu ft
Thickness	6"
Sail Area	69 sq ft
Mast Length	14'10"
Mast Step	Adjustable
Surface	Traction Coated
Hull Shell	Polyethylene
Core	Polyurethane
Mast	Epoxy
Boom	Aluminum
Price	$1,250

Length	12'9"
Beam	2'3"
Daggerboard	Pivoting
Skeg	Retractable
Weight	46 lbs
Sail Area	
Standard	61 sq ft
Regatta	68 sq ft
Storm	50 sq ft
Hull Shell	ABS
Core	Foam
Foot Straps	none
First Built	1980
Price	$1,045

BIC LEISURE PRODUCTS INC.
1070 Sherman Avenue
Hamdam, CT 06514
(800) 243-6699

ALPHA INTERNATIONAL INC.
2832 Westin Building
2001 Sixth Avenue
Seattle, WA 98121
(206) 621-9914

PERFORMANCE SAILCRAFT
824 W. 18th St.
Costa Mesa, CA 92627

Windsurfer Sprint

Windsurfer Win

Blue Marlin 702

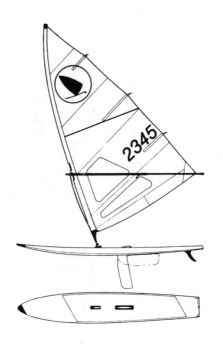

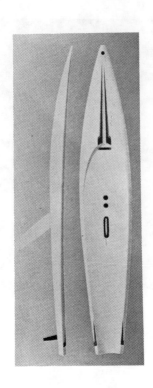

Length	12'9''
Beam	2'1''
Daggerboard	Pivoting
Weight	52 lbs
Bottom	V
Sail Area	65 sq ft
Mast Length	14'8''
Boom Length	9'6''
Hull Shell	Polyethylene
Core	Polyurethane Foam
Mast	Fiberglass
Boom	Aluminum/Rubber
Foot Straps	none
Designer	Hoyle Schweitzer
First Built	1981
Price	$1,260

Length	12'9''
Beam	2'2''
Daggerboard	Pivoting
Weight	69 lbs
Bottom	Round
Sail Area	65 sq ft
Sail Material	Dura-Lam
Mast Length	14'8''
Boom Length	9'
Hull Shell	Polyethylene
Core	Polyurethane Foam
Mast	Fiberglass
Boom	Aluminum/Rubber
Foot Straps	none
Designer	Hoyle Schweitzer
First Built	1983
Price	$1,195

Length	12'10''
Beam	2'2''
Daggerboard	Pivoting/Fiberglass
Skeg	Fixed/Nylon
Weight	44 lbs
Thickness	6''
Sail Area	
Standard	60 sq ft
Regatta	68 sq ft
Storm	41 sq ft
Sail Material	Tetoron
Mast Length	15'
Boom Length	9'2''
No. Mast Steps	2
Surface	Non-skid
Hull Shell	Fiberglass
Core	Polyurethane Foam
Mast	Fiberglass
Boom	Aluminum/Rubber
Foot Straps	none
Builder	Wah Lee, Taiwan
First Built	1981
Price	na

WINDSURFING INTERNATIONAL, INC.
1955 W. 190th St.
P. O. Box 2950
Torrance, CA 90509
(213) 515-4900

WINDSURFING INTERNATIONAL, INC.
1955 W. 190th St.
P. O. Box 2950
Torrance, CA 90509
(213) 515-4900

RAY ENTERPRISES
4962 El Camino Real
Suite 206
Los Altos, CA 94022
(800) 227-8218

Cyclone Competition

Phantom

Crit 650

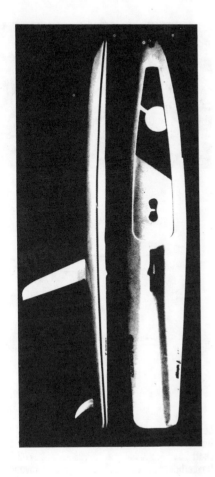

Length	12'10"
Beam	2'4"
Daggerboard	Pivoting
Weight	46 lbs
Volume	11.3 cu ft
Sail Area	70 sq ft
No. Mast Steps	2
Hull Shell	ABS
Core	Polyurethane
Mast	Epoxy
Builder	Sainval, France
Price	$1,300

Length	12'10"
Beam	2'1"
Daggerboard	Pivoting/Wood
Skeg	Retracting
Weight	40 lbs
Volume	9.9 cu ft
Thickness	8"
Bottom	Round
Sail Area	69 sq ft
Mast Length	14'10"
Mast Step	Adjustable
Surface	High-Traction
Hull Shell	Lupolen
Core	Polyurethane
Mast	Aluminum
Boom	Aluminum
Price	$1,495

Length	13'
Beam	2'4"
Draft	3'4"
Daggerboard	Wood
Skeg	Adjustable
Weight	44 lbs
Volume	10.9 cu ft
Sail Area	70 sq ft
Mast Length	15'
Mast Step	Adjustable
No. Mast Steps	2
Hull Shell	Fiberglass
Core	Foam
Mast	Aluminum
Designer	Crit, France
Builder	Crit, France
First Built	1980
No. Built	8000
Price	$1,495

Crit D2

Turbo

Pan Am

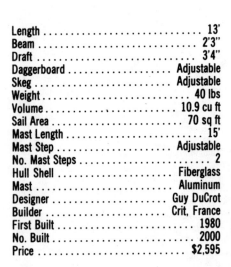

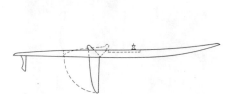

Length	13'
Beam	2'3"
Draft	3'4"
Daggerboard	Adjustable
Skeg	Adjustable
Weight	40 lbs
Volume	10.9 cu ft
Sail Area	70 sq ft
Mast Length	15'
Mast Step	Adjustable
No. Mast Steps	2
Hull Shell	Fiberglass
Mast	Aluminum
Designer	Guy DuCrot
Builder	Crit, France
First Built	1980
No. Built	2000
Price	$2,595

Length	13'
Beam	2'2"
Draft	2'6"
Daggerboard	Pivoting
Volume	8.8 cu ft
Sail Area	70 sq ft
Mast Length	15'
No. Mast Steps	3
Hull Shell	Polyethylene
Mast	Fiberglass
Builder	Spanel
First Built	1980
No. Built	5000
Price	$895

Length	13'2"
Beam	2'1"
Draft	2'2"
Daggerboard	Pivoting
Skeg	One
Weight	39 lbs
Sail Area	
Standard	60 sq ft
Regatta	75 sq ft
Sail Material	Mylar
Mast Length	17'
Hull Shell	Fiberglass
Mast	Carbon
Foot Straps	none
Designer	Ken Winner
First Built	1982
No. Built	25
Price	$1,700

THE ROMNEY GROUP
165-B New Boston St.
Woburn, MA 01801
(617) 935-6802

SHOREWIND INC.
701 S. Highlands Drive
Hollywood, FL 33021

**FLEETWOOD SAILBOARDS
INTERNATIONAL**
P. O. Box 1385
Santa Cruz, CA 95061
(408) 427-1235

MULTIHULLS

Abbreviations:

Alum .... Aluminum
cb .... Centerboard
Cockpit .... Cockpit Length
db .... Daggerboard
Disp .... Displacement
dn .... Down
FR .... Fractional
FRP .... Fiberglass
Fr. Water .... Fresh Water
Fuel Cap .... Fuel Capacity
gal .... Gallons
hp .... Horsepower
Ht .... Height
inbd .... Inboard
lbs .... Pounds
LOA .... Length Overall
LOD .... Length on Deck
LWL .... Length at Waterline
MH .... Masthead
na .... Not Available
No. .... Number
outbd .... Outboard
opt .... Optional
Pos Float .... Positive Floatation
SA .... Sail Area
sq ft .... Square Feet

Prices:

Prices are subject to change without notice.

Price listed is for a completed boat unless specifically labeled kit price.

Photos and drawings may show optional equipment.

The base price is listed. Optional rigs or layouts may be higher priced.

Note:

For all performance prediction ratios (SA/DISP, DISP/LWL), if an item in the ratio is listed more than once, the first value was used to compute the ratio. That is, if two sail areas are listed, the first one was used for the SA/DISP ratio.

Topcat

LOD	9'1"	Hull	FRP
LWL	na	Spar	Alum
Beam	5'1"	Pos Float	yes
Draft	na	SA/Disp	36.2
Disp	110 lbs	1 Design	yes
Sail Area		Price	$1,125
Cat	52 sq ft		with sails
Mast	unstayed		

VANDESTADT & McGRUER LTD.
Box 7, Owen Sound
Ontario, Canada N4K 5P1
(519) 376-8548

Doodle Cat

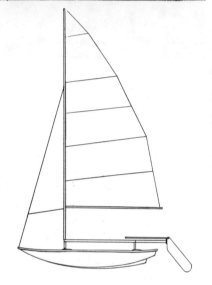

LOD	12'	Hull	FRP
LWL	11'	Deck	FRP
Beam	7'2"	Spar	Alum
Draft	7"	Pos Float	yes
Disp	150 lbs	SA/Disp	56.7
Sail Area		Disp/LWL	50
Sloop	100 sq ft	Designer	Furman Shaw
Mast Ht	19'	First Built	1970
		No. Built	25
		1 Design	yes
		Price	$1,695
			with sails

AQUA MOTION INDUSTRIES
P. O. Box 884
Lansdale, PA 19446
(215) 362-8016

Aqua Cat

LOD	12'2"	Hull	FRP/Foam
LWL	12'2"	Deck	FRP/Foam
Beam	6'	Spar	Alum
Draft		Pos Float	yes
db up	5"	SA/Disp	47.9
db dn	2'	Disp/LWL	40
Disp	165 lbs	First Built	1961
Sail Area		No. Built	17,000
Cat	90 sq ft	Price	na
Mast Ht	22'		

AMERICAN SAIL
7325 Pepperdam Ave.
Pepperdam Industrial Park
Charleston, SC 29405
(803) 552-8548

Cheshire

LOD . . . . 14'	Hull . . . . FRP
LWL . . . . na	Deck . . . . FRP
Beam . . . . 6'5"	SA/Disp 66.5
Draft	Price $3,700
cb up . . . . 5"	with sails
cb dn . . . . . . 2'1"	
Disp . . . . . . 185 lbs	
Sail Area	
Sloop . . . . 135 sq ft	
Mast Ht . . . . 21'	

FIBERGLASS UNLIMITED
2212 S. Miami Blvd.
Durham, NC 27703
(919) 596-2887

Hobie 14

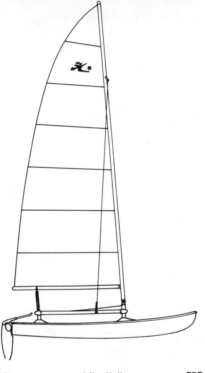

LOD . . . . 14'	Hull . . . . FRP
LWL . . . . 13'5"	Deck . . . . FRP
Beam . . . . 7'8"	Spar . . . . Alum
Draft	Pos Float . . . . . . yes
Rudder up . . . . . 8"	SA/Disp 48.9
Rudder dn . . . 2'6"	Disp/LWL 44
Disp . . . . . . 240 lbs	Designer . Hobie Alter
Sail Area	First Built 1969
Cat . . . . . 118 sq ft	1 Design . . . . . . yes
Mast Ht . . . . . . 24'3"	Price $1,995
	with sails

HOBIE CAT
Box 1008, 4925 E. Oceanside Blvd.
Oceanside, CA 92054
(714) 758-9100

Hobie 14 Turbo

LOD . . . . 14'	Hull . . . . FRP
LWL . . . . 13'5"	Deck . . . . FRP
Beam . . . . 7'8"	Spar . . . . Alum
Draft	Pos Float . . . . . . yes
Rudder up . . . . . 8"	SA/Disp 61.3
Rudder dn . . . 2'6"	Disp/LWL 44
Disp . . . . . . 240 lbs	Designer . Hobie Alter
Sail Area	First Built 1981
Sloop . . . . 148 sq ft	1 Design . . . . yes
Mast Ht . . . . . . 24'3"	Price $2,995
	with sails

HOBIE CAT
Box 1008, 4925 E. Oceanside Blvd.
Oceanside, CA 92054
(714) 758-9100

Trac 14 Catamaran

Aqua Cat II

Prindle 15

LOD .... 14'1"	Hull .... FRP
LWL .... na	Deck .... FRP
Beam .... 7'6"	Spar .... Alum
Draft .... 6"	Pos Float ...... yes
Disp ...... 195 lbs	SA/Disp 70.4
Sail Area	Designer
Sloop .... 148 sq ft	R. MacFarland
Mast Ht ...... 22'8"	First Built 1977
	1 Design .... yes
	Price $2,695
	with sails

LOD .... 14'4"	Hull ...... FRP/Foam
LWL .... 14'4"	Deck .... FRP/Foam
Beam .... 6'	Spar .... Alum
Draft .... 8"	Pos Float ...... yes
Disp ...... 195 lbs	SA/Disp 50
Sail Area	Disp/LWL 30
Cat ..... 105 sq ft	Price $1,995
Mast Ht .... 25'	with sails

LOD .... 15'	Hull ...... FRP/Foam
LWL .... 14'	Deck ..... FRP/Foam
Beam .... 8'	Spar .... Alum
Draft .... 7"	Pos Float .... no
Disp ...... 260 lbs	SA/Disp 55.8
Sail Area	Disp/LWL 42
Cat ..... 142 sq ft	Designer
Mast Ht .... 25'	Geoff Prindle
	First Built 1979
	No. Built 1000
	1 Design .... yes
	Price $2,795
	with sails

Sea Spray 15

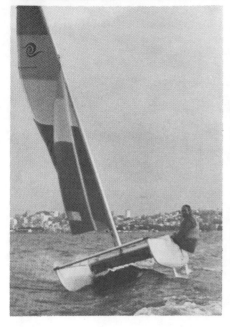

LOD . . . . 15'	Hull . . . . FRP
LWL . . . . 14'	Deck . . . . FRP
Beam . . . . 6'5"	Spar . . . . Alum
Draft	Pos Float . . . . yes
db up . . . . 6"	SA/Disp 60.5
db dn . . . . . . 2'3"	Disp/LWL 30
Disp . . . . . . 190 lbs	Designer . Alan Arnold
Sail Area	First Built 1966
Sloop . . . . 125 sq ft	No. Built 7000
Mast Ht . . . . . . 20'3"	1 Design . . . . . . yes
	Price $2,835
	with sails

DYNACAT
P. O. Box 4846
Foster City, CA 94404
(415) 573-1955

Spark

LOD . . . . 15'	Hull . . . . FRP
LWL . . . . na	Deck . . . . FRP
Beam . . . . 6'11"	Spar . . . . Alum
Draft . . . . na	SA/Disp 49
Disp . . . . . . 230 lbs	Designer
Sail Area	Rodney March
Cat . . . . . . 115 sq ft	Builder
	Panthercraft, England
	Price . . . . na

SAILCRAFT — OLYMPIC
3 Davey St.
Simsbury, CT 06070
(203) 658-5052

Sundowner

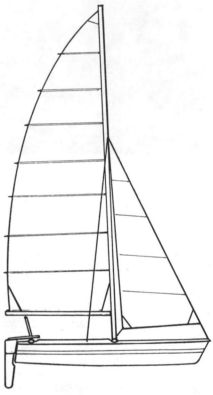

LOD . . . . 15'	Hull . . . . FRP
LWL . . . . na	Deck . . . . FRP
Beam . . . . 7'11"	Spar . . . . Alum
Draft . . . . 6"	Pos Float . . . . yes
Disp . . . . . . 230 lbs	SA/Disp 66.9
Sail Area	First Built 1979
Sloop . . . . 157 sq ft	1 Design . . . . . . yes
Mast Ht . . . . . . 25'6"	Price $2,595
	with sails

SUNDOWNER INDUSTRIES
292 South State St.
Otisville, MI 48463
(313) 631-4607

Windspeed 15

Windspeed International developed the Windspeed 15 to be the best catamaran value available. Regardless of where you live, you will find the Windspeed offers the top in catamaran technology at the lowest price around.

Specially designed hand layed symmetrical hulls (no boards) give the performance and flotation customary in symmetrical designs but without the problems inherent with daggerboards.

Our large one piece mesh trampoline provides seating for a family of four, yet the Windspeed can be easily rigged, launched and sailed by one person. For safety all Windspeeds have 100% flotation.

A boomless main sail eliminates being hit while tacking and gives plenty of room under the main sail for people.

Modern technology has allowed us to provide the newest in catamaran features at an outstanding low price.
* colored main & jib sails standard
* deep symmetric hulls (no boards)
* built in ice box & storage
* boomless main sail (full battens)
* large seating area (tent option)
* 8 bolt cross bar design for sturdiness

Windspeed International is looking for dealers from coast to coast or individuals wishing to represent us in their area. If you don't already have a Windspeed dealer in your area, we expect to have one soon. "LET THE WIND SPEED YOU ALONG"

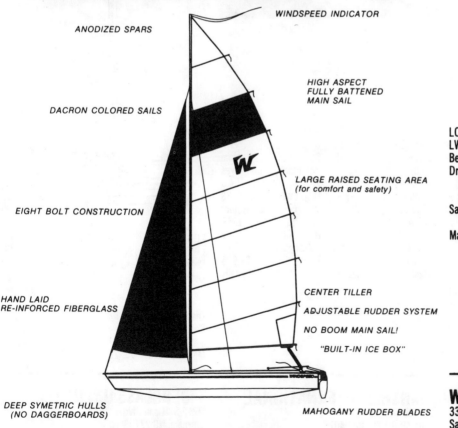

ANODIZED SPARS

WINDSPEED INDICATOR

HIGH ASPECT FULLY BATTENED MAIN SAIL

DACRON COLORED SAILS

LARGE RAISED SEATING AREA (for comfort and safety)

EIGHT BOLT CONSTRUCTION

HAND LAID RE-INFORCED FIBERGLASS

CENTER TILLER

ADJUSTABLE RUDDER SYSTEM

NO BOOM MAIN SAIL!

"BUILT-IN ICE BOX"

DEEP SYMETRIC HULLS (NO DAGGERBOARDS)

MAHOGANY RUDDER BLADES

AN OUTSTANDING VALUE

LOD	15'3"	Hull	FRP
LWL	14'4"	Deck	FRP
Beam	7'7"	Spar	Alum
Draft		Pos Float	yes
Rudder up	8"	SA/Disp	59.8
Rudder dn	10"	Designer	
Sail Area			Steve Kincaid
Sloop	160 sq ft	1 Design	yes
Mast Ht	25'	Kit	$1,996
		Price	$2,098
			with sails

WINDSPEED INTERNATIONAL
3302 Jewell St.
San Diego, CA 92109
(714) 273-7245

Supercat 15

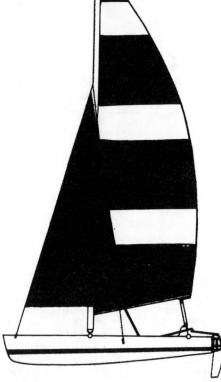

LOD	15'3"	Hull	FRP
LWL	na	Deck	FRP
Beam	8'	Spar	Alum
Draft		SA/Disp	73.8
Rudder up	10"	1 Design	yes
Rudder dn	2'	Price	$4,490
Disp	305 lbs		with sails
Sail Area			
Sloop	209 sq ft		
Mast Ht	26'		

BOSTON WHALER INC.
P. O. Box 10184
Riviera Beach, FL 33404
(305) 842-5171

Kalia CT

LOD	15'6"	Hull	FRP
LWL	14'	Deck	FRP
Beam	8'	Spar	Alum
Draft		Pos Float	yes
db up	4"	SA/Disp	54.6
db dn	2'6"	Disp/LWL	38
Disp	235 lbs	Designer	Ron Holder
Sail Area		First Built	1977
Sloop	130 sq ft	No. Built	85
Cat	95 sq ft	1 Design	yes
Mast Ht	21'6"	Price	$1,995
Mast	unstayed		with sails

BANSHEE INTERNATIONAL
12186 Winton Way
Los Altos Hills, CA 94022
(415) 969-3334

Isotope

LOD	16'	Hull	FRP
LWL	na	Deck	FRP
Beam	7'4"	SA/Disp	70
Draft		Price	$4,250
cb up	6"		with sails
cb dn	2'6"		
Disp	275 lbs		
Sail Area			
Sloop	185 sq ft		
Mast Ht	26'		

FIBERGLASS UNLIMITED
2212 S. Miami Blvd.
Durham, NC 27703
(919) 596-2887

Prindle 16

LOD	16'	Hull	FRP/Foam
LWL	15'	Deck	FRP/Foam
Beam	8'	Spar	Alum
Draft	7"	Pos Float	no
Disp	300 lbs	SA/Disp	67.5
Sail Area		Disp/LWL	40
Sloop	189 sq ft	Designer	
Mast Ht	26'		Geoff Prindle
		First Built	1972
		No. Built	7000
		1 Design	yes
		Price	$3,595
			with sails

SURFGLAS
1810 E. Borchard
Santa Ana, CA 92705

Super — 16

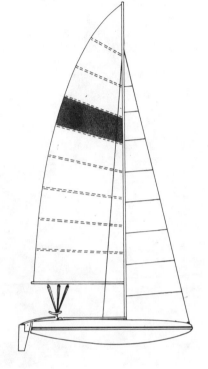

LOD	16'5"	Hull	Alum or Fg
LWL	na	Deck	Alum or Fg
Beam	8'	Spar	Alum
Draft	10"	Pos Float	yes
Disp	300 lbs	SA/Disp	78.5
Sail Area		Price	$3,395
Sloop	220 sq ft		with sails

GREAT LAKES SPORTS MFG.
480 S. Green Rd.
Cleveland, OH 44121
(216) 481-6895

Hobie 16

LOD	16'7"	Hull	FRP
LWL	16'	Deck	FRP
Beam	7'11"	Spar	Alum
Draft		Pos Float	yes
Rudder up	10"	SA/Disp	71.6
Rudder dn	2'6"	Disp/LWL	37
Disp	340 lbs	Designer . Hobie Alter
Sail Area		First Built	1971
Sloop	218 sq ft	1 Design	yes
Mast Ht	28'3"	Price	$3,395
			with sails

HOBIE CAT
Box 1008, 4925 E. Oceanside Blvd.
Oceanside, CA 92054
(714) 758-9100

G—Cat 5.0 Meter

Nacra 5.0

Nacra 5.2

LOD .... 16'8''	Hull .... FRP		
LWL .... 15'6''	Deck .... FRP		
Beam .... 8'	Spar .... Alum		
Draft .... na	Pos Float .... yes		
Disp ...... 340 lbs	SA/Disp 69		
Sail Area	Disp/LWL 40		
Sloop .... 210 sq ft	Designer		
Mast Ht .... 27'	Hans Geissler		
	First Built 1976		
	No. Built 1200		
	1 Design .... yes		
	Price $3,995		
	with sails		

LOD .... 16'8''	Hull .... FRP
LWL .... 16'8''	Deck .... FRP
Beam .... 8'	Spar .... Alum
Draft	Pos Float .... yes
Rudder up ..... 9''	SA/Disp 66.3
Rudder dn ... 2'3''	Disp/LWL 32
Disp ...... 335 lbs	First Built 1982
Sail Area	1 Design .... yes
Sloop .... 200 sq ft	Price $3,795
Mast Ht .... 27'	with sails

LOD .... 17'	Hull .... FRP
LWL .... 17'	Deck .... FRP
Beam .... 8'	Spar .... Alum
Draft	Pos Float .... yes
db up .... 4''	SA/Disp 68.9
db dn ..... 2'10''	Disp/LWL 33
Disp ...... 365 lbs	Designer . Tom Roland
Sail Area	First Built 1975
Sloop .... 220 sq ft	No. Built 2500
Mast Ht .... 28'	1 Design .... yes
	Price $4,600
	with sails

G—CAT INTERNATIONAL
269 16th St. North
St. Petersburg, FL 33705
(813) 821-6881

NACRA
6382 Rose Ln.
Carpinteria, CA 93013
(805) 684-8756

NACRA
6382 Rose Ln.
Carpinteria, CA 93013
(805) 684-8756

Supercat 17

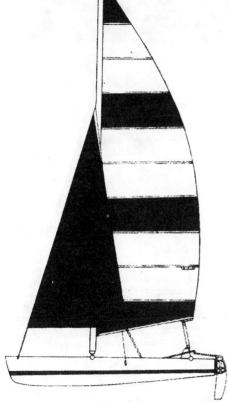

LOD .... 17'	Hull .... FRP
LWL .... na	Deck .... FRP
Beam .... 8'	Spar .... Alum
Draft	SA/Disp 79.2
Rudder up .... 10"	1 Design .... yes
Rudder dn ..... 2'	Price $5,670
Disp ...... 325 lbs	with sails
Sail Area	
Sloop .... 234 sq ft	
Mast Ht ...... 28'9"	

BOSTON WHALER INC.
P. O. Box 10184
Riviera Beach, FL 33404
(305) 842-5171

Hobie 18

LOD .... 18'	Hull .... FRP
LWL .... 17'9"	Deck .... FRP
Beam .... 8'	Spar .... Alum
Draft	Pos Float ...... yes
db up ...... 10"	SA/Disp 70.7
db dn ..... 2'6"	Disp/LWL 31
Disp ...... 400 lbs	Designer . Hobie Alter
Sail Area	First Built 1977
Sloop .... 240 sq ft	1 Design .... yes
Mast Ht .... 30'	Price $4,595
	with sails

HOBIE CAT
Box 1008, 4925 E. Oceanside Blvd.
Oceanside, CA 92054
(714) 758-9100

Nacra 5.5

LOD .... 18'	Hull .... FRP
LWL .... 18'	Deck .... FRP
Beam .... 11'	Spar .... Alum
Draft	Pos Float .... no
db up ...... 4"	SA/Disp 62.5
db dn .... 2'10"	Disp/LWL 26
Disp ...... 350 lbs	First Built 1977
Sail Area	1 Design .... no
Cat ..... 194 sq ft	Price $4,700
Mast Ht .... 30'	with sails

NACRA
6382 Rose Ln.
Carpinteria, CA 93013
(805) 684-8756

Prindle 18

LOD	18'	Hull	FRP/Foam
LWL	17'	Deck	FRP/Foam
Beam	8'	Spar	Alum
Draft	7"	Pos Float	no
Disp	335 lbs	SA/Disp	72.3
Sail Area		Disp/LWL	30
Sloop	218 sq ft	Designer	
Mast Ht	28'9"		Geoff Prindle
		First Built	1978
		No. Built	2000
		1 Design	yes
		Price	$4,195
			with sails

SURFGLAS
1810 E. Borchard
Santa Ana, CA 92705

Trac 18 Catamaran

LOD	18'	Hull	FRP
LWL	na	Deck	FRP
Beam	8'	Spar	Alum
Draft		Pos Float	yes
db up	4"	SA/Disp	78
db dn	2'7"	Designer	
Disp	341 lbs		David Hubbard
Sail Area		First Built	1982
Sloop	238 sq ft	1 Design	yes
Mast Ht	30'1"	Price	$6,495
			with sails

AMF ALCORT/SAILBOATS
Box 1345
Waterbury, CT 06708
(203) 756-7091

Star Cat 5.6

LOD	18'4"	Hull	FRP
LWL	na	Deck	FRP
Beam	7'7"	Spar	Alum
Draft		SA/Disp	64
cb up	4"	Price	$4,400
cb dn	3'		with sails
Disp	380 lbs		
Sail Area			
Sloop	210 sq ft		
Mast Ht	26'		

STAR CATAMARANS INC.
1209 S. Brown St.
Jackson, MI 49203
(517) 787-6154

G – Cat 5.7 Meter

G – Cat 5.7 Meter Day Sailor

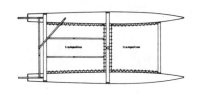

P – Cat 2 – 18

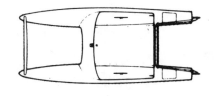

LOD . . . . 18'8"	Hull . . . . FRP
LWL . . . . 17'6"	Deck . . . . FRP
Beam . . . . 8'	Spar . . . . Alum
Draft . . . . na	Pos Float . . . . . . yes
Disp . . . . . . 360 lbs	SA/Disp 74.3
Sail Area	Disp/LWL 29
Sloop . . . . 235 sq ft	Designer
Mast Ht . . . . 28'	Hans Geissler
	First Built 1980
	No. Built 250
	1 Design . . . . yes
	Price $4,995
	with sails

LOD . . . . 18'8"	Hull . . . . FRP
LWL . . . . 17'6"	Deck . . . . FRP
Beam . . . . 8'	Spar . . . . Alum
Draft . . . . na	Pos Float . . . . . . yes
Disp . . . . . 345 lbs	SA/Disp 51.4
Sail Area	Disp/LWL 28
Sloop . . . . 158 sq ft	Designer
Mast Ht . . . . 24'	Hans Geissler
	First Built 1981
	1 Design . . . . yes
	Price $4,295
	with sails

LOD . . . . 18'9"	Hull . . . . FRP
LWL . . . . na	Deck . . . . FRP
Beam . . . . 7'11"	Spar . . . . Alum
Draft	SA/Disp 73.6
db up . . . . na	Price $5,075
db dn . . . . na	with sails
Disp . . . . . 450 lbs	
Sail Area	
Sloop . . . . 270 sq ft	

G – CAT INTERNATIONAL
269 16th St. North
St. Petersburg, FL 33705
(813) 821-6881

G – CAT INTERNATIONAL
269 16th St. North
St. Petersburg, FL 33705
(813) 821-6881

WESTPORT PACIFIC BOATS
447 N. Newport Blvd.
Newport Beach, CA 92663
(714) 645-4524

Seafire

Smoothie

Nacra 5.8

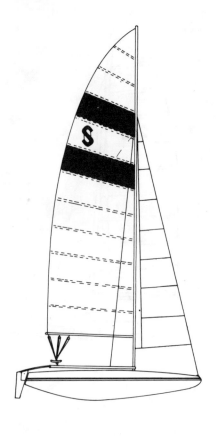

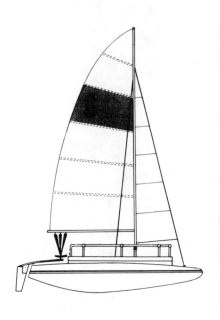

Seafire		
LOD .... 18'10"	Hull .... Alum	
LWL .... na	Deck .... Alum	
Beam ...... 8' or 10'	Spar .... Alum	
Draft .... 1'	Pos Float .... yes	
Disp ...... 400 lbs	SA/Disp 76.6	
Sail Area	Price $4,195	
Sloop .... 260 sq ft	with sails	

Smoothie		
LOD .... 18'10"	Hull .... Alum	
LWL .... na	Deck .... Alum	
Beam .... 8'	Spar .... Alum	
Draft .... 1'	Pos Float .... yes	
Disp ...... 465 lbs	SA/Disp 40	
Sail Area	Price $4,595	
Sloop .... 150 sq ft	with sails	
Sloop .... 220 sq ft		
Auxiliary .... opt		
40 hp		

Nacra 5.8		
LOD .... 19'	Hull .... FRP	
LWL .... 19'	Deck .... FRP	
Beam .... 8'	Spar .... Alum	
Draft	Pos Float .... yes	
db up .... 5"	SA/Disp 69.6	
db dn ...... 3'2"	Disp/LWL ..:... 26	
Disp .... 410 lbs	First Built 1981	
Sail Area	No. Built 250	
Sloop .... 240 sq ft	1 Design .... yes	
Mast Ht .... 30'	Price $5,995	
	with sails	

GREAT LAKES SPORTS MFG.
480 S. Green Rd.
Cleveland, OH 44121
(216) 481-6895

GREAT LAKES SPORTS MFG.
480 S. Green Rd.
Cleveland, OH 44121
(216) 481-6895

NACRA
6382 Rose Ln.
Carpinteria, CA 93013
(805) 684-8756

Sea Spray 19

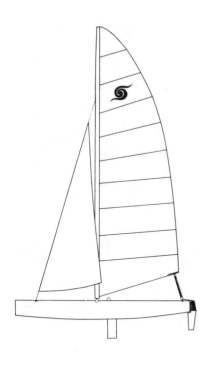

LOA	19'	Hull	FRP
LOD	19'	Deck	FRP
LWL	18'10"	Spar	Alum
Beam	8'3"	Pos Float	yes
Draft		SA/Disp	82.8
db up	5"	Disp/LWL	22
db dn	3'	Designer	Julian Cane
Disp	330 lbs	First Built	1981
Sail Area		No. Built	125
Sloop	247 sq ft	1 Design	yes
Mast Ht	28'6"	Price	$5,695
			with sails

DYNACAT
P. O. Box 4846
Foster City, CA 94404
(415) 573-1955

Supercat 19

LOD	19'	Hull	FRP
LWL	na	Deck	FRP
Beam	8'	Spar	Alum
Draft		SA/Disp	80
db up	10"	1 Design	yes
db dn	3'6"	Price	$6,980
Disp	375 lbs		with sails
Sail Area			
Sloop	260 sq ft		
Mast Ht	28'9"		

BOSTON WHALER INC.
P. O. Box 10184
Riviera Beach, FL 33404
(305) 842-5171

Tramp

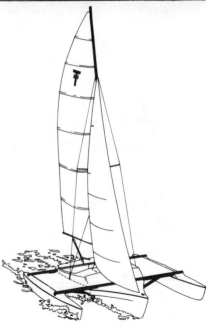

LOD	19'6"	Hull	FRP/Coremat
LWL	18'1"	Deck	FRP/Coremat
Beam	14'9"	Spar	Alum
Draft		Pos Float	yes
cb up	1'2"	SA/Disp	26.6
cb dn	4'	Disp/LWL	106
Disp	1400 lbs	Designer	Ian Farrier
Sail Area		Builder	
Sloop	208 sq ft	Haines Hunter, Australia	
Auxiliary	opt	First Built	1980
	6 hp	No. Built	200
		1 Design	yes
		Price	$15,021
			with sails

VAN ORDER ASSOCIATES
12625 Memorial Drive, No. 89
Houston, TX 77024
(713) 461-3885

Shark

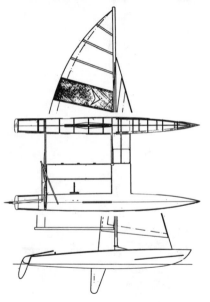

LOD . . . . 20'	Hull . . . . Wood
LWL . . . . 18'	Deck . . . . Wood
Beam . . . . 10'	Spar . . . . Alum
Draft	Pos Float . . . . . . yes
cb up . . . . 6"	Cockpit . . . . 7'3"
cb dn . . . . . . 3'6"	SA/Disp 74.9
Disp . . . . . . 450 lbs	Disp/LWL 34
Sail Area	Designer
Sloop . . . . 275 sq ft	J. R. Macalpine-Downie
Mast Ht . . . . . . 28'6"	First Built 1963
	No. Built 550
	1 Design . . . . yes
	Price $11,500
	with sails

JOHN ROGERS
72 Maiden Lane
Canandaigua, NY 14424
(716) 394-6853

Supercat 20

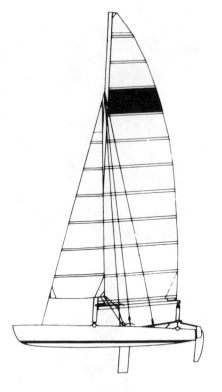

LOD . . . . 20'	Hull . . . . FRP
LWL . . . . na	Deck . . . . FRP
Beam . . . . 12'	Spar . . . . Alum
Draft	SA/Disp 74.9
db up . . . . 6"	1 Design . . . . . . yes
db dn . . . . . . 3'6"	Price $9,950
Disp . . . . . . 450 lbs	with sails
Sail Area	
Sloop . . . . 275 sq ft	
Mast Ht . . . . . . 33'	

BOSTON WHALER INC.
P. O. Box 10184
Riviera Beach, FL 33404
(305) 842-5171

Tornado Cat

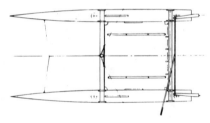

LOD . . . . 20'	Hull . . . . FRP
LWL . . . . 18'	Deck . . . . FRP
Beam . . . . 10'	Spar . . . . Alum
Draft	Pos Float . . . . . . yes
cb up . . . . 5"	SA/Disp 85
cb dn . . . . . . 2'5"	Disp/LWL 23
Disp . . . . . . 300 lbs	Designer
Sail Area	Rodney Marsh
Sloop . . . . 238 sq ft	First Built 1974
Mast Ht . . . . . . 32'	No. Built 50
	1 Design . . . . yes
	Price $5,800
	without sails

SOUTHERN YACHTS
3550 South East Blvd.
Wichita, KS 67216

Tornado Olympic

Tremolino

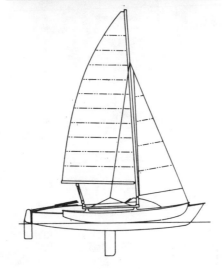

Sirocco 26

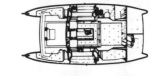

Tornado Olympic

LOD	20'	Hull	FRP/Foam
LWL	na	Deck	FRP/Foam
Beam	10'	Spar	Alum
Draft		Pos Float	yes
cb up	6"	Designer	
cb dn	2'6"		Rodney March
Disp	na	First Built	1967
Sail Area		No. Built	3600
Sloop	235 sq ft	1 Design	yes
Mast Ht	31'6"	Kit	available
		Price	$9,000
			without sails

Tremolino

LOD	22'10"	Hull	FRP
LWL	21'	Deck	FRP
Beam	16'6"	Spar	Alum
Draft		Pos Float	yes
cb up	1'1"	SA/Disp	40.5
cb dn	4'4"	Disp/LWL	39
Disp	800 lbs	Kit	$3,975
Sail Area			
Sloop	218 sq ft		
Mast Ht	28'3"		

Sirocco 26

LOD	25'11"	Hull	FRP
LWL	22'6"	Deck	FRP/Balsa
Beam	12'9"	Spar	Alum
Draft	2'4"	Pos Float	yes
Disp	5000 lbs	Cockpit	5'
Sail Area		Headroom	6'
Sloop	300 sq ft	Fr. Water	44 gal
Auxiliary	opt	SA/Disp	16.4
	15 hp	Disp/LWL	196
		Builder	
			Prout, England
		1 Design	no
		Kit	available
		Price	na

SAILCRAFT OF CANADA
316 Beaconsfield Blvd.
Canada H9W 4A8
(514) 695-9394

TREMOLINO BOAT CO.
5840 Ridge Road, P. O. Box D
Excelsior, MN 55331
(612) 474-7402

SYMONS — SAILING INC.
Box 415
Amityville, NY 11701
(516) 264-6330

Stiletto 27

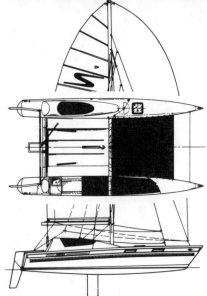

LOA	26'10"	Hull	FRP/Nomex
LOD	26'6"	Deck	FRP/Nomex
LWL	24'	Spar	Alum
Beam	13'10"	Pos Float	yes
Draft		Cockpit	10'
db up	9"	Headroom	4'6"
db dn	4'	Fr. Water	5 gal
Disp	1100 lbs	SA/Disp	50.5
Sail Area		Disp/LWL	35
Sloop	336 sq ft	Designer	Higgins
Mast Ht	40'	First Built	1975
Auxiliary	opt	No. Built	330
	15 hp	1 Design	yes
	outbd	Price	$22,980
			with sails

FORCE ENGINEERING CO.
5329 Ashton Ct.
Sarasota, FL 33583
(813) 923-1857

Stiletto 30

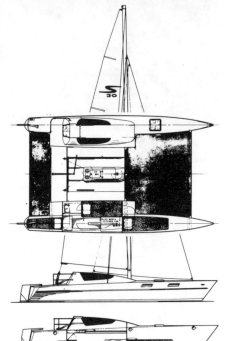

LOA	29'4"	Hull	FRP/Nomex
LOD	29'	Deck	FRP/Nomex
LWL	26'10"	Spar	Alum
Beam	17'10"	Pos Float	yes
Draft		Cockpit	10'
cb up	10"	Headroom	54"
cb dn	4'	Fr. Water	25 gal
Disp	2200 lbs	Disp/LWL	50
Sail Area		Designer	
Sloop	na		Peter Wormwood
Mast Ht	39'	First Built	1981
Auxiliary	opt	No. Built	8
	15 hp	1 Design	no
	outbd	Price	$42,000
			with sails

FORCE ENGINEERING CO.
5329 Ashton Ct.
Sarasota, FL 33583
(813) 923-1857

Turissimo 30

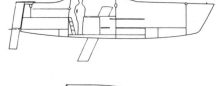

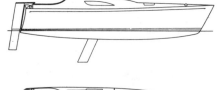

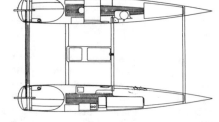

LOD	29'6"	Hull	Wood
LWL	na	Deck	Wood
Beam	17'	Spar	Alum
Draft		Fr. Water	20 gal
db up	1'	SA/Disp	31.1
db dn	4'6"	Price	$19,900
Disp	4982 lbs		with sails
Sail Area			
Sloop	567 sq ft		
Auxiliary	opt		

MULTIHULL CONSTRUCTORS
3833 176th S.W.
Lynnwood, WA 98036
(206) 743-4514

Newick 30

LOD	29'8"	Hull . . .	Wood + FRP
LWL	28'10"	Deck . .	Wood + FRP
Beam	25'	Spar	Alum
Draft		Pos Float	yes
db up	2'6"	Cockpit	4'
db dn	6'	Headroom	6'2"
Disp	3600 lbs	SA/Disp	44.3
Sail Area		Disp/LWL	67
Sloop	650 sq ft	Designer	
Mast Ht	43'		Richard Newick
		First Built	1982
		1 Design	no
		Kit	available
		Price	$42,000
			without sails

DAMIAN McLAUGHLIN JR. CORP.
Box 538
N. Falmouth, MA 02556
563-3075

Kaulua 31

LOA	31'	Hull	FRP
LOD	30'4"	Deck	FRP
LWL	29'	Spar	Alum
Beam	14'	Pos Float	yes
Draft		Cockpit	3'6"
db up	1'8"	Headroom	6'3"
db dn	4'	Fr. Water	20 gal
Disp	4200 lbs	SA/Disp	25.3
Sail Area		Disp/LWL	76
Sloop	412 sq ft	Designer	
Mast Ht	42'11"		Harold Stilson Jr.
Auxiliary	opt	First Built	1977
	25 hp	No. Built	7
	outbd	Kit	$21,342
		Price	$39,871
			with sails

HARSTIL INDUSTRIES INC.
17150 15 Mile Rd. Box 26
Fraser, MI 48026
(313) 294-6850

Gemini 31

LOD	30'6"	Hull	FRP
LWL	27'7"	Deck	FRP
Beam	14'	Spar	Alum
Draft		Pos Float	yes
cb up	1'4"	Cockpit	8'6"
cb dn	4'9"	Headroom	6'5"
Disp	6520 lbs	Fr. Water	25 gal
Sail Area		SA/Disp	19.5
Sloop	425 sq ft	Disp/LWL	139
Mast Ht	41'6"	Designer . Tony Smith	
Auxiliary	opt	First Built	1980
	40 hp	No. Built	11
		Kit	available
		Price	$38,500
			with sails

PERFORMANCE CRUISING
P. O. Box 381
Mayo, MD 21106
(301) 798-5150

Quest 31

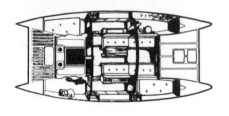

LOD	31'	Hull	FRP
LWL	28'6"	Deck	FRP/Balsa
Beam	14'3"	Spar	Alum
Draft	2'6"	Pos Float	yes
Disp	7000 lbs	Cockpit	6'
Sail Area		Headroom	6'2"
Sloop	443 sq ft	Fr. Water	64 gal
Cutter	500 sq ft	SA/Disp	19.4
Auxiliary	std	Disp/LWL	135
Yanmar	15 hp	Builder	Prout, England
Diesel		Kit	available
Fuel Cap	12 gal	Price	na

SYMONS — SAILING INC.
Box 415
Amityville, NY 11701
(516) 264-6330

Catfisher 32

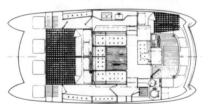

LOD	32'	Hull	FRP
LWL	na	Deck	FRP/Balsa
Beam	13'1"	Spar	Alum
Draft	2'8"	Pos Float	yes
Disp	8000 lbs	Cockpit	7'
Sail Area		Headroom	6'4"
Sloop	325 sq ft	Fr. Water	60 gal
Auxiliary	std	SA/Disp	13
Yanmar	30 hp	Designer	
Diesel			Terry Compton
Fuel Cap	60 gal	Price	na

SYMONS — SAILING INC.
Box 415
Amityville, NY 11701
(516) 264-6330

Turissimo 10

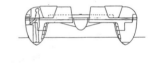

LOD	32'7"	Hull	Wood
LWL	na	Deck	Wood
Beam	19'	Spar	Alum
Draft		Fr. Water	20 gal
db up	1'	SA/Disp	25.9
db dn	4'6"	Price	$29,900
Disp	6160 lbs		without sails
Sail Area			
Sloop	544 sq ft		
Auxiliary	opt		

MULTIHULL CONSTRUCTORS
3833 176th S.W.
Lynnwood, WA 98036
(206) 743-4514

Wildwind

Imagine a 1400 pound catamaran with 600 square feet of sail. 32 feet long with a substantial amount of Go Fast hardware. It is fast, trailerable, and all hand built.

THAT IS WHAT WE OFFER
PLUS MUCH, MUCH MORE!

The Wildwind MK!! is a 32'6 Daysailing "D" Class Catamaran, designed to aircraft structural principles. This concept offers high strength with

low weight. WILDWIND MKII is unrivaled by any other catamaran in speed and maneuverability. She demonstrates remarkable performance with handling qualities achieved by few. WILDWIND MKII has been a constant race winner since her inception in 1965. Conceived primarily for out and out racing, she has superb stability for around the buoys and off-shore racing.

LOD	32'6"	Hull	FRP/Kledgecell
LWL	29'5"	Deck	FRP/Kledgecell
Beam	16'	Spar	Alum
Draft		Pos Float	yes
db up	10"	SA/Disp	73.6
db dn	3'4"	Disp/LWL	25
Disp	1400 lbs	Designer	Judson Grant
Sail Area		First Built	1965
Sloop	576 sq ft	1 Design	yes
Mast Ht	44'	Price	na
Auxiliary	opt		
	5 hp		
	outbd		

KW 33

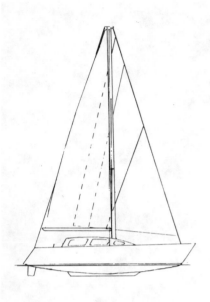

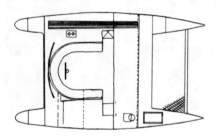

LOD . . . . 34'	Hull . . . . Wood
LWL . . . . 30'	Deck . . . . Wood
Beam . . . . 20'	Spar . . . . Alum
Draft	Headroom . . . . . . 6'
cb up . . . . 1'8"	SA/Disp 34.7
cb dn . . . . 4'6"	Disp/LWL 66
Disp . . . . . . 4000 lbs	First Built 1983
Sail Area	Kit $19,000
Sloop . . . . 547 sq ft	Price $38,000
Mast Ht . . . . . . 45'9"	with sails
Auxiliary . . . . opt	

KUSTOM WATERCRAFT
P. O. Box 898
Scarborough, ME 04074

Witness 35

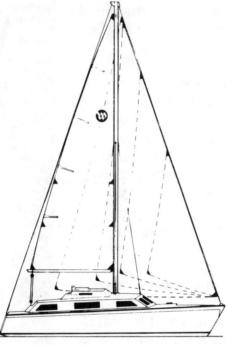

LOD . . . . 34'8"	Hull . . . . FRP
LWL . . . . 30'3"	Deck . . FRP/Klegecell
Beam . . . . . . 16'10"	Spar . . . . Alum
Draft	Fr. Water . . . 100 gal
db up . . . . . . 2'6"	SA/Disp 17.6
db dn . . . . 5'	Disp/LWL 218
Disp . . . . 13,500 lbs	Designer
Sail Area	Lock Crowther
Sloop . . . . 625 sq ft	Kit $19,900
Auxiliary . . . . std	Price $52,500
Gas	with sails
Fuel Cap . . . . . . 36 gal	

WITNESS CATAMARANS
2771 Hanson Street
Fort Myers, FL 33901
(813) 334-0100

Witness 35 "Sightseer"

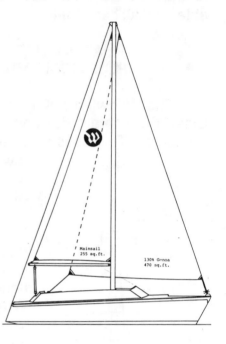

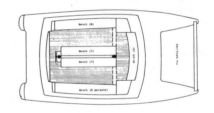

LOD . . . . 34'8"	Hull . . . . FRP
LWL . . . . 30'3"	Deck . . FRP/Klegecell
Beam . . . . 17'10"	Spar . . . . Alum
Draft	SA/Disp 20.5
db up . . . . . . 2'6"	Disp/LWL 218
db dn . . . . 5'	Designer
Disp . . 13,500 lbs	Lock Crowther
Sail Area	Price . . . . na
Sloop . . . . 725 sq ft	
Mast Ht . . . . . . 51'	
Auxiliary . . . . std	
Diesel . . . . 2-20 hp	

WITNESS CATAMARANS
2771 Hanson Street
Fort Myers, FL 33901
(813) 334-0100

Meyers 36

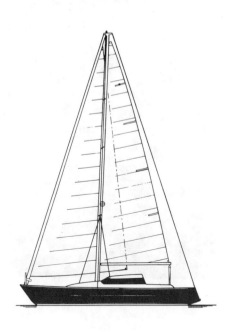

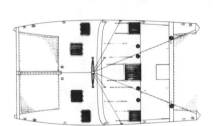

LOD	35'6"	Hull	FRP/Foam
LWL	28'3"	Deck	FRP/Foam
Beam	18'	Spar	Alum
Draft		Cockpit	5'
cb up	1'6"	Headroom	6'4"
cb dn	4'2"	Fr. Water	120 gal
Disp	4900 lbs	SA/Disp	38
Sail Area		Disp/LWL	97
Sloop	685 sq ft	Designer	Hugo Meyers
Mast Ht	50'4"	First Built	1982
Auxiliary	std	No. Built	1
	25 hp	Kit	available
	outbd	Price	$90,000
Fuel Cap	25 gal		with sails

HIDDEN HARBOR BOATWORKS
2029 Whitfield Park Ave.
Sarasota, FL 33580
(813) 775-7533

MacGregor 36

LOD	36'	Hull	FRP
LWL	33'6"	Deck	FRP
Beam	18'	Spar	Alum
Draft		Pos Float	yes
db up	8"	Cockpit	6'
db dn	5'	Headroom	5'
Disp	3000 lbs	Fr. Water	5 gal
Sail Area		SA/Disp	41.1
Sloop	534 sq ft	Disp/LWL	35
Mast Ht	48'	Designer	
Auxiliary	opt		R. N. MacGregor
	10 hp	First Built	1977
		No. Built	200
		1 Design	yes
		Price	$18,836
			with sails

MacGREGOR
1631 Placentia
Costa Mesa, CA 92627
(714) 642-6830

Trice III Trimaran

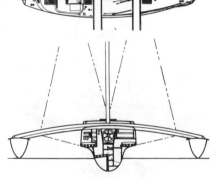

LOD	36'11"	Hull	FRP
LWL	35'4"	Deck	FRP
Beam	27'4"	Spar	Alum
Draft		Pos Float	yes
cb up	30"	Cockpit	5'9"
cb dn	5'6"	Headroom	6'4"
Disp	5240 lbs	Fr. Water	40 gal
Sail Area		SA/Disp	31.8
Sloop (FR)	600 sq ft	Disp/LWL	53
Sloop (MH)	650 sq ft	Designer	
Mast Ht	46'		Richard Newick
Auxiliary	opt	First Built	1981
	15 hp	No. Built	3
	outbd	1 Design	yes
		Kit	$32,800
		Price	$67,500
			with sails

HUDSON RIVER BOATBUILDING
P. O. Box 248
Glasco, NY 12433
(914) 336-6582

Snowgoose 37

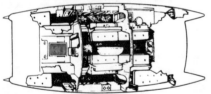

LOD	37'	Hull	FRP
LWL	33'	Deck	FRP/Balsa
Beam	15'3"	Spar	Alum
Draft	2'8"	Pos Float	yes
Disp	9600 lbs	Cockpit	7'
Sail Area		Headroom	6'6"
Cutter	672 sq ft	Fr. Water	70 gal
Auxiliary	std	SA/Disp	23.8
Yanmar	22 hp	Disp/LWL	119
Diesel		Designer	Prout
Fuel Cap	18 gal	Builder	Prout
		Kit	available
		Price	na

Quark 38

LOD	38'	Hull	FRP/Foam
LWL	32'6"	Deck	FRP/Wood
Beam	22'	Spar	Alum
Draft		Disp/LWL	156
cb up	2'4"	Designer	
cb dn	4'6"		Spiegel/Blass
Disp	12,000 lbs	Price	$105,000
Sail Area	na		with sails

40' Polycat

LOA	40'	Hull	FRP
LOD	39'	Deck	FRP
LWL	36'	Pos Float	yes
Beam	20'	Headroom	6'4"
Draft	18"	Designer	Paul Stovall
Disp	na	First Built	1972
Sail Area		No. Built	42
Sloop	na	Kit	$12,000
Ketch	na		

Quasar 50

The **new Prout Quasar 50** developed from the well known **Ocean Ranger 45.** This latest design offers the finest ocean-going comfort; capable of meeting the toughest conditions and already the Ocean Ranger has many thousands of miles of blue water under her keels.

The Prout Quasar 50 has the same tough, fast design capabilities, and will sail at speeds well in excess of 15 knots. Her performance to windward is unmatched, and those who have sailed in the Ocean Ranger will know how exceptional this is.

With over 1,000 sq. ft. of sail her performance in light winds is good, and 10-12 knots in only light to moderate winds is possible on a reach.

The Quasar has the same shallow draft, only 3'0", which opens up large areas of cruising not possible or safe in a deep-draft yacht; and it is even possible to nose right up on to the beach. Taking the bottom in harbours which dry out is quite normal practice with a catamaran.

Power is by **two 20-hp diesel engines,** one in each hull. The twin-engine control, wide apart in each hull, makes for quite exceptional maneuverability; probably better than any motor cruiser. Cruising speeds are around 8 knots and the cruising range is in excess of 400 miles.

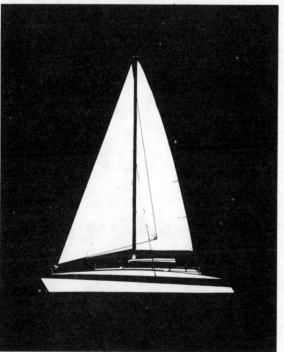

LOD	49'	Hull	FRP
LWL	45'	Deck	FRP/Balsa
Beam	20'	Spar	Alum
Draft	3'	Pos Float	yes
Disp	20,000 lbs	Cockpit	7'
Sail Area		Headroom	7'
Sloop	1000 sq ft	Fr. Water	90 gal
Cutter	1125 sq ft	SA/Disp	21.7
Auxiliary	std	Disp/LWL	98
Yanmar	20 twin hp	Designer	Prout
Diesel		Builder	Prout
Fuel Cap	60 gal	Kit	available
		Price	na

SYMONS — SAILING INC.
Box 415
Amityville, NY 11701
(516) 264-6330

MONOHULLS

Abbreviations:

Alum	Aluminum
Blst	Ballast
Can	Canadian Dollars
cb	Centerboard
Cockpit	Cockpit Length
db	Daggerboard
Disp	Displacement
dn	Down
FR	Fractional
FRP	Fiberglass
Fr. Water	Fresh Water
Fuel Cap	Fuel Capacity
gal	Gallons
hp	Horsepower
Ht	Height
inbd	Inboard
I/O	Inboard or Outboard
lb	Leeboards
lbs	Pounds
LOA	Length Overall
LOD	Length on Deck
LWL	Length at Waterline
MH	Masthead
na	Not Available
No.	Number
outbd	Outboard
opt	Optional
Pos Float	Positive Floatation
SA	Sail Area
Scnr	Schooner
sq ft	Square Feet
Ver ret	Vertically Retracting

Prices:

Prices are subject to change without notice.

Price listed is for a completed boat unless specifically labeled kit price.

Photos and drawings may show optional equipment.

The base price is listed. Optional rigs or layouts may be higher priced.

Note:

For all performance prediction ratios (SA/DISP, DISP/LWL, BLST/DISP), if an item in the ratio is listed more than once, the first value was used to compute the ratio. That is, if two sail areas are listed, the first one was used for the SA/DISP ratio.

M O N O H U L L S

Optimist Dinghy

C Y T Optimist Pram

No Photo
or
Line Drawing
Available

Int'l Optimist Dinghy

LOD	7'6"	Hull	FRP
LWL	7'	Deck	FRP
Beam	3'8"	Spar	Alum
Draft		Pos Float	yes
db up	4"	Cockpit	7'
db dn	2'8"	SA/Disp	35.8
Disp	70 lbs	Disp/LWL	91
Ballast	0 lbs	Designer	Clark Mills
Sail Area		First Built	1960
Cat (sprit)	38 sq ft	No. Built	10,000
Mast Ht	7'6"	1 Design	yes
Mast	unstayed	Kit	available
		Price	$725
			without sails

LOA	7'9"	Hull	FRP
LOD	7'7"	Deck	FRP
LWL	6'5"	Spar	Alum
Beam	44"	Pos Float	yes
Draft		Designer	Clark Mills
db up	5"	First Built	1983
db dn	33"	1 Design	yes
Disp	na	Price	$895
Ballast	na		with sails
Sail Area			
Cat (sprit)	35 sq ft		
Mast Ht	13'		
Mast	unstayed		

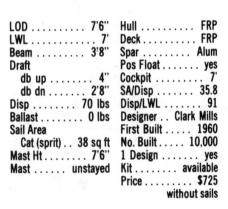

LOD	7'8"	Hull	FRP
LWL	na	Deck	FRP
Beam	3'8"	Spar	Alum
Draft		SA/Disp	30.9
db up	na	Designer	Clark Mills
db dn	na	1 Design	yes
Disp	77 lbs	Price	$1,585
Ballast	0 lbs		with sails
Sail Area			
Cat (sprit)	35 sq ft		
Mast	unstayed		

DYNAMIC PLASTICS
Route 1, Box 6
New Paris, OH 45347
(513) 437-7261

CUSTOM YACHT TENDERS
804 Grace Ave.
Lake Worth, FL 33461

VANGUARD
1251 E. Wisconsin Ave.
Pewaukee, WI 53072
(414) 691-3320

International Optimist Dinghy

LOD	7'8"	Hull	FRP
LWL	na	Deck	FRP
Beam	3'8"	Spar	Alum
Draft		Pos Float	yes
db up	na	SA/Disp	30.9
db dn	na	Designer	Clark Mills
Disp	77 lbs	First Built	1947
Ballast	0 lbs	No. Built	260,000
Sail Area		1 Design	yes
Cat (Sprit)	35 sq ft	Price	$1,190
			with sails

ELVSTROM — USA
727 Boston Post Rd.
P. O. Box A
Guilford, CT 06437
(203) 453-6594

Murray Peterson Yacht Tender

LOD	7'9"	Hull	Wood
LWL	na	Spar	Wood
Beam	3'9"	SA/Disp	18.8
Draft		Price	na
db up	na		
db dn	na		
Disp	110 lbs		
Ballast	0 lbs		
Sail Area			
Cat (sprit)	27 sq ft		
Mast	unstayed		

AMERICAN BOAT HOUSE
Atlantic Ave., P. O. Box 911
Camden, ME 04843
(207) 236-4188

Sabot

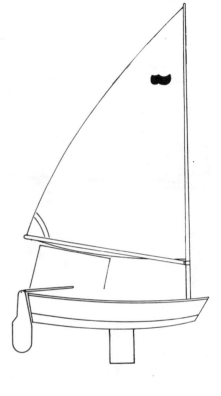

LOD	7'10"	Hull	FRP/Foam
LWL	na	Pos Float	yes
Beam	3'10"	SA/Disp	39.7
Draft		1 Design	yes
lb up	na	Price	$845
lb dn	na		with sails
Disp	60 lbs		
Ballast	0 lbs		
Sail Area			
Cat	38 sq ft		
Mast	unstayed		
Auxiliary	opt		

SIDNEY CO.
11825 Major St.
Culver City, CA 90230
(213) 390-9838

Drifter 8

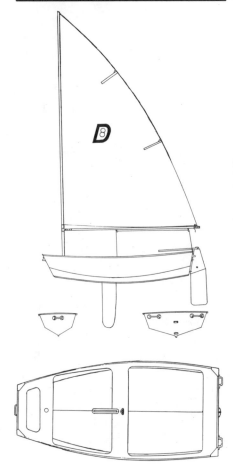

Dyer Dhow "Midget"

C Y T Pram

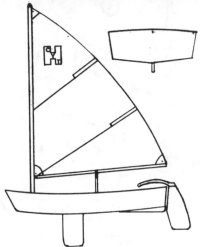

LOD	7'11"	Hull	FRP
LWL	7'3"	Deck	FRP
Beam	3'10"	Spar	Alum
Draft		Pos Float	yes
cb up	6"	Cockpit	7'9"
cb dn	2'9"	SA/Disp	29
Disp	85 lbs	Disp/LWL	99
Ballast	0 lbs	Designer	
Sail Area			Michael Schallmann
Cat	35 sq ft	First Built	1983
Cat (tall)	40 sq ft	No. Built	2
Mast Ht		1 Design	no
Cat	12'	Price	$761
Cat (tall)	13'		with sails
Mast	unstayed		
Auxiliary	opt		
	2 hp		

LOD	7'11"	Hull	FRP
LWL	na	Deck	FRP
Beam	4'1"	Spar	Wood
Draft		Pos Float	yes
db up	5"	SA/Disp	27.9
db dn	2'4"	Designer	William Dyer
Disp	90 lbs	First Built	1946
Ballast	0 lbs	No. Built	8700
Sail Area		1 Design	yes
Cat	35 sq ft	Price	$1,370
Auxiliary	opt		with sails
	2 hp		

LOD	8'	Hull	FRP
LWL	7'	Deck	FRP
Beam	4'	Spar	Alum
Draft		Pos Float	yes
db up	5"	Designer	Drew Hansen
db dn	3'	First Built	1975
Disp	na	No. Built	145
Ballast	0 lbs	1 Design	no
Sail Area		Kit	available
Cat	35 sq ft	Price	$525
Mast Ht	12'6"		with sails
Mast	unstayed		
Auxiliary	opt		
	2 hp		

DRIFTER MARINE ENTERPRISES
P. O. Box 11163
Phoenix, AZ 85061
(602) 246-0227

THE ANCHORAGE
57 Miller St.
Warren, RI 02885
(401) 245-3300

CUSTOM YACHT TENDERS
804 Grace Ave.
Lake Worth, FL 33461

C Y T Sailing Dinghy

LOD	8'	Hull	FRP
LWL	7'	Deck	FRP
Beam	4'	Spar	Alum
Draft		Pos Float	yes
db up	4"	Designer	Drew Hansen
db dn	2'	First Built	1975
Disp	na	No. Built	245
Ballast	0 lbs	1 Design	no
Sail Area		Price	$650
Cat	35 sq ft		with sails
Mast Ht	12'6"		
Mast	unstayed		
Auxiliary	opt		
	2 hp		

CUSTOM YACHT TENDERS
804 Grace Ave.
Lake Worth, FL 33461

8' Folding Porta — Bote

LOA	8'8"	Hull	Polypropylene
LOD	8'	Deck	Polypropylene
LWL	7'3"	Pos Float	yes
Beam	3'10"	SA/Disp	48.7
Draft		Disp/LWL	46
lb up	4"	Designer	Stansbury
lb dn	na	First Built	1969
Disp	39 lbs	No. Built	17,500
Ballast	0 lbs	1 Design	yes
Sail Area		Price	$1,084
Cat	35 sq ft		with sails
Mast Ht	12'		
Auxiliary	opt		
	2 hp		

Note: Also available in 10' and 12' lengths.

PORTA—BOTE INT'L.
Div. Sandy Kaye Ent. Inc.
P. O. Box 2287
Menlo Park, CA 94025

Lem

LOD	8'	Pos Float	yes
LWL	8'	SA/Disp	27.9
Beam	3'11"	Disp/LWL	78
Draft		First Built	1974
cb up	6"	No. Built	200
cb dn	3'	1 Design	no
Disp	90 lbs	Kit	available
Ballast	0 lbs	Price	$995
Sail Area			with sails
Lateen	35 sq ft		
Mast Ht	12'		
Mast	unstayed		

NYE YACHTS
25 Dundas St. W.
Belleville, Ontario
Canada K8P 3M7

Norwegian Sailing Pram

LOD	8'	Hull	Wood
LWL	na	Spar	Wood
Beam	4'	Pos Float	yes
Draft		SA/Disp	30.1
cb up	3"	Designer	Frank Danie
cb dn	na	Builder	C. W. Carter
Disp	70 lbs	First Built	1980
Ballast	0 lbs	No. Built	7
Sail Area		Price	$1,795
Cat (gaff)	32 sq ft		with sails
Mast	unstayed		

CHARLES W. CARTER
Box 226
Miller Plains, NY 11764

Quartermaster 8

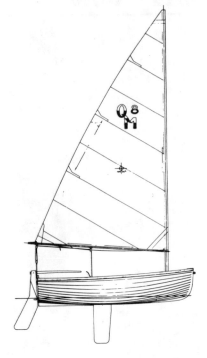

LOD	8'	Hull	FRP
LWL	8'	Spar	Alum
Beam	4'	Pos Float	yes
Draft		SA/Disp	30.7
db up	na	Disp/LWL	96
db dn	na	Price	$1,095
Disp	110 lbs		with sails
Ballast	0 lbs		
Sail Area			
Cat	44 sq ft		
Mast Ht	15'6"		
Mast	unstayed		

VASHON BOAT WORKS
P. O. Box Q
Vashon, WA 98070
(206) 463-2750

8' Scout Sailor

LOD	8'	Hull	FRP
LWL	na	Spar	Alum
Beam	4'	Pos Float	yes
Disp	82 lbs	SA/Disp	33.1
Ballast	0 lbs	Price	$668
Sail Area			with sails
Cat	39 sq ft		
Mast	unstayed		

ELI LAMINATES CO. INC.
1439 Montauk Hwy.
Oakdale, NY 11769
(516) 589-4020

Sinbad the Sailer

Thunderbird Sailing Dinghy

Howmar 8' Havler

LOD .... 8'	Hull .... FRP	LOD .... 8'	Hull ..... FRP/Foam
LWL .... na	Spar .... Alum	LWL .... na	Deck .... FRP/Foam
Beam .... 3'11"	Pos Float .... yes	Beam .... 4'	Spar .... Alum
Draft	SA/Disp 33.4	Draft	Pos Float .... yes
db up .... 4"	Designer ..... T. Lotz	db up .... 4"	Cockpit .... na
db dn ...... 2'8"	First Built 1977	db dn ...... 2'4"	Headroom .... na
Disp ...... 87 lbs	No. Built 327	Disp ...... 110 lbs	SA/Disp 29.3
Ballast .... 0 lbs	1 Design .... yes	Ballast .... 0 lbs	Designer
Sail Area	Price $749	Sail Area	Ross A. Sackett
Cat .... 41 sq ft	with sails	Cat .... 42 sq ft	First Built 1947
Mast Ht .... 13'		Mast Ht .... 12'	No. Built 1500
Mast ...... unstayed		Mast ...... unstayed	1 Design .... yes
Auxiliary .... opt		Auxiliary .... opt	Price $995
2 hp			with sails

LOD .... 8'1"	Hull .... FRP
LWL .... na	Deck .... FRP
Beam .... 4'3"	Spar .... Alum
Draft	Pos Float .... yes
db up .... na	Designer
db dn ...... 19"	Howmar Boats
Disp .... na	First Built 1979
Ballast .... na	No. Built 800
Sail Area	1 Design .... no
Gunter .... 37 sq ft	Price $895
Mast Ht .... 12'	with sails
Mast ...... unstayed	
Auxiliary .... opt	
2 hp	

SINBAD THE SAILER
P. O. Box 143
West Bend, WI 53095
(414) 338-8619

SNUG HARBOR BOAT WORKS
10121 Snug Harbor Rd.
St. Petersburg, FL 33702
(813) 576-1094

HOWMAR BOATS
29 Mack Drive
Edison, NJ 08817

SMR Performer

The *SMR* PERFORMER is a sound example of Old World design and craftsmanship. She is built to ensure durability and safety.

The *SMR* PERFORMER is not only a sailing delight, but provides mountings for motoring and rowing.

The wine glass shaped fiberglass hull makes for ease in towing and her hand-rubbed mahogany trim is a beauty to behold — a pride of ownership. Truly a "Dinghy of Distinction" — befit for the discriminating yachtsman at an affordable price.

At *SMR* we specialize in building "Dinghies of Distinction" and bringing an end to the "Dinghy Dilemma."

What is the **"Dinghy Dilemma"**? Simply, it is the tendency for Dinghies to perform in some areas and not others. Thousands of both custom and production Dinghies are produced each year. Some will row, some will sail. Some will motor and some will tow. Some sacrifice speed and performance for other needs. Some neglect beauty for durability. We know, because at *SMR* we are also cruising yachtsmen and have experienced the very same **"Dinghy Dilemma."**

If you have been plagued by the **"Dinghy Dilemma,"** then we invite you to test sail the *SMR* Dinghies. We are sure you will agree in beauty, durability and performance at sail, under power, towed or rowed, the *SMR* dinghies have no equal. Truly, the *SMR* dinghies are "Dinghies of Distinction," a compliment to any yacht; a yacht for work or pleasure in its own right.

LOD	8'6"	Hull	FRP
LWL	na	Spar	Alum
Beam	4'	Pos Float	yes
Draft		SA/Disp	25.1
cb up	6"	First Built	1979
cb dn	2'	1 Design	no
Disp	110 lbs	Price	$1,150
Ballast	0 lbs		with sails
Sail Area			
Cat	36 sq ft		
Mast Ht	12'		
Mast	unstayed		
Auxiliary	opt		
	2 hp		

SMR INDUSTRIES
1301 3rd Street South
St. Petersburg, FL 33701
(813) 322-5521

Patriot 8

Beachcomber Dingy

9' Sailing Dinghy

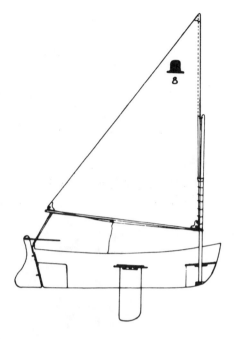

LOD .... 9'	Hull .... FRP
LWL .... 7'6"	Spar .... Alum
Beam .... 4'	Pos Float ...... yes
Draft	Designer .. Jack Smith
db up .... 3"	First Built 1980
db dn .... 3'	No. Built 22
Disp .... na	1 Design ...... yes
Ballast .... na	Price $1,450
Sail Area	with sails
Cat (Sprit) .. 35 sq ft	
Mast Ht .... 8'4"	
Mast ...... unstayed	
Auxiliary .... opt	
2 hp	

LOD .... 8'6"	Hull .... FRP
LWL .... na	Spar .... Alum
Beam .... 4'	SA/Disp 26.3
Draft	Kit .... available
db up .... 5"	Price $990
db dn ...... 1'11"	with sails
Disp .... 90 lbs	
Ballast .... 0 lbs	
Sail Area	
Cat ...... 33 sq ft	
Mast ...... unstayed	
Auxiliary .... opt	
1.9 hp	

LOD .... 9'	Hull .... FRP
LWL .... na	Spar .... Alum
Beam .... 4'4"	Pos Float ...... yes
Draft	SA/Disp 28
lb up .... na	First Built 1972
lb dn .... na	No. Built 2519
Disp ...... 105 lbs	Price $889
Ballast .... 0 lbs	with sails
Sail Area	
Cat (sprit) .. 39 sq ft	
Sloop .... na	
Auxiliary .... opt	
2 hp	

Note: Also available in 7' and 8' lengths.

LIBERTY YACHT CORP.
Rt. 2 Box 548
Leland, NC 28451
(919) 371-3999

**BEACHCOMBER
BOAT BUILDING**
P. O. Box 206
Port Salerno, FL 33492

SUMNER BOAT CO.
334 S. Bayview Ave.
Amityville, NY 11701
(516) 264-1830

9' Dyer Dhow

Minto

Admiral Sailing Dinghy

LOD . . . . 9'1"	Hull . . . . FRP
LWL . . . . na	Deck . . . . FRP
Beam . . . . 4'6"	Spar . . . . . Wood or Al
Draft	Pos Float . . . . . . yes
cb up . . . . 5"	SA/Disp 32.1
cb dn . . . . 2'9"	Designer William Dyer
Disp . . . . . . 106 lbs	First Built 1949
Ballast . . . . 0 lbs	No. Built 5700
Sail Area	1 Design . . . . . . yes
Cat . . . . . . 45 sq ft	Price $1,385
Auxiliary . . . . . . opt	with sails
2 hp	

LOD . . . . 9'1"	Hull . . . . FRP
LWL . . . . na	Spar . . . . Alum
Beam . . . . 51"	Pos Float . . . . . . yes
Draft	SA/Disp 35.6
db up . . . . 6"	First Built 1962
db dn . . . . 2'6"	No. Built 1188
Disp . . . . . . 100 lbs	Price $1,295
Ballast . . . . na	with sails
Sail Area	
Cat . . . . . . 48 sq ft	
Mast Ht . . . . 15'	
Auxiliary . . . . opt	
3 hp	

LOD . . . . 9'2"	Hull . . . . FRP
LWL . . . . na	Spar . . . . Alum
Beam . . . . 4'4"	Pos Float . . . . . . yes
Draft	SA/Disp 30.7
cb up . . . . 6"	First Built 1982
cb dn . . . . 2'	No. Built 25
Disp . . . . . . 125 lbs	1 Design . . . . no
Ballast . . . . 0 lbs	Price $1,350
Sail Area	with sails
Cat . . . . . . 48 sq ft	
Sloop . . . . . 65 sq ft	
Mast Ht . . . . 15'	
Mast . . . . . . unstayed	
Auxiliary . . . . opt	
4 hp	

THE ANCHORAGE
57 Miller St.
Warren, RI 02885
(401) 245-3300

RANGER BOAT CO.
25802 Pacific Hwy. S.
Kent, WA 98031
(206) 839-5213

SMR INDUSTRIES
1301 3rd Street South
St. Petersburg, FL 33701
(813) 322-5521

Chaser 9

LOD . . . . 9'3"	Hull . . . . FRP
LWL . . . . na	Spar . . . . Alum
Beam . . . . 4'2"	Pos Float . . . . . . yes
Draft	SA/Disp 49.8
db up . . . . 6"	No. Built 400
db dn . . . . 2'	Price $695
Disp . . . . 55 lbs	with sails
Ballast . . . . . . 0 lbs	
Sail Area	
Cat . . . . . . 45 sq ft	
Mast Ht . . . . 14'	
Mast . . . . . . unstayed	
Auxiliary . . . . opt	
2 hp	

MORETTE'S
17 Sideroad
Erin, Ontario
Canada N0B 1T0
(519) 833-2263

Nordic IX

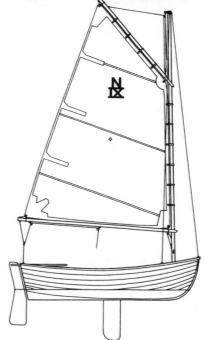

LOD . . . . 9'3"	Hull . . . . FRP
LWL . . . . 8'2"	Spar . . . . Wood
Beam . . . . 3'11"	Pos Float . . . . . . yes
Draft	SA/Disp 32.4
db up . . . . na	Disp/LWL 107
db dn . . . . 2'6"	Price $1,595
Disp . . . . 130 lbs	with sails
Ballast . . . . 0 lbs	
Sail Area	
Cat (Gaff) . . 52 sq ft	

NORDIC DINGHY CO.
2635 175th Ave. NE
Redmond, WA 98052
(206) 881-2622

Shrimp

LOD . . . . 9'7"	Hull . . . . FRP
LWL . . . . na	Spar . . . . Alum
Beam . . . . 4'10"	Pos Float . . . . . . yes
Draft	SA/Disp 32.9
cb up . . . . 6"	1 Design . . . . yes
cb dn . . . . 2'6"	Price $1,195
Disp . . . . 120 lbs	with sails
Ballast . . . . 0 lbs	
Sail Area	
Cat . . . . . . 50 sq ft	
Mast . . . . . . unstayed	
Auxiliary . . . . opt	

VANDESTADT & McGRUER LTD.
Box 7, Owen Sound
Ontario, Canada N4K 5P1
(519) 376-8548

10' Dyer Dink   Quartermaster 10   Sailing Wherry

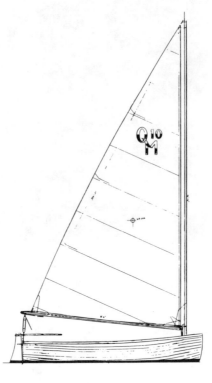

LOD . . . . 10'	Hull . . . . FRP	LOD . . . . 10'	Hull . . . . FRP
LWL . . . . na	Deck . . . . FRP	LWL . . . . 10'	Spar . . . . Alum
Beam . . . . 4'6"	Spar . . . . Wood	Beam . . . . 4'1"	SA/Disp 40
Draft	Pos Float . . . . . . yes	Draft	Disp/LWL 65
cb up . . . . 5"	SA/Disp 40.1	db up . . . . na	Price $1,295
cb dn . . . . . 3'10"	Designer	db dn . . . . na	with sails
Disp . . . . . . 135 lbs	Philip Rhodes	Disp . . . . . . 145 lbs	
Ballast . . . . 0 lbs	First Built 1934	Ballast . . . . 0 lbs	
Sail Area	No. Built 1240	Sail Area	
Cat . . . . . . 66 sq ft	1 Design . . . . yes	Cat . . . . . . 69 sq ft	
Auxiliary . . . . opt	Price $2,120	Mast . . . . . . unstayed	
2 hp	with sails		

LOD . . . . 10'	Hull . . . . . . FRP/Foam
LWL . . . . na	Spar . . . . Alum
Beam . . . . 4'6"	Pos Float . . . . yes
Draft	Cockpit . . . . na
db up . . . . 4"	Headroom . . . . na
db dn . . . . . . 2'4"	SA/Disp 36.8
Disp . . . . . . 150 lbs	Designer
Ballast . . . . 0 lbs	Ross A. Sackett
Sail Area	First Built 1981
Cat . . . . . . 65 sq ft	No. Built 52
Mast Ht . . . . 16'	1 Design . . . . yes
Auxiliary . . . . opt	Price $1,495
2 hp	with sails

The Ten

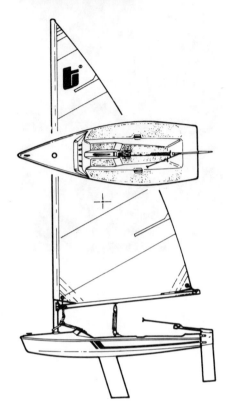

LOD	10'3"	Hull	FRP
LWL	9'10"	Deck	FRP
Beam	3'9"	Spar	Alum
Draft		Pos Float	yes
db up	2"	Cockpit	6'
db dn	2'4"	SA/Disp	62.1
Disp	85 lbs	Disp/LWL	39
Ballast	0 lbs	Designer	Jim Melton
Sail Area		First Built	1981
Cat	75 sq ft	No. Built	16
Mast Ht	19'	Price	$1,295
Mast	unstayed		with sails

J. MELTON SAILBOATS
124 S. Main St.
Andover, OH 44003
(216) 293-5822

Turnabout

LOD	10'4"	Hull	FRP/Airex
LWL	9'6"	Deck	FRP
Beam	5'3"	Spar	Alum
Draft		Pos Float	yes
cb up	6"	Cockpit	9'
cb dn	2'6"	Designer	
Disp	na		Harold R. Turner
Ballast	na	First Built	1948
Sail Area		No. Built	3505
Cat	60 sq ft	1 Design	yes
Mast Ht	18'	Price	$1,995
			with sails

PARKER RIVER MARINA
292 High Road
Newbury, MA 01950
(617) 462-4551

Mirror Dingy

LOD	10'10"	Hull	Wood
LWL	na	Deck	Wood
Beam	4'7"	Spar	Alum
Draft		Designer	Jack Holt
cb up	na	No. Built	70,000
cb dn	na	Kit	$1250 with sails
Disp	135 lbs		
Ballast	0 lbs		
Sail Area			
Sloop	69 sq ft		

COUNTRY WAYS INC.
15235 Minnetonka Blvd.
Minnetonka, MN 55343
(612) 935-1218

Free Spirit

LOD	11'	Hull	ABS plastic
LWL	10'	Spar	Alum
Beam	3'2''	Pos Float	yes
Draft		Price	$470
db up	na		with sails
db dn	na		
Disp	na		
Ballast	na		
Sail Area			
Lateen	45 sq ft		

SEARS ROEBUCK & CO.
25-04 Sears Tower
Chicago, IL 60684

Ranger 11

LOD	11'	Hull	FRP
LWL	na	Spar	Alum
Beam	4'9''	Pos Float	yes
Draft		SA/Disp	48
db up	6''	Designer	
db dn	2'9''		Raymond Richards
Disp	125 lbs	First Built	1973
Ballast	na	No. Built	271
Sail Area		Price	$1,575
Sloop	75 sq ft		with sails
Auxiliary	opt		
	3 hp		

RANGER BOAT CO.
25802 Pacific Hwy. S.
Kent, WA 98031
(206) 839-5213

Sea Snark

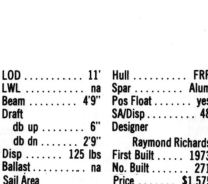

LOD	11'	Hull	Polystyrene
LWL	na	Spar	Alum
Beam	3'2''	Pos Float	yes
Draft		SA/Disp	46
db up	na	Price	$249
db dn	na		with sails
Disp	62 lbs		
Ballast	0 lbs		
Sail Area			
Lateen	45 sq ft		
Mast	unstayed		

KRANSCO MFG.
501 Forbes Blvd.
South San Francisco, CA 94080
(415) 871-9440

Sundancer

LOD	11'	Hull	Cycolac
LWL	na	Spar	Alum
Beam	3'6"	Pos Float	yes
Draft		SA/Disp	68.9
cb up	na	First Built	1982
cb dn	na	Price	$598
Disp	52 lbs		with sails
Ballast	0 lbs		
Sail Area			
Cat	60 sq ft		
Mast	unstayed		

KRANSCO MFG.
501 Forbes Blvd.
South San Francisco, CA 94080
(415) 871-9440

Sunflower

LOD	11'	Hull	Cycolac
LWL	na	Spar	Alum
Beam	3'6"	Pos Float	yes
Draft		SA/Disp	69.6
cb up	na	Price	$499
cb dn	na		with sails
Disp	45 lbs		
Ballast	0 lbs		
Sail Area			
Lateen	55 sq ft		
Mast	unstayed		

KRANSCO MFG.
501 Forbes Blvd.,
South San Francisco, CA 94080
(415) 871-9440

Super Snark

LOD	11'	Hull	Cycolac
LWL	na	Spar	Alum
Beam	3'2"	Pos Float	yes
Draft		SA/Disp	61.6
db up	na	Price	$399
db dn	na		with sails
Disp	40 lbs		
Ballast	0 lbs		
Sail Area			
Lateen	45 sq ft		
Mast	unstayed		

KRANSCO MFG.
501 Forbes Blvd.
South San Francisco, CA 94080
(415) 871-9440

Gloucester 11

Skunk

Topper

Gloucester 11	
LOD .... 11'1"	Hull .... FRP
LWL .... 10'3"	Deck .... FRP
Beam .... 5'2"	Spar .... Alum
Draft	Pos Float ...... yes
db up .... 3"	SA/Disp 41.2
db dn ...... 2'9"	Disp/LWL 82
Disp ...... 200 lbs	Designer
Ballast .... 0 lbs	Harry R. Sindle
Sail Area	First Built 1972
Sloop ..... 88 sq ft	No. Built 812
Mast Ht ...... 19'8"	1 Design .... yes
Auxiliary .... opt	Price $1,795
3 hp	with sails

GLOUCESTER YACHTS
P. O. Box 307, Rte. 623
Gloucester, VA 23061
(804) 693-3818

Skunk	
LOD .... 11'1"	Hull .... FRP
LWL .... na	Spar .... Alum
Beam .... 5'5"	Pos Float ...... yes
Draft	SA/Disp 33.9
cb up .... 6"	1 Design .... yes
cb dn ...... 2'6"	Price $1,530
Disp ...... 190 lbs	with sails
Ballast .... 0 lbs	
Sail Area	
Sloop ..... 70 sq ft	
Mast ...... unstayed	
Auxiliary .... opt	
5 hp	

VANDESTADT & McGRUER LTD.
Box 7, Owen Sound
Ontario, Canada N4K 5P1
(519) 376-8548

Topper	
LOD .... 11'2"	Hull ... Polypropylene
LWL .... na	Deck .. Polypropylene
Beam .... 3'10"	Spar .... Alum
Draft	Pos Float .... yes
db up .... 3"	SA/Disp 43
db dn ...... 2'6"	Builder
Disp .... 95 lbs	J. V. Dunhill, England
Ballast .... 0 lbs	1 Design .... yes
Sail Area	Price $1,150
Cat ...... 56 sq ft	with sails
Mast Ht .... 17'	
Mast ...... unstayed	

TOPPER SAILCRAFT INC.
P. O. Box 3349
Deland, FL 32720
(904) 734-5308

CL 11

Sandpiper 100

Super Snark 2

LOD	11'3"	Hull	FRP
LWL	10'	Deck	FRP
Beam	4'10"	Spar	Alum
Draft		Pos Float	yes
cb up	8"	SA/Disp	44.8
cb dn	3'	Disp/LWL	75
Disp	170 lbs	Price	na
Ballast	0 lbs		
Sail Area			
Sloop	86 sq ft		

LOD	11'4"	Hull	Cycolac
LWL	na	Spar	Alum
Beam	4'10"	Pos Float	yes
Draft		SA/Disp	69.7
cb up	na	Designer	
cb dn	na		A. Kostanecki
Disp	110 lbs	First Built	1970
Ballast	0 lbs	Price	$1,198
Sail Area			with sails
Sloop	100 sq ft		
Mast	unstayed		
Auxiliary	opt		
	4 hp		

LOD	11'4"	Hull	Cycolac
LWL	na	Spar	Alum
Beam	58"	Pos Float	yes
Draft		SA/Disp	53.5
db up	na	Price	$995
db dn	na		with sails
Disp	100 lbs		
Ballast	0 lbs		
Sail Area			
Lateen	72 sq ft		
Mast	unstayed		
Auxiliary	opt		
	4 hp		

C&L BOAT WORKS
884 Dillingham Rd.
Pickering, Ontario
Canada L1W 1Z6
(416) 839-7991

KRANSCO MFG.
501 Forbes Blvd.
South San Francisco, CA 94080
(415) 871-9440

KRANSCO MFG.
501 Forbes Blvd.
South San Francisco, CA 94080
(415) 871-9440

Breezy 12

Minifish

Sailing Tender

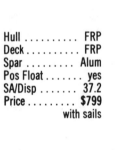

LOD	11'7"	Hull	FRP
LWL	na	Deck	FRP
Beam	3'10"	Spar	Alum
Draft		Pos Float	yes
db up	na	SA/Disp	37.2
db dn	na	Price	$799
Disp	85 lbs		with sails
Ballast	0 lbs		
Sail Area			
Cat	45 sq ft		
Mast	unstayed		

LOD	11'9"	Hull	FRP
LWL	na	Deck	FRP
Beam	3'10"	Spar	Alum
Draft		Pos Float	yes
db up	4"	SA/Disp	52.6
db dn	na	First Built	1971
Disp	88 lbs	1 Design	yes
Ballast	0 lbs	Price	$895
Sail Area			with sails
Lateen	65 sq ft		

LOD	11'9"	SA/Disp	30.6
LWL	na	Price	$1,995
Beam	4'2"		with sails
Disp	150 lbs		
Ballast	0 lbs		
Sail Area	54 sq ft		
Auxiliary	opt		
	5 hp		

DOLPHIN INDUSTRIES
395 S. Earlham St.
Orange, CA 92669
(714) 633-5520

AMF ALCORT/SAILBOATS
Box 1345
Waterbury, CT 06708
(203) 756-7091

JARVIS NEWMAN BOATS
P. O. Box 707
Southwest Harbor, ME 04679
(207) 244-3860

Holder 12

Lowell Sailing Skiff

Sea Devil

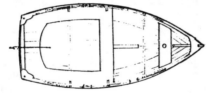

LOD	12'	Hull	FRP
LWL	11'3"	Deck	FRP
Beam	5'	Spar	Alum
Draft		Pos Float	yes
db up	4"	Cockpit	8'
db dn	3'	SA/Disp	46
Disp	115 lbs	Disp/LWL	36
Ballast	0 lbs	Designer	Ron Holder
Sail Area		First Built	1982
Cat	68 sq ft	1 Design	yes
Mast Ht	18'	Price	$1,395
Mast	unstayed		with sails

LOD	12'	Hull	Wood
LWL	10'6"	Spar	Wood
Beam	5'	Pos Float	yes
Draft		First Built	1920
db up	5"	No. Built	1200
db dn	3'2"	Price	$3,600
Disp	na		with sails
Ballast	0 lbs		
Sail Area			
Sloop (Gaff)	70 sq ft		
Sloop	na		
Mast Ht			
Gunter	12'6"		
Sloop	18'		
Mast	unstayed		
Auxiliary	opt		
	9.9 hp		
	tbd		

LOD	12'	Hull	ABS
LWL	na	Spar	Alum
Beam	3'3"	Pos Float	yes
Draft		Designer	
db up	na		J. T. Lockley
db dn	na	Builder	Lockley
Disp	na	First Built	1970
Ballast	na	Price	$459
Sail Area			with sails
Sloop	70 sq ft		

HOBIE CAT
Box 1008, 4925 E. Oceanside Blvd.
Oceanside, CA 92054
(714) 758-9100

LOWELL'S BOAT SHOP INC.
459 Main Street
Amesbury, MA 01913

LOCKLEY MANUFACTURING CO.
310 Grove Street
New Castle, PA 16103

Sea Swinger

Sea Witch

Sumner Sprite

LOD	12'	Hull	ABS
LWL	na	Designer	
Beam	3'3"		J. T. Lockley
Draft		Builder	Lockley
db up	na	First Built	1970
db dn	na	Price	$445
Disp	na		with sails
Ballast	na		
Sail Area			
Lateen	55 sq ft		

LOD	12'	Hull	ABS
LWL	na	Spar	Alum
Beam	4'8"	Pos Float	yes
Draft		Designer	
db up	na		J. T. Lockley
db dn	na	Builder	Lockley
Disp	na	First Built	1975
Ballast	na	Price	$1,064
Sail Area			with sails
Sloop	100 sq ft		
Auxiliary	opt		
	6 hp		

LOD	12'	Hull	FRP
LWL	11'	Deck	FRP
Beam	4'7"	Spar	Alum
Draft		Pos Float	yes
db up	6"	SA/Disp	40.4
db dn	2'6"	Disp/LWL	65
Disp	195 lbs	First Built	1981
Ballast	0 lbs	No. Built	317
Sail Area		1 Design	no
Sloop	85 sq ft	Price	$1,695
Mast Ht	16'8"		with sails
Auxiliary	opt		
	4.5 hp		

Wingsailer

LOD	12'	Hull	FRP
LWL	10'8"	Deck	FRP
Beam	na	Spar	FRP
Draft		SA/Disp	28.2
cb up	3"	Disp/LWL	22
cb dn	2'1"	Price	$1,495
Disp	60 lbs		with sails
Ballast	0 lbs		
Sail Area			
Wing	27 sq ft		

FIBERGLASS UNLIMITED
2212 S. Miami Blvd.
Durham, NC 27703
(919) 596-2887

Butterfly

LOD	12'2"	Hull	FRP
LWL	na	Deck	FRP
Beam	4'6"	Spar	Alum
Draft		Pos Float	yes
db up	2'	Designer	John Barnett
db dn	4'	First Built	1960
Disp	na	No. Built	8900
Ballast	na	1 Design	yes
Sail Area		Price	$1,795
Cat	75 sq ft		with sails
Mast Ht	18'		

BARNETT BOAT CO.
534 Commercial Ave.
Green Lake, WI 54941
(414) 294-6351

Howmar 12

LOD	12'2"	Hull	FRP
LWL	11'5"	Deck	FRP
Beam	5'	Spar	Alum
Draft		Pos Float	yes
cb up	4"	Designer	
cb dn	2'6"	Sparkman & Stephens	
Disp	na	First Built	1981
Ballast	na	No. Built	250
Sail Area		1 Design	yes
Sloop	90 sq ft	Price	$2,195
Mast Ht	21'		with sails
Auxiliary	opt		
	4 hp		

HOWMAR BOATS
29 Mack Drive
Edison, NJ 08817

The Twelve

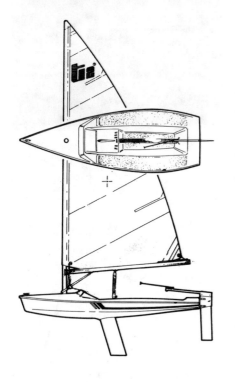

LOD .... 12'3"	Hull .... FRP
LWL .... 10'6"	Deck .... FRP
Beam .... 4'	Spar .... Alum
Draft	Pos Float .... yes
db up .... 2"	Cockpit .... 8'
db dn .... 2'6"	SA/Disp 55.7
Disp .... 100 lbs	Disp/LWL 38
Ballast ...... 0 lbs	Designer .. Jim Melton
Sail Area	First Built 1982
Cat ...... 75 sq ft	No. Built 4
Mast Ht ...... 19'4"	1 Design .... yes
Mast ..... unstayed	Price $1,475
	with sails

J. MELTON SAILBOATS
124 S. Main St.
Andover, OH 44003
(216) 293-5822

Beetle Cat Boat

LOD .... 12'4"	Hull .... Wood
LWL .... 11'8"	Deck .... Wood
Beam .... 6'	Spar .... Wood
Draft	Pos Float .... no
cb up .... 9"	Cockpit .... 6'
cb dn .... 2'	SA/Disp 27.2
Disp .... 450 lbs	Disp/LWL 126
Ballast ..... 50 lbs	Blst/Disp 11%
Sail Area	Designer
Cat (gaff) . 100 sq ft	Beetle Family
Mast Ht .... 14'	First Built 1921
	No. Built 3000
	1 Design .... yes
	Price $3,400
	without sails

CONCORDIA CO.
South Wharf
S. Dartmouth, MA 02748

Widgeon

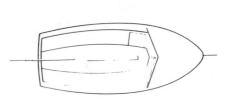

LOD .... 12'4"	Hull .... FRP
LWL .... 11'6"	Deck .... FRP
Beam .... 5'	Spar .... Alum
Draft	Pos Float .... yes
cb up .... 5"	Cockpit .... 7'7"
cb dn .... 3'6"	SA/Disp 31.1
Disp .... 315 lbs	Disp/LWL 92
Ballast ...... 0 lbs	Designer Robert Baker
Sail Area	First Built 1964
Sloop ..... 90 sq ft	No. Built 4474
Mast Ht .... 18'8"	1 Design .... yes
	Price .... na

BANGOR PUNTA MARINE
848 Airport Rd.
Box 991
Fall River, MA 02722
(617) 678-5291

12' Dyer Dhow

LOD .... 12'6"	Hull .... FRP
LWL .... na	Deck .... FRP
Beam .... 5'2"	Spar .... Alum
Draft	Pos Float ...... yes
cb up .... 8"	SA/Disp 31.6
cb dn .... 3'11"	Designer William Dyer
Disp ...... 220 lbs	First Built 1945
Ballast .... 0 lbs	No. Built 425
Sail Area	1 Design .... yes
Cat ...... 72 sq ft	Price $2,990
Sloop ..... 91 sq ft	with sails
Auxiliary .... opt	
2 hp	

THE ANCHORAGE
57 Miller St.
Warren, RI 02885
(401) 245-3300

Mistral 12

LOD .... 12'6"	Hull .... FRP
LWL .... na	Deck .... FRP
Beam .... 5'	Spar .... Alum
Draft	SA/Disp 44
cb up .... na	Price .... na
cb dn ...... 3'4"	
Disp ...... 200 lbs	
Ballast .... 0 lbs	
Sail Area	
Sloop ..... 94 sq ft	

MISTRAL INC.
2187 De La Province
Longueuil, Quebec
Canada J4G 1R2
(514) 679-6221

Puffer

LOD .... 12'6"	Hull .... FRP
LWL .... na	Deck .... FRP
Beam .... 4'10"	Spar .... Alum
Draft	Pos Float ...... yes
db up .... 8"	SA/Disp 48.9
db dn .... na	First Built 1972
Disp ...... 160 lbs	1 Design .... yes
Ballast .... 0 lbs	Price $1,995
Sail Area	with sails
Sloop ..... 90 sq ft	

AMF ALCORT/SAILBOATS
Box 1345
Waterbury, CT 06708
(203) 756-7091

Tech Dinghy

LOD	12'8"	Hull	FRP
LWL	12'	Deck	FRP
Beam	5'2"	Spar	Alum
Draft		SA/Disp	29
cb up	6"	Disp/LWL	65
cb dn	na	Designer	
Disp	250 lbs		H. Herreshoff
Ballast	0 lbs	Price	$3,014
Sail Area			with sails
Cat	72 sq ft		

VANGUARD
1251 E. Wisconsin Ave.
Pewaukee, WI 53072
(414) 691-3320

Streaker

LOD	12'9"	Hull	Wood
LWL	na	Deck	Wood
Beam	4'7"	Spar	Alum
Draft		Pos Float	yes
cb up	na	Designer	Jack Holt
cb dn	na	1 Design	yes
Disp	100 lbs	Kit	$1540 with sails
Ballast	0 lbs		
Sail Area			
Sloop	70 sq ft		

COUNTRY WAYS INC.
15235 Minnetonka Blvd.
Minnetonka, MN 55343
(612) 935-1218

Banshee

LOD	13'	Hull	FRP
LWL	12'4"	Deck	FRP
Beam	4'1"	Spar	Alum
Draft		Pos Float	yes
db up	4"	Cockpit	8'
db dn	2'6"	SA/Disp	53.9
Disp	120 lbs	Disp/LWL	28
Ballast	0 lbs	Designer	Richard Reed
Sail Area		First Built	1979
Cat	82 sq ft	No. Built	8500
Mast Ht	20'6"	1 Design	yes
Mast	unstayed	Price	$1,875
			with sails

BANSHEE INTERNATIONAL
12186 Winton Way
Los Altos Hills, CA 94022
(415) 969-3334

Banshee T

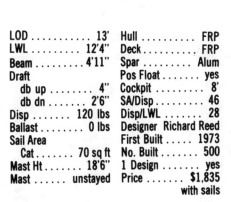

LOD . . . . 13'	Hull . . . . FRP
LWL . . . . 12'4"	Deck . . . . FRP
Beam . . . . 4'11"	Spar . . . . Alum
Draft	Pos Float . . . . yes
db up . . . . 4"	Cockpit . . . . 8'
db dn . . . . . 2'6"	SA/Disp 46
Disp . . . . . . 120 lbs	Disp/LWL 28
Ballast . . . . 0 lbs	Designer Richard Reed
Sail Area	First Built 1973
Cat . . . . . . 70 sq ft	No. Built 500
Mast Ht . . . . . . 18'6"	1 Design . . . . yes
Mast . . . . . unstayed	Price $1,835
	with sails

BANSHEE INTERNATIONAL
12186 Winton Way
Los Altos Hills, CA 94022
(415) 969-3334

Cyclone 13

LOD . . . . 13'	Hull . . . . FRP
LWL . . . . na	Deck . . . . FRP
Beam . . . . 4'11"	Spar . . . . Alum
Draft	Pos Float . . . . yes
db up . . . . na	SA/Disp 42.3
db dn . . . . na	Designer . Frank Butler
Disp . . . . . . 148 lbs	First Built 1972
Ballast . . . . 0 lbs	No. Built 2355
Sail Area	1 Design . . . . yes
Cat . . . . . . 74 sq ft	Price $1,395
	with sails

CATALINA YACHTS
21200 Victory Blvd.
Woodland Hills, CA 91367
(213) 884-7700

Salisbury Point Skiff

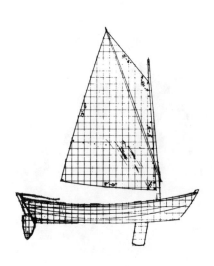

LOD . . . . 13'	Hull . . . . Wood
LWL . . . . 11'6"	Spar . . . . Wood
Beam . . . . 4'6"	Pos Float . . . . yes
Draft	First Built 1860
cb up . . . . 4"	No. Built 2000
cb dn . . . . . 2'11"	Price $2,800
Disp . . . . na	with sails
Ballast . . . . 0 lbs	
Sail Area	
Sprit . . . . . 60 sq ft	
Mast Ht . . . . . . 12'6"	
Mast . . . . . . unstayed	
Auxiliary . . . . opt	
4.5 hp	
outbd	

LOWELL'S BOAT SHOP INC.
459 Main Street
Amesbury, MA 01913

Code 40

LOD	13'1"	Spar	Alum
LWL	13'1"	Pos Float	yes
Beam	5'1"	SA/Disp	52.8
Draft		Disp/LWL	37
cb up	na	Designer	Andre Cornu
cb dn	3'4"	Price	na
Disp	187 lbs		
Ballast	0 lbs		
Sail Area			
Sloop	108 sq ft		

C&L BOAT WORKS
884 Dillingham Rd.
Pickering, Ontario
Canada L1W 1ZF
(416) 839-7991

Gryphon

LOD	13'1"	Hull	CF
LWL	12'1"	Deck	CF
Beam	5'	Spar	CF
Draft		Pos Float	yes
db up	3"	Cockpit	8'
db dn	2'6"	SA/Disp	67
Disp	85 lbs	Disp/LWL	21
Ballast	0 lbs	Designer	Barry Bruch
Sail Area		First Built	1980
Cat	81 sq ft	No. Built	90
Mast Ht	21'6"	1 Design	yes
Mast	unstayed	Price	$3,850
			with sails

BANSHEE INTERNATIONAL
12186 Winton Way
Los Altos Hills, CA 94022
(415) 969-3334

Thundercat

LOD	13'2"	Hull	FRP/Foam
LWL	na	Deck	FRP/Foam
Beam	5'2"	Spar	Alum
Draft		Pos Float	yes
db up	5"	Cockpit	na
db dn	3'	Headroom	na
Disp	300 lbs	SA/Disp	39.3
Ballast	0 lbs	Designer	
Sail Area			Ross A. Sackett
Cat	110 sq ft	First Built	1969
Mast Ht	20'6"	No. Built	183
Auxiliary	opt	1 Design	yes
	2 hp	Price	$2,495
			with sails

SNUG HARBOR BOAT WORKS
10121 Snug Harbor Rd.
St. Petersburg, FL 33702
(813) 576-1094

Flying Junior

International Enterprise

Mistral 4.04

LOD . . . . 13'3"	Hull . . . . FRP	LOD . . . . 13'3"	Hull . . . . FRP
LWL . . . . na	Deck . . . . FRP	LWL . . . . na	Deck . . . . FRP
Beam . . . . 4'11"	Spar . . . . Alum	Beam . . . . 5'3"	Spar . . . . Alum
Draft	Pos Float . . . . yes	Draft	Pos Float . . . . yes
cb up . . . . 6"	SA/Disp 53.2	cb up . . . . 7"	SA/Disp 51.7
cb dn . . . . na	1 Design . . . . . . yes	cb dn . . . . . 3'3"	Designer . . . Jack Holt
Disp . . . . . . 165 lbs	Price $3,477	Disp . . . . . . 207 lbs	First Built 1956
Ballast . . . . 0 lbs	with sails	Ballast . . . . 0 lbs	No. Built 20,700
Sail Area		Sail Area	1 Design . . . . yes
Sloop . . . . 100 sq ft		Sloop . . . . 113 sq ft	Price $2,860
Mast Ht . . . . 20'		Mast Ht . . . . 22'	without sails

LOD . . . . 13'3"	Hull . . . . FRP		
LWL . . . . 12'4"	Deck . . . . FRP		
Beam . . . . 4'9"	Spar . . . . Alum		
Draft	SA/Disp 51.1		
cb up . . . . 6"	Disp/LWL 42		
cb dn . . . . . . 3'6"	Price . . . . na		
Disp . . . . . . 175 lbs			
Ballast . . . . 0 lbs			
Sail Area			
Sloop . . . . 100 sq ft			

VANGUARD
1251 E. Wisconsin Ave.
Pewaukee, WI 53072
(414) 691-3320

TURNER MARINE
RR 1, Lake Mattoon
Neoga, IL 62447
(217) 895-3395

MISTRAL INC.
2187 De La Province
Longueuil, Quebec
Canada J4G 1R2
(514) 679-6221

Sailboat Buyers' Guide

Page 79

Spindrift

Blue Jay

Starwind 13.5

LOD .... 13'4"	Hull ...... FRP/Foam
LWL .... na	Spar .... Alum
Beam .... 5'2"	Pos Float .... yes
Draft	SA/Disp 46
cb up .... 4"	1 Design .... yes
cb dn .... 3'	Price $1,975
Disp ...... 205 lbs	with sails
Ballast .... 0 lbs	
Sail Area	
Sloop .... 100 sq ft	

LOD .... 13'6"	Hull .... FRP
LWL .... na	Deck .... FRP
Beam .... 5'2"	Spar .... Alum
Draft	Pos Float .... yes
cb up .... 6"	SA/Disp 34.1
cb dn .... 3'8"	1 Design .... yes
Disp ...... 275 lbs	Price $2,895
Ballast .... 0 lbs	without sails
Sail Area	
Sloop .... 90 sq ft	

LOD .... 13'6"	Hull .... FRP
LWL .... 12'6"	Deck .... FRP
Beam .... 4'9"	Spar .... Alum
Draft	SA/Disp 44.5
db up .... 5"	Disp/LWL 32
db dn .... 3'2"	Price .... na
Disp ...... 140 lbs	
Ballast .... 0 lbs	
Sail Area	
Lateen .... 75 sq ft	

VANDESTADT & McGRUER LTD.
Box 7, Owen Sound
Ontario, Canada N4K 5P1
(519) 376-8548

SAYBROOK YACHT YARD
Ferry Rd., P. O. Box 492
Old Lyme, CT 06371
(203) 434-7025

STARWIND
8151 Bradenton Road
Sarasota, FL 33580
(813) 756-1811

Sundowner II

Holder 14

Vagabond 14

LOD .... 13'6"	Hull .... FRP
LWL .... na	Deck .... FRP
Beam .... 4'	Spar .... FRP
Draft	Pos Float .... yes
db up .... 4"	SA/Disp 69.3
db dn .... 2'6"	First Built 1983
Disp .... 65 lbs	1 Design .... yes
Ballast ...... 0 lbs	Price $995
Sail Area	with sails
Cat .... 70 sq ft	
Mast ...... unstayed	

LOD .... 13'8"	Hull .... FRP
LWL .... 12'6"	Deck .... FRP
Beam .... 6'2"	Spar .... Alum
Draft	Pos Float .... yes
db up .... 6"	Cockpit .... 9'
db dn ...... 3'10"	SA/Disp 42.7
Disp ...... 265 lbs	Disp/LWL 60
Ballast .... 0 lbs	Designer . Ron Holder
Sail Area	First Built 1977
Sloop .... 110 sq ft	1 Design .... yes
Mast Ht .... 20'8"	Price .... na

LOD .... 13'8"	Hull .... FRP
LWL .... 12'6"	Deck .... FRP
Beam .... 6'2"	Spar .... Alum
Draft	Pos Float .... yes
db up .... 6"	SA/Disp 42.7
db dn ..... 3'10"	Disp/LWL 61
Disp ...... 265 lbs	Price .... na
Ballast .... 0 lbs	
Sail Area	
Sloop .... 110 sq ft	
Auxiliary .... opt	

SUNDOWNER INDUSTRIES
292 South State St.
Otisville, MI 48463
(313) 631-4607

HOBIE CAT
Box 1008, 4925 E. Oceanside Blvd.
Oceanside, CA 92054
(714) 758-9100

VAGABOND SAILBOATS
3401 West Fordham
Santa Ana, CA 92704
(714) 979-9361

Aqua Finn

LOD	13'9"	Hull	FRP/Coremat
LWL	13'9"	Deck	FRP/Coremat
Beam	4'2"	Spar	Alum
Draft		SA/Disp	48
db up	4"	Disp/LWL	21
db dn	2'10"	Price	$1,095
Disp	125 lbs		with sails
Ballast	0 lbs		
Sail Area			
Lateen	75 sq ft		

AMERICAN SAIL
7325 Pepperdam Ave.
Pepperdam Industrial Park
Charleston, SC 29405
(803) 552-8548

Omega 14

LOD	13'9"	Hull	FRP
LWL	na	Deck	FRP
Beam	5'8"	Spar	Alum
Draft		Pos Float	yes
cb up	4"	SA/Disp	39
cb dn	3'6"	Designer	Frank Butler
Disp	295 lbs	First Built	1970
Ballast	0 lbs	No. Built	2007
Sail Area		1 Design	yes
Sloop	108 sq ft	Price	$1895
			with sails

CATALINA YACHTS
21200 Victory Blvd.
Woodland Hills, CA 91367
(213) 884-7700

Star Dancer

LOD	13'9"	Hull	FRP
LWL	na	Deck	FRP
Beam	4'	Spar	Alum
Draft		Pos Float	yes
cb up	12"	Headroom	na
cb dn	3'	SA/Disp	44.5
Disp	140 lbs	Designer	Edo Western
Ballast	0 lbs	First Built	1963
Sail Area		No. Built	6720
Lateen	75 sq ft	1 Design	yes
Mast Ht	18'	Price	$1,195
Mast			with sails
Lateen	unstayed		

LOFTY SAILS
111 E. Pacific
Salina, KS 67401

Vanguard 420

Laser

Sunfish

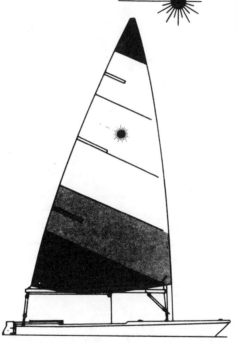

	Vanguard 420	
LOD	13'9"	Hull . . . . FRP
LWL	13'2"	Deck . . . . FRP
Beam	5'5"	Spar . . . . Alum
Draft		SA/Disp 56
cb up	6"	Disp/LWL 34
cb dn	3'2"	Designer
Disp	176 lbs	Christian Maury, France
Ballast	0 lbs	1 Design . . . . yes
Sail Area		Price $3,716
Sloop	110 sq ft	with sails

	Laser	
LOD	13'10"	Hull . . . . FRP
LWL	12'6"	Deck . . . . FRP
Beam	4'6"	Spar . . . . Alum
Draft		Pos Float . . . . yes
db up	na	Designer . Bruce Kirby
db dn	na	First Built 1970
Disp	na	No. Built . . . 120,000
Ballast	na	1 Design . . . . yes
Sail Area		Price $1,995
Cat	76 sq ft	with sails
Mast	unstayed	

	Sunfish	
LOD	13'10"	Hull . . . . FRP
LWL	na	Deck . . . . FRP
Beam	4'1"	Spar . . . . Alum
Draft		Pos Float . . . . yes
db up	6"	SA/Disp 47
db dn	na	First Built 1952
Disp	129 lbs	No. Built . . 200,000+
Ballast	0 lbs	1 Design . . . . yes
Sail Area		Price $1,259
Lateen	75 sq ft	with sails

VANGUARD
1251 E. Wisconsin Ave.
Pewaukee, WI 53072
(414) 691-3320

PERFORMANCE SAILCRAFT
824 West 18th St.
Costa Mesa, CA 92627
(714) 642-0846

AMF ALCORT/SAILBOATS
Box 1345
Waterbury, CT 06708
(203) 756-7091

Force 5

LOD .... 13'11"	Hull .... FRP
LWL .... na	Deck .... FRP
Beam .... 4'10"	Spar .... Alum
Draft	Pos Float ...... yes
db up .... 6"	SA/Disp 52.8
db dn .... na	Designer .. Fred Scott
Disp ...... 145 lbs	First Built 1973
Ballast .... na	1 Design ...... yes
Sail Area	Price $1,995
Cat ...... 91 sq ft	with sails

AMF ALCORT/SAILBOATS
Box 1345
Waterbury, CT 06708
(203) 756-7091

Javelin

LOD .... 14'	Hull .... FRP
LWL .... 13'2"	Deck .... FRP
Beam .... 5'8"	Spar .... Alum
Draft	Pos Float ...... yes
cb up .... 6"	Cockpit .... 9'
cb dn .... 3'10"	SA/Disp 30.8
Disp ...... 524 lbs	Disp/LWL 102
Ballast .... 0 lbs	Designer ... Uffa Fox
Sail Area	First Built 1962
Sloop .... 125 sq ft	No. Built 4518
Mast Ht ...... 23'1"	1 Design ...... yes
Auxiliary .... opt	Price .... na
8 hp	

BANGOR PUNTA MARINE
848 Airport Rd.
Box 991
Fall River, MA 02722
(617) 678-5291

Lido 14

LOD .... 14'	Hull .... FRP
LWL .... na	Deck .... FRP
Beam .... 6'	Spar .... Alum
Draft	SA/Disp 38.8
cb up .... 5"	1 Design ...... yes
cb dn ...... 4'3"	Price $2,839
Disp ...... 310 lbs	with sails
Ballast .... 0 lbs	
Sail Area	
Sloop .... 111 sq ft	

W. D. SCHOCK CORP.
3502 S. Greenville St.
Santa Ana, CA 92704
(714) 549-2277

Nomad 14

LOD	14'	Hull	FRP/Coremat
LWL	13'	Deck	FRP/Coremat
Beam	6'	Spar	Alum
Draft		Pos Float	yes
db up	3"	SA/Disp	38.1
db dn	3'8"	Disp/LWL	63
Disp	310 lbs	Designer	
Ballast	0 lbs		Geoff Prindle
Sail Area		First Built	1983
Sloop	109 sq ft	1 Design	yes
		Price	$2,898
			with sails

SURFGLAS
1810 E. Borchard
Santa Ana, CA 92705
(714) 835-6416

Rhodes Bantam

LOD	14'	Hull	FRP
LWL	13'10"	Spar	Alum
Beam	5'6"	Pos Float	yes
Draft		Cockpit	13'
cb up	6"	SA/Disp	42.3
cb dn	4'	Disp/LWL	13
Disp	325 lbs	Designer	
Ballast	0 lbs		Philip Rhodes
Sail Area		First Built :	1948
Sloop	125 sq ft	No. Built	1850
Mast Ht	20'	1 Design	yes
		Kit	available
		Price	$3,275
			without sails

DYNAMIC PLASTICS
Route 1, Box 6
New Paris, OH 45347
(513) 437-7261

Sailing Surf Dory

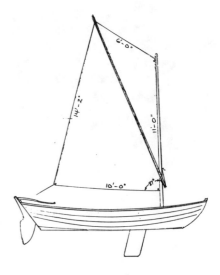

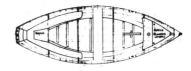

LOD	14'	Hull	Wood
LWL	11'	Spar	Wood
Beam	5'	Pos Float	yes
Draft		First Built	1793
cb up	4"	No. Built	10,000
cb dn	2'6"	1 Design	yes
Disp	na	Kit	available
Ballast	0 lbs	Price	$4,600
Sail Area			with sails
Sloop (Gaff)	72 sq ft		
Spirit	72 sq ft		
Mast Ht			
Sloop (Gaff)	13'6"		
Spirit	12'		
Mast	unstayed		
Auxiliary	opt		
	7.5 hp		

LOWELL'S BOAT SHOP INC.
459 Main Street
Amesbury, MA 01913

Phantom

LOD	14'1"	Hull	FRP
LWL	10'6"	Deck	FRP
Beam	4'5"	Spar	Alum
Draft		Pos Float	yes
db up	na	First Built	1977
db dn	2'10"	No. Built	10,000
Disp	na	1 Design	yes
Ballast	0 lbs	Price	$1,269
Sail Area			with sails
Lateen	84 sq ft		
Mast Ht	15'6"		
Mast	unstayed		

HOWMAR BOATS
29 Mack Drive
Edison, NJ 08817

CL 14

LOD	14'2"	Hull	FRP
LWL	14'2"	Deck	FRP
Beam	5'6"	Spar	Alum
Draft		Pos Float	yes
cb up	8"	SA/Disp	49.7
cb dn	3'6"	Disp/LWL	37
Disp	240 lbs	Price	na
Ballast	0 lbs		
Sail Area			
Sloop	120 sq ft		

C&L BOAT WORKS
884 Dillingham Rd.
Pickering, Ontario
Canada L1W 1Z6
(416) 839-7991

Doodle

LOD	14'2"	Hull	FRP
LWL	14'2"	Deck	FRP
Beam	53"	Spar	Alum
Draft		Pos Float	yes
cb up	6"	SA/Disp	42.3
cb dn	29"	Disp/LWL	39
Disp	250 lbs	Designer	Furman Shaw
Ballast	0 lbs	First Built	1967
Sail Area		No. Built	355
Sloop	105 sq ft	1 Design	yes
Mast Ht	18'6"	Price	$2,295
			with sails

AQUA MOTION INDUSTRIES
P. O. Box 884
Lansdale, PA 19446
(215) 362-8016

Pulsar

PULSAR

LOD	14'3"	Hull	FRP
LWL	13'	Deck	FRP
Beam	5'3"	Spar	Alum
Draft		Pos Float	yes
cb up	4"	SA/Disp	53.3
cb dn	3'6"	Disp/LWL	38
Disp	190 lbs	Designer	Robert Dufour
Ballast	0 lbs	First Built	1981
Sail Area		1 Design	yes
Sloop	110 sq ft	Price	$3,380 Can.
Mast Ht	21'6"		with sails

Manchac

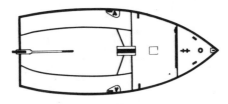

LOD	14'4"	Hull	FRP
LWL	12'6"	Deck	FRP
Beam	6'2"	Spar	Alum
Draft		Pos Float	yes
db up	6"	SA/Disp	31.7
db dn	2'9"	Disp/LWL	88
Disp	385 lbs	1 Design	yes
Ballast	0 lbs	Price	$2500
Sail Area			with sails
Sloop	105 sq ft		

Laser II

LOD	14'5"	Hull	FRP
LWL	na	Deck	FRP
Beam	4'8"	Spar	Alum
Draft		Pos Float	yes
db up	na	Designer	
db dn	na		Bethwaite/Bruce
Disp	na	First Built	1980
Ballast	na	No. Built	5000
Sail Area		1 Design	yes
Sloop	124 sq ft	Price	$2,995
			with sails

NAVIBEC SPORTS
289 Savage Granby
P.Q. Canada J2G 4T5
(514) 372-5201

RON CHAPMAN SHIPWRIGHT
3500 Buffon St.
Chalmette, LA 70043
(504) 277-6526

PERFORMANCE SAILCRAFT
824 West 18th St.
Costa Mesa, CA 92627
(714) 642-0846

Rascal

Dolphin Senior

Triggerfish

Rascal

LOD	14'5"	Hull	FRP
LWL	13'10"	Deck	FRP
Beam	6'	Spar	Alum
Draft		Pos Float	yes
cb up	4"	Cockpit	8'6"
cb dn	3'	SA/Disp	37.2
Disp	375 lbs	Disp/LWL	63
Ballast	na	Designer	Ray Greene
Sail Area		First Built	1962
Sloop	121 sq ft	No. Built	4018
Mast Ht	26'	1 Design	yes
Auxiliary	opt	Price	$2,895
			with sails

Dolphin Senior

LOD	14'6"	Hull	FRP
LWL	14'	Deck	FRP
Beam	4'3"	Spar	Alum
Draft		Pos Float	no
db up	6"	Cockpit	3'3"
db dn	3'	SA/Disp	44.3
Disp	170 lbs	Disp/LWL	28
Ballast	0 lbs	Designer	
Sail Area			Glen Corcorran
Lateen	85 sq ft	First Built	1963
Mast Ht	16'	No. Built	7000
Mast	unstayed	1 Design	yes
		Price	$1,650
			with sails

Triggerfish

LOD	14'6"	Hull	FRP
LWL	na	Deck	FRP
Beam	3'10"	Spar	Alum
Draft		Pos Float	yes
cb up	na	1 Design	yes
cb dn	2'9"	Price	$2,195
Disp	na		with sails
Ballast	na		
Sail Area			
Sloop	85 sq ft		

SPINDRIFT ONE DESIGNS
1220 Tallevast Rd.
Tallevast, FL 33588
(813) 355-8455

MIDWEST DOLPHIN
16400 E. Truman Rd.
Independence, MO 64050
(816) 254-5600

TRIGGERFISH SAILBOATS
158 Pickett St.
S. Portland, ME 04106

Gloucester 15

LOD	14'7"	Hull	FRP
LWL	14'	Deck	FRP
Beam	5'3"	Spar	Alum
Draft		Pos Float	yes
cb up	4"	SA/Disp	35.4
cb dn	3'10"	Disp/LWL	56
Disp	350 lbs	Blst/Disp	14%
Ballast	50 lbs	Designer	Harry Sindle
Sail Area		First Built	1969
Sloop	110 sq ft	No. Built	790
Mast Ht	21'2"	1 Design	yes
Auxiliary	opt	Price	$2,795
	3 hp		with sails

GLOUCESTER YACHTS
P. O. Box 307, Rte. 623
Gloucester, VA 23061
(804) 693-3818

O'Day 15

LOD	14'7"	Hull	FRP
LWL	13'6"	Deck	FRP
Beam	5'11"	Spar	Alum
Draft		Pos Float	yes
db up	5"	Cockpit	10'
db dn	2'9"	SA/Disp	35.1
Disp	350 lbs	Disp/LWL	63
Ballast	0 lbs	Designer	
Sail Area			C. R. Hunt Assoc.
Sloop	108.8 sq ft	First Built	1981
Mast Ht	22'9"	No. Built	178
Auxiliary	opt	1 Design	yes
	4 hp	Price	na

BANGOR PUNTA MARINE
848 Airport Rd.
Box 991
Fall River, MA 02722
(617) 678-5291

Skeltic

LOD	14'7"	Hull	FRP
LWL	13'	Deck	FRP
Beam	4'6"	Spar	Alum
Draft		Pos Float	yes
db up	3"	SA/Disp	81.1
db dn	4'	Disp/LWL	28
Disp	136 lbs	Designer	
Ballast	0 lbs		Jacques Fauroux
Sail Area		Builder	
Sloop	134 sq ft		Keltic Marine, France
		First Built	1982
		No. Built	2000
		1 Design	yes
		Price	$2,995
			with sails

THE ROMNEY GROUP
165—B New Boston St.
Woburn, MA 01801
(617) 935-6802

Arrow 15

 (Arrow 15 photo)

LOD .... 14'8"	Hull .... FRP
LWL .... 14'8"	Deck .... FRP
Beam .... 4'1"	Spar .... Alum
Draft	Pos Float .... yes
db up .... na	SA/Disp 47.1
db dn .... na	Disp/LWL 21
Disp ...... 155 lbs	Price .... na
Ballast .... 0 lbs	
Sail Area	
Lateen .... 85 sq ft	
Mast Ht .... 10'	
Mast ...... unstayed	

AYR—WAY IND.
P. O. Box 426
Kendallville, IN 46755
(219) 347-4515

Mistral 15

(Mistral 15 photo)

LOD .... 14'8"	Hull .... FRP
LWL .... na	Deck .... FRP
Beam .... 5'	Spar .... Alum
Draft	Pos Float .... yes
db up .... na	SA/Disp 49.9
db dn .... na	Price .... na
Disp ...... 145 lbs	
Ballast .... 0 lbs	
Sail Area	
Cat .... 86 sq ft	

MISTRAL INC.
2187 De La Province
Longueuil, Quebec
Canada J4G 1R2
(514) 679-6221

MK II Finn

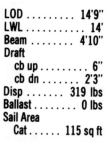

LOD .... 14'9"	Hull .... FRP
LWL .... 14'	Deck .... FRP
Beam .... 4'10"	Spar .... Alum
Draft	SA/Disp 39.4
cb up .... 6"	Disp/LWL 52
cb dn ...... 2'3"	Designer
Disp ...... 319 lbs	Rickard Sarby
Ballast .... 0 lbs	Price $4,805
Sail Area	with sails
Cat ...... 115 sq ft	

VANGUARD
1251 E. Wisconsin Ave.
Pewaukee, WI 53072
(414) 691-3320

Scaffie

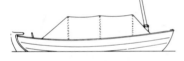

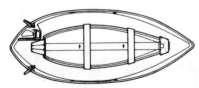

LOD .... 14'9"	Hull .... FRP
LWL .... 12'3"	Spar .... Wood
Beam .... 5'9"	Pos/Float ...... yes
Draft .... 1'3"	SA/Disp 26.9
Disp ...... 460 lbs	Disp/LWL 111
Ballast .... 0 lbs	Designer
Sail Area	John Watkinson
Lugsail ... 100 sq ft	Price $3,795
Mast ..... unstayed	with sails
Auxiliary .... opt	
3 hp	

MAINE MARINE CORP.
Rte. 32
Waldoboro, ME 04572
(207) 832-5323

Whitehall

LOD .... 14'9"	Hull .... Wood
LWL .... na	Spar .... Wood
Beam .... 4'	SA/Disp 29
Draft	Price .... na
db up .... na	
db dn .... na	
Disp .... 200 lbs	
Ballast .... 0 lbs	
Sail Area	
Cat (sprit) .. 62 sq ft	
Mast ...... unstayed	

AMERICAN BOAT HOUSE
Atlantic Ave., P. O. Box 911
Camden, ME 04843
(207) 236-4188

Designer's Choice

LOD .... 14'10"	Hull .... FRP
LWL .... 12'9"	Deck .... FRP
Beam .... 6'1"	Spar .... Alum
Draft	Pos Float .... yes
cb up .... 5"	Designer
cb dn .... 3'	Sparkman & Stephens
Disp .... na	First Built 1979
Ballast .... na	No. Built 1000
Sail Area	1 Design .... yes
Sloop .... 120 sq ft	Price $3,195
Mast Ht .... 24'	with sails
Auxiliary .... opt	
4 hp	

HOWMAR BOATS
29 Mack Drive
Edison, NJ 08817

Bateau

Albacore

Falcon

LOD . . . . 14'11"	Hull . . . . FRP
LWL . . . . 14'6"	Spar . . . . Alum
Beam . . . . 3'6"	Pos Float . . . . . . yes
Draft	Cockpit . . . . open
cb up . . . . 3"	SA/Disp 41.3
cb dn . . . . . 2'10"	Disp/LWL 16
Disp . . . . . . 112 lbs	Designer
Ballast . . . . 0 lbs	H. Raymond Bond
Sail Area	First Built 1981
Lateen . . . . 60 sq ft	No. Built 12
Mast Ht . . . . . . 10'8"	1 Design . . . . . . yes
Mast . . . . . . unstayed	Price $1,475
Auxiliary . . . . opt	with sails
4 hp	

LOD . . . . 15'	Hull . . . . FRP
LWL . . . . na	Deck . . . . FRP
Beam . . . . 5'4"	Spar . . . . Alum
Draft	Pos Float . . . . yes
cb up . . . . 9"	SA/Disp 51.8
cb dn . . . . . . 4'9"	Designer
Disp . . . . 240 lbs	Uffa Fox
Ballast . . . . 0 lbs	Price . . . . $3,995 Can
Sail Area	with sails
Sloop . . . . 125 sq ft	

LOD . . . . 15'	Hull . . . . FRP/Coremat
LWL . . . . 14'1"	Deck . . . FRP/Coremat
Beam . . . . 5'8"	Spar . . . . Alum
Draft	Pos Float . . . . yes
cb up . . . . 4"	SA/Disp 48.6
cb dn . . . . . . 3'3"	Disp/LWL 45
Disp . . . . . . 280 lbs	Designer Bruce Kelley
Ballast . . . . 0 lbs	1 Design . . . . yes
Sail Area	Price $2,985
Sloop . . . . 130 sq ft	with sails

Galilee 15

Harpoon 4.6

Mercury

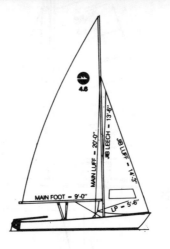

LOD	15'	Hull	FRP
LWL	13'	Deck	FRP
Beam	6'8"	Spar	Alum
Draft		Pos Float	yes
db up	7"	SA/Disp	27
db dn	3'7"	Disp/LWL	106
Disp	525 lbs	Blst/Disp	23%
Ballast	120 lbs	Designer	Steven Dileo
Sail Area		First Built	1981
Sloop	110 sq ft	No. Built	100
Mast Ht	21'10"	1 Design	yes
Auxiliary	opt	Price	$3,395
	2 hp		with sails

LOD	15'	Hull	FRP
LWL	13'4"	Deck	FRP
Beam	6'7"	Spar	Alum
Draft		Pos Float	yes
cb up	6"	SA/Disp	36.5
cb dn	3'4"	Disp/LWL	80
Disp	425 lbs	1 Design	yes
Ballast	0 lbs	Price	$4,390
Sail Area			without sails
Sloop	129 sq ft		
Mast Ht	23'		

LOD	15'	Hull	FRP
LWL	13'10"	Deck	FRP
Beam	5'5"	Spar	Alum
Draft		Pos Float	yes
Deep	2'5"	SA/Disp	23.5
Shoal cb up	na	Disp/LWL	123
Shoal cb dn	3'3"	Designer	
Disp			Sparkman & Stephens
Deep	730 lbs	1 Design	yes
Shoal	470 lbs	Price	$4,260
Ballast	na		with sails
Sail Area			
Sloop	119 sq ft		
Auxiliary	opt		

GALILEE BOATWORKS
P. O. Box 403
Mayo, MD 21106
(301) 798-6224

BOSTON WHALER INC.
P. O. Box 10184
Riviera Beach, FL 33404
(305) 842-5171

CAPE COD SHIPBUILDING CO.
Narrows Rd.
Box 152
Wareham, MA 02571
(617) 295-3550

Montgomery 15   Starwind 15   Wing Dinghy

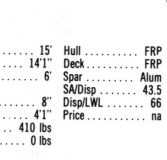

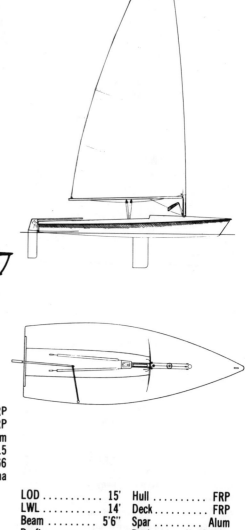

LOD . . . . 15'	Hull . . . . FRP
LWL . . . . 13'3"	Deck . . . . FRP
Beam . . . . 6'4"	Spar . . . . Alum
Draft	Pos Float . . . . . . yes
cb up . . . . 15"	Cockpit . . . . 5'6"
cb dn . . . . 2'6"	Headroom . . . . . . 4'
Disp . . . . . . 750 lbs	SA/Disp 23.6
Ballast . . . . . . 275 lbs	Disp/LWL 144
Sail Area	Blst/Disp 37%
Sloop . . . . 122 sq ft	Designer
	Jerry Montgomery
	First Built 1980
	No. Built 230
	1 Design . . . . no
	Price $4,295
	with sails

LOD . . . . 15'	Hull . . . . FRP
LWL . . . . 14'1"	Deck . . . . FRP
Beam . . . . 6'	Spar . . . . Alum
Draft	SA/Disp 43.5
db up . . . . 8"	Disp/LWL 66
db dn . . . . . . 4'1"	Price . . . . na
Disp . . . . . . 410 lbs	
Ballast . . . . 0 lbs	
Sail Area	
Sloop . . . . 150 sq ft	

LOD . . . . 15'	Hull . . . . FRP
LWL . . . . 14'	Deck . . . . FRP
Beam . . . . 5'6"	Spar . . . . Alum
Draft	Designer . . Jim Antrim
db up . . . . na	1 Design . . . . yes
db dn . . . . . . 2'7"	Price $2,315
Disp . . . . na	with sails
Ballast . . . . na	
Sail Area	
Cat . . . . . . 108 sq ft	

MONTGOMERY MARINE
935 W. 18th St.
Costa Mesa, CA 92626
(714) 548-9452

STARWIND
8151 Bradenton Road
Sarasota, FL 33580
(813) 756-1811

PYRAMID BOATWORKS
2429 Pratt Ave.
Hayward, CA 94544
(415) 489-8025

West Wight Potter 15

The World famous West Wight Potter 15 cabin sloop is one of the best known and oldest sailboat models in the cruising fraternity, with thousands of these attractive compact cruisers sailing the waters of the USA and all over the world. Continuously improved over her long 19 year history, she has achieved a noteworthy record of sailing successes, including being sailed single-handed from California to Hawaii, from Seattle to Ketchikan, and from England to Sweden across the North Atlantic. Her wide beam and unique hull configuration combine to provide the stability and sea-going attributes of far larger boats. Yet the Potter easily trails behind today's smaller cars — even the newest mini-compact models.

Designed for safety and ease of sailing, the Potter is self bailing, self righting, non-sinkable (bonded closed cell foam flotation) and is extremely stable under sail. Even in stronger winds the Potter sails more level than comparable boats and is especially known for her high dry cockpit. Excellent performance is achieved with the highly efficient simulated gaff rig, loose footed mainsail, and deep fin keel. The standard kick-up rudder, fully retracting swing keel, and molded in hull skegs make her one of the few completely beachable cruisers—great for going ashore in remote areas for that special picnic or exploring new shoreline. With carefully designed fittings and hardware, the Potter can be rigged, launched, and sailed with the minimum of effort by one person. Just push the mast up from cabin top cradle position, connect the forestay and you have completed the standing rigging. Everything else slides and snaps into place without a single nut, bolt or cotter pin anywhere. Even the trailer is specially designed to allow the Potter to be easily rolled off and on the trailer. For unprepared launching areas, the trailer has a special tilting mechanism which allows the Potter to be launched at shoreside with the trailer completely out of the water. No other cabin sloop has so many convenience and safety features as the West Wight Potter.

The roomy cabin features 6½' bunks, two food lockers, room for a portable head, chain locker in the forepeak, and over 14 cubic feet of storage under the cockpit seats for sail bags, ice chest and personal gear. Hull, deck and inside liner are of the highest quality hand-laid fiberglass construction. Mast and boom are anodized with the boom well over the head of the tallest crew member. The deck has molded-in toerails and non-skid step surfaces. Cockpit coamings are high enough for comfortable back rest while sailing.

Sail-a-way price includes ALL of the following: quality dacron main and jibsails, mooring cleats, mainsheet and jibsheet cam jams, bow chocks, S.S. standing rigging, S.S. bow eye, forward air scoop, 3" bunk cushions, mahogany handrails and trim, motor mount, cockpit table, tinted side and front windows, running lights, and choice of standard hull colors in blue, orange, yellow, and smoke white. A partial list of options includes color coordinated sails, genoa, spinnaker, cockpit and bow rails, self-contained head, and trailer specially designed for easy launching.

The Potter represents the original of the compact ocean cruisers and remains one of the best sailboat values available anywhere for a completely equipped, expertly finished cabin sloop.

LOD	15'	Hull	FRP/Foam
LWL	12'	Deck	FRP/Foam
Beam	5'6"	Spar	Alum
Draft		Pos Float	yes
Swing Keel up	7"	Cockpit	5'
Swing keel dn	3'	Headroom	3'9"
Disp	475 lbs	SA/Disp	23.9
Ballast	100 lbs	Disp/LWL	123
Sail Area		Blst/Disp	21%
Sloop	91 sq ft	First Built	1962
Mast Ht	17'11"	No. Built	2000
Auxiliary	opt	1 Design	yes
	4 hp outbd	Price	$3,795 with sails

HMS MARINE
904 W. Hyde Park Blvd.
Inglewood, CA 90302
(213) 674-4540

Island 15

LOD	15'3"	Hull	FRP
LWL	13'5"	Deck	FRP
Beam	6'8"	Spar	Alum
Draft		Pos Float	yes
cb up	6"	SA/Disp	36.5
cb dn	3'4"	Disp/LWL	75
Disp	405 lbs	First Built	1983
Ballast	0 lbs	1 Design	no
Sail Area		Price	$2,595
Sloop	125 sq ft		with sails
Mast Ht	23'2"		
Auxiliary	opt		
	4.5 hp		

SUMNER BOAT CO.
334 S. Bayview Ave.
Amityville, NY 11701
(516) 264-1830

Coronado 15

LOD	15'4"	Hull	FRP
LWL	na	Deck	FRP
Beam	5'8"	Spar	Alum
Draft		Pos Float	yes
cb up	4"	SA/Disp	42
cb dn	3'6"	Designer	Frank Butler
Disp	385 lbs	First Built	1970
Ballast	0 lbs	No. Built	3303
Sail Area		1 Design	yes
Sloop	139 sq ft	Price	$1,995
			with sails

CATALINA YACHTS
21200 Victory Blvd.
Woodland Hills, CA 91367
(213) 884-7700

Int'l 470

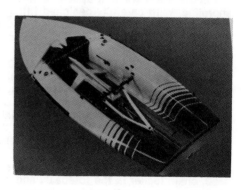

LOD	15'5"	Hull	FRP
LWL	14'7"	Deck	FRP
Beam	5'6"	Spar	Alum
Draft		SA/Disp	53.8
cb up	6"	Disp/LWL	37
cb dn	3'2"	Price	$4,240
Disp	260 lbs		with sails
Ballast	0 lbs		
Sail Area			
Sloop	137 sq ft		
Mast Ht	23'3"		

VANGUARD
1251 E. Wisconsin Ave.
Pewaukee, WI 53072
(414) 691-3320

Mistral 4.7

Dabber

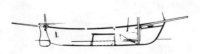

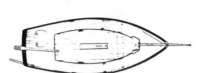

Sandpiper

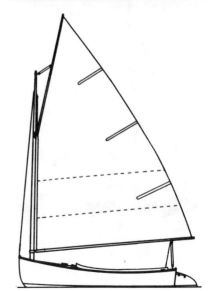

LOD	15'5"	Hull	FRP
LWL	na	Deck	FRP
Beam	5'2"	Spar	Alum
Draft		SA/Disp	62.7
cb up	na	Price	na
cb dn	3'2"		
Disp	225 lbs		
Ballast	0 lbs		
Sail Area			
Sloop	145 sq ft		

MISTRAL INC.
2187 De La Province
Longeuil, Quebec
Canada J4G 1R2
(514) 679-6221

LOD	15'6"	Hull	FRP
LWL	13'7"	Spar	Wood
Beam	5'10"	Pos Float	yes
Draft		SA/Disp	28.1
cb up	8"	Disp/LWL	97
cb dn	3'	Designer	
Disp	550 lbs		John Watkinson
Ballast	0 lbs	Price	$6,136
Sail Area			with sails
Yawl	118 sq ft		
Auxiliary	opt		
	4 hp		

MAINE MARINE CORP.
Rte. 32
Waldoboro, ME 04572
(207) 832-5323

LOD	15'6"	Hull	FRP
LWL	na	Deck	FRP
Beam	7'1"	Spar	Alum
Draft		Pos Float	yes
cb up	1'4"	SA/Disp	25.7
cb dn	3'9"	Blst/Disp	19%
Disp	1050 lbs	First Built	1972
Ballast	200 lbs	Price	$5,500
Sail Area			with sails
Cat (gaff)	166 sq ft		
Auxiliary	opt		

MARSHALL MARINE CORP.
P. O. Box P-266
S. Dartmouth, MA 02748
(617) 994-0414

Snipe

LOD .... 15'6"	Hull .... FRP
LWL .... 13'6"	Deck .... FRP
Beam .... 5'	Spar .... Alum
Draft	Pos Float ...... yes
db up .... 5"	Cockpit .... 6'
db dn ...... 3'3"	SA/Disp 35.9
Disp ...... 381 lbs	Disp/LWL 69
Ballast .... 0 lbs	First Built 1969
Sail Area	No. Built 130
Sloop .... 118 sq ft	1 Design .... yes
Mast Ht .... 21'6"	Price $3,500
	without sails

SOUTHERN YACHTS
3550 South East Blvd.
Wichita, KS 67216

Gloucester 16

LOD .... 15'7"	Hull .... FRP
LWL .... 14'	Deck .... FRP
Beam .... 6'3"	Spar .... Alum
Draft	Pos Float ...... no
Swing keel up .. 9"	Cockpit .... 7'6"
Swing keel dn . 3'9"	Headroom .... 4'
Disp .... 900 lbs	SA/Disp 23.5
Ballast ..... 350 lbs	Disp/LWL 146
Sail Area	Blst/Disp 39%
Sloop .... 137 sq ft	Designer W. Lapworth
Mast Ht .... 24'	First Built 1967
Auxiliary .... opt	No. Built 1100
4 hp	1 Design .... yes
	Price $3,995
	with sails

GLOUCESTER YACHTS
P. O. Box 307, Rte. 623
Gloucester, VA 23061
(804) 693-3818

Bull's Eye

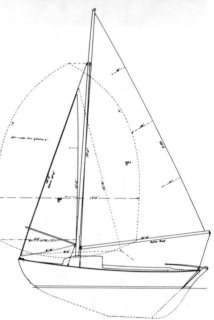

LOD .... 15'8"	Hull .... FRP
LWL .... 12'7"	Deck .... FRP
Beam .... 5'10"	Spar .... Alum
Draft .... 2'5"	Pos Float ...... yes
Disp ...... 1350 lbs	SA/Disp 18.3
Ballast .... 750 lbs	Disp/LWL 302
Sail Area	Blst/Disp 56%
Sloop .... 140 sq ft	Designer
	N. Herreshoff
	1 Design .... yes
	Price $6,683
	with sails

CAPE COD SHIPBUILDING CO.
Narrows Rd.
Box 152
Wareham, MA 02571
(617) 295-3550

H – 12

LOD . . . . 15'8"	Hull . . . . FRP
LWL . . . . 12'6"	Deck . . . . FRP/Wood
Beam . . . . 5'10"	Spar . . . . Wood
Draft . . . . 2'5"	Pos Float . . . . yes
Disp . . . . . 1350 lbs	SA/Disp 18.3
Ballast . . . . . 750 lbs	Disp/LWL 308
Sail Area	Blst/Disp 56%
Sloop (gaff) 140 sq ft	Designer
	N. Herreshoff
	Price $8,595
	with sails

CAPE COD SHIPBUILDING CO.
Narrows Rd.
Box 152
Wareham, MA 02571
(617) 295-3550

Neptune 16

LOD . . . . 15'9"	Hull . . . . FRP
LWL . . . . 13'6"	Deck . . . . FRP
Beam . . . . 6'2"	Spar . . . . Alum
Draft	SA/Disp 23.5
Swing keel up . . 10"	Disp/LWL 163
Swing keel dn . . 4'	Blst/Disp 22%
Fixed . . . . . . 2'2"	Price . . . . na
Disp . . . . . 900 lbs	
Ballast	
Swing . . . . 200 lbs	
Fixed . . . . 275 lbs	
Sail Area	
Sloop . . . . 137 sq ft	

CAPITAL YACHTS INC.
25914 President Ave.
Harbor City, CA 90710
(213) 530-1311

Doughdish

THE DOUGHDISH

LOD . . . . 15'10"	Hull . . . . FRP
LWL . . . . 12'6"	Deck . . . . FRP
Beam . . . . 5'10"	Spar . . . . Wood
Draft . . . . 2'6"	Pos Float . . . . yes
Disp . . . . . 1500 lbs	Cockpit . . . . 11'
Ballast . . . . . 735 lbs	SA/Disp 17.1
Sail Area	Disp/LWL 343
Sloop (Gaff) 140 sq ft	Blst/Disp 49%
Sloop . . . 140 sq ft	Designer
Mast Ht	N. G. Herreshoff
Sloop (Gaff) . . . . 16'	First Built 1972
Sloop . . . . 22'	No. Built 140
Auxiliary . . . . opt	1 Design . . . . yes
2-3 hp	Price $9,125
	with sails

DOUGHDISH
380 Wareham St.
Marion, MA 02738

Mistral 16

Lil' Pirate

Balboa 16

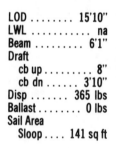

LOD	15'10"	Hull	FRP
LWL	na	Deck	FRP
Beam	6'1"	Spar	Alum
Draft		SA/Disp	44.2
cb up	8"	Price	na
cb dn	3'10"		
Disp	365 lbs		
Ballast	0 lbs		
Sail Area			
Sloop	141 sq ft		

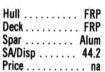

LOD	15'11"	Hull	FRP
LWL	na	Deck	FRP
Beam	5'9"	Spar	Alum
Draft		Pos Float	yes
cb up	8"	SA/Disp	31.9
cb dn	4'2"	Price	na
Disp	550 lbs		
Ballast	0 lbs		
Sail Area			
Sloop	134 sq ft		
Mast Ht	23'5"		
Auxiliary	opt		
	6 hp		

LOD	16'	Hull	FRP
LWL	14'8"	Deck	FRP
Beam	7'5"	Spar	Alum
Draft	2'5"	Pos Float	no
Disp	1000 lbs	SA/Disp	18.7
Ballast	400 lbs	Disp/LWL	141
Sail Area		Blst/Disp	40%
Sloop	117 sq ft	Designer	
Mast Ht	19'		W. Shad Turner
Auxiliary	opt	1 Design	yes
	6 hp	Price	$4,476
			with sails

MISTRAL INC.
2187 De La Province
Longueuil, Quebec
Canada J4G 1R2
(514) 679-6221

RINKERBUILT BOAT CO.
207 Chicago St.
Syracuse, IN 46567
(219) 457-5731

LAGUNA YACHTS INC.
10960 Boatman
Stanton, CA 90680
(714) 527-7262

Catboat

CL 16

Com—Pac 16

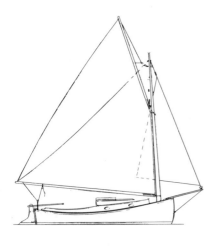

LOA . . . . 18'	Hull . . . . Wood
LOD . . . . 16'	Deck . . . Canvas/Wood
LWL . . . . 15'6"	Spar . . . . Wood
Beam . . . . 7'6"	Pos Float . . . . . . no
Draft	Cockpit . . . . 6'
cb up . . . . . . 1'10"	Headroom . . . . . 3'4"
cb dn . . . . 4'	SA/Disp 18.3
Disp . . . . . . 2500 lbs	Disp/LWL 299
Ballast . . . . . 600 lbs	Blst/Disp 24%
Sail Area	Designer S. S. Crocker
Sloop (gaff) 211 sq ft	First Built 1980
Mast . . . . . . unstayed	No. Built 2
Auxiliary . . . . opt	1 Design . . . . no
6 hp	Price $12,500
	with sails

LOD . . . . 16'	Hull . . . . FRP
LWL . . . . . . 14'10"	Deck . . . . FRP
Beam . . . . 6'1"	Spar . . . . Alum
Draft	Pos Float . . . . . . yes
cb up . . . . 8"	SA/Disp 44.2
cb dn . . . . . 3'10"	Disp/LWL 49
Disp . . . . 365 lbs	Price . . . . na
Ballast . . . . . . 0 lbs	
Sail Area	
Sloop . . . . 141 sq ft	

LOD . . . . 16'	Hull . . . . FRP
LWL . . . . 14'	Deck . . . . FRP
Beam . . . . 6'	Spar . . . . Alum
Draft . . . . 1'6"	Pos Float . . . . . . no
Disp . . . . . . 1100 lbs	Cockpit . . . . . . 6'11"
Ballast . . . . . 450 lbs	SA/Disp 17.3
Sail Area	Disp/LWL 179
Sloop . . . . 115 sq ft	Blst/Disp 41%
Mast Ht . . . . 21'	Designer . . Clark Mills
Auxiliary . . . . opt	First Built 1975
4 hp	No. Built 1880
	1 Design . . . . yes
	Price $3,988
	with sails

THE LANDING BOATSHOP
P. O. Box 461
Kennebunkport, ME 04046
(207) 985-7976

C&L BOAT WORKS
884 Dillingham Rd.
Pickering, Ontario
Canada L1W 1Z6
(416) 839-7991

HUTCHINS CO. INC.
1195 Kapp Dr.
Clearwater, FL 33515
(813) 443-4408

Johnson Daysailer 16

M — 16 Scow

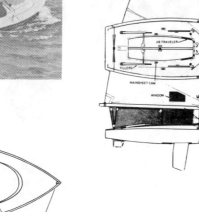

MC Scow

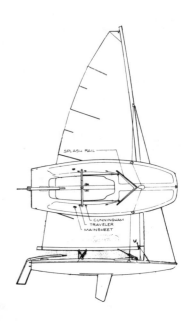

LOD . . . . 16'	Hull . . . . FRP
LWL . . . . na	Deck . . . . FRP
Beam . . . . 6'1"	Spar . . . . Alum
Draft	Price $3,395
cb up . . . . na	without sails
cb dn . . . . na	
Disp . . . . na	
Ballast . . . . na	
Sail Area	
Sloop . . . . 106 sq ft	

JOHNSON BOAT WORKS
323 S. Lake Ave.
White Bear Lake, MN 55110

LOD . . . . 16'	Hull . . . . FRP
LWL . . . . na	Deck . . . . FRP
Beam . . . . 5'8"	Spar . . . . Alum
Draft	Pos Float . . . . yes
lb up . . . . 9"	Designer Henry McKee
lb dn . . . . 2'8"	1 Design . . . . yes
Disp . . . . . . 440 lbs	Price $4,350
Ballast . . . . 0 lbs	without sails
Sail Area	
Sloop . . . . na	

MELGES BOAT WORKS
Zenda, WI 53195

JOHNSON BOAT WORKS
323 S. Lake Ave.
White Bear Lake, MN 55110

LOD . . . . 16'	Hull . . . . FRP
LWL . . . . na	Deck . . . . FRP
Beam . . . . 5'8"	Spar . . . . Alum
Draft	Pos Float . . . . yes
lb up . . . . na	Designer Harry Mekes
lb dn . . . . na	First Built 1972
Disp . . . . na	No. Built 800
Ballast . . . . na	1 Design . . . . yes
Sail Area	Price $3,368
Cat . . . . . 135 sq ft	without sails
Mast Ht . . . . 30'	

MELGES BOAT WORKS
Zenda, WI 53195

JOHNSON BOAT WORKS
323 L. Lake Ave.
White Bear Lake, MN 55110

Nordica 16   # X Boat   # Gemini

   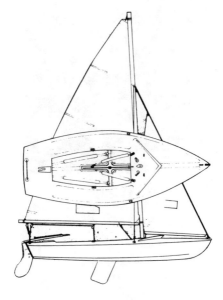   

LOD	16'	Hull	FRP
LWL	13'1"	Deck	FRP
Beam	6'2"	Spar	Alum
Draft	1'8"	Pos Float	yes
Disp	925 lbs	SA/Disp	21.9
Ballast	400 lbs	Disp/LWL	184
Sail Area		Blst/Disp	43%
Sloop	130 sq ft	Price	$4,400
Auxiliary	opt		with sails
	5 hp		

LOD	16'	Hull	FRP
LWL	na	Deck	FRP
Beam	6'1"	Spar	Alum
Draft		Pos Float	yes
cb up	1'3"	SA/Disp	27.9
cb dn	2'6"	1 Design	no
Disp	500 lbs	Price	$3,085
Ballast	0 lbs		without sails
Sail Area			
Sloop	10 sq ft		

LOD	16'1"	Hull	FRP
LWL	14'9"	Deck	FRP
Beam	5'7"	Spar	Alum
Draft		Pos Float	yes
lb up	7"	SA/Disp	38.7
lb dn	3'4"	Disp/LWL	61
Disp	440 lbs	Designer	
Ballast	0 lbs		Sidney Herreshoff
Sail Area		Price	$4,325
Sloop	140 sq ft		with sails
Auxiliary	opt		

EXE FIBRECRAFT LTD.
London Rd. S
Exeter, Ontario
Canada Nom 1SO
(519) 235-0610

MELGES BOAT WORKS
Zenda, WI 53195

JOHNSON BOAT WORKS
323 S. Lake Ave.
White Bear Lake, MN 55110

CAPE COD SHIPBUILDING CO.
Narrows Rd.
Box 152
Wareham, MA 02571
(617) 295-3550

Rebel

Precision 16

Tanzer 16

Rebel

LOD	16'1"	Hull	FRP
LWL	15'10"	Deck	FRP
Beam	6'6"	Spar	Alum
Draft		Pos Float	yes
cb up	6"	Cockpit	9'6"
cb dn	3'4"	SA/Disp	36
Disp	675 lbs	Disp/LWL	76
Ballast	na	Designer	Ray Greene
Sail Area		First Built	1947
Sloop	173 sq ft	No. Built	4000
Mast Ht	26'	1 Design	yes
Auxiliary	opt	Price	$3,795
			with sails

Precision 16

LOD	16'3"	Hull	FRP
LWL	14'	Deck	FRP
Beam	6'8"	Spar	Alum
Draft		Pos Float	yes
cb up	8"	SA/Disp	46.5
cb dn	3'8"	Disp/LWL	63
Disp	390 lbs	Designer	Steve Seaton
Ballast	0 lbs	First Built	1981
Sail Area		No. Built	70
Sloop	155 sq ft	1 Design	yes
Mast Ht	23'9"	Price	$2,595
			with sails

Tanzer 16

LOD	16'4"	Hull	FRP
LWL	15'7"	Deck	FRP
Beam	6'2"	Spar	Alum
Draft		Pos Float	yes
cb up	7"	Headroom	na
cb dn	2'9"	SA/Disp	36.8
Disp	450 lbs	Disp/LWL	53
Ballast	na	Designer	
Sail Area			Johann Tanzer
Sloop	135 sq ft	First Built	1963
Mast Ht	25'	No. Built	1455
Auxiliary	opt	1 Design	yes
	3 hp	Price	$3,395
			with sails

SPINDRIFT ONE DESIGNS
1220 Tallevast Rd.
Tallevast, FL 33588
(813) 355-8455

HUTCHINS CO. INC.
1195 Kapp Dr.
Clearwater, FL 33515
(813) 443-4408

TANZER INDUSTRIES
P. O. Box 67
Dorion, PQ Canada J7V 5V8
(514) 455-5681

Tanzer Overnighter

Islands 17

Leeward 16

LOD .... 16'4"	Hull .... FRP
LWL .... 15'7"	Deck .... FRP
Beam .... 6'2"	Spar .... Alum
Draft	Pos Float ...... yes
cb up .... 7"	SA/Disp 34.3
cb dn .... 2'9"	Disp/LWL 59
Disp ...... 500 lbs	Designer
Ballast .... na	Johann Tanzer
Sail Area	First Built 1969
Sloop ... 135 sq ft	No. Built 403
Mast Ht .... 25'	1 Design ...... yes
Auxiliary ...... opt	Price $3,900
3 hp	with sails

LOD .... 16'7"	Hull .... FRP
LWL .... 15'10"	Deck .... FRP
Beam .... 6'2"	Spar .... Alum
Draft	Pos Float ...... yes
cb up .... 7"	SA/Disp 35.5
cb dn .... 3'6"	Disp/LWL 53
Disp ...... 475 lbs	Designer
Ballast .... 0 lbs	Island Class Assoc.
Sail Area	First Built 1981
Sloop ... 135 sq ft	No. Built 1010
Mast Ht .... 23'3"	1 Design ...... yes
Auxiliary ...... opt	Price $3,395
	with sails

LOD .... 16'8"	Hull .... FRP
LWL .... 15'	Deck .... FRP
Beam .... 6'3"	Spar .... Alum
Draft	Pos Float ...... no
cb up .... 18"	Cockpit ...... 7'7"
cb dn .... 3'9"	SA/Disp 29.9
Disp ...... 650 lbs	Disp/LWL 85
Ballast .... 0 lbs	Designer ..... Luger
Sail Area	1 Design .... no
Sloop .... 140 sq ft	Kit $2,218
Mast Ht .... 22'	
Auxiliary .... opt	
7 hp	

TANZER INDUSTRIES
P. O. Box 67
Dorion, PQ Canada J7V 5V8
(514) 455-5681

SUMNER BOAT CO.
334 S. Bayview Ave.
Amityville, NY 11701
(516) 264-1830

LUGER INDUSTRIES INC.
3800 West Hwy 13
Burnsville, MN 55337
(612) 890-3000

Day Sailer

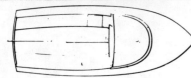

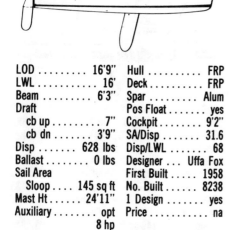

LOD	16'9"	Hull	FRP
LWL	16'	Deck	FRP
Beam	6'3"	Spar	Alum
Draft		Pos Float	yes
cb up	7"	Cockpit	9'2"
cb dn	3'9"	SA/Disp	31.6
Disp	628 lbs	Disp/LWL	68
Ballast	0 lbs	Designer	Uffa Fox
Sail Area		First Built	1958
Sloop	145 sq ft	No. Built	8238
Mast Ht	24'11"	1 Design	yes
Auxiliary	opt	Price	na
	8 hp		

BANGOR PUNTA MARINE
848 Airport Rd.
Box 991
Fall River, MA 02722
(617) 678-5291

Daysailer I

LOD	16'9"	Hull	FRP
LWL	16'	Deck	FRP
Beam	6'3"	Spar	Alum
Draft		Pos Float	yes
cb up	7"	Cockpit	7'5"
cb dn	3'9"	SA/Disp	36.9
Disp	525 lbs	Disp/LWL	57
Ballast	na	Designer	
Sail Area			Uffa Fox/George O'Day
Sloop	150 sq ft	First Built	1958
Mast Ht	28'	No. Built	11,500
Auxiliary	opt	1 Design	yes
		Price	$3,895
			with sails

SPINDRIFT ONE DESIGNS
1220 Tallevast Rd.
Tallevast, FL 33588
(813) 355-8455

Dolphin 17

LOD	16'9"	Hull	FRP
LWL	na	Deck	FRP
Beam	6'	Spar	Alum
Draft		Pos Float	no
cb up	8"	Cockpit	6'6"
cb dn	3'4"	SA/Disp	31.7
Disp	725 lbs	Blst/Disp	28%
Ballast	200 lbs	Designer	
Sail Area			Glen Corcorran
Sloop	160 sq ft	First Built	1970
Mast Ht	24'	No. Built	750
Auxiliary	opt	1 Design	no
	7.5 hp	Price	$4,595
			with sails

DOLPHIN 17 COMPANY
Municipal Airport
P. O. Box 817
Coffeyville, KN 67337
(316) 251-4110

Dolphin 17 C

LOD	16'9"	Hull	FRP
LWL	na	Deck	FRP
Beam	6'	Spar	Alum
Draft		Pos Float	no
cb up	8"	Cockpit	6'
cb dn	3'4"	Headroom	4'
Disp	800 lbs	SA/Disp	25.6
Ballast	200 lbs	Blst/Disp	25%
Sail Area		Designer	
Sloop	138 sq ft		Glen Corcorran
Mast Ht	22'10"	First Built	1970
Auxiliary	opt	No. Built	750
	7.5 hp	1 Design	no
	outbd	Price	$5,150
			with sails

DOLPHIN 17 COMPANY
Municipal Airport
P. O. Box 817
Coffeyville, KN 67337
(316) 251-4110

17' Centerboard Knockabout

LOD	16'10"	Hull	Wood
LWL	13'11"	Spar	Wood
Beam	5'	SA/Disp	33.8
Draft		Disp/LWL	74
cb up	4"	Designer	
cb dn	na		Mr. Herreshoff
Disp	450 lbs	Price	na
Ballast	0 lbs		
Sail Area			
Sloop	124 sq ft		

AMERICAN BOAT HOUSE
Atlantic Ave., P. O. Box 911
Camden, ME 04843
(207) 236-4188

Seabreeze 16

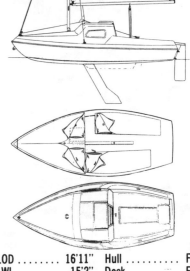

LOD	16'11"	Hull	FRP
LWL	15'2"	Deck	FRP
Beam	6'4"	Spar	Alum
Draft		Pos Float	no
Swing keel up	1'7"	Headroom	4'5"
Swing keel dn	4'2"	SA/Disp	28.4
Disp	700 lbs	Disp/LWL	89
Ballast	100 lbs	Blst/Disp	14%
Sail Area		Designer	Luger
Sloop	140 sq ft	1 Design	no
Mast Ht	21'10"	Kit	$2,877
Auxiliary	opt		
	7 hp		

LUGER INDUSTRIES INC.
3800 West Hwy 13
Burnsville, MN 55337
(612) 890-3000

Cape Cod Cat

Dockrell 17

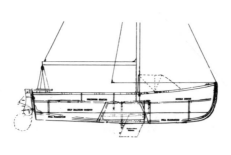

Harpoon 5.2

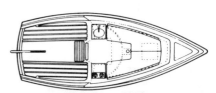

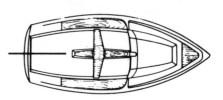

LOD	17'	Hull	FRP
LWL	16'5"	Deck	FRP
Beam	7'11"	Spar	Alum
Draft		Cockpit	6'5"
Shoal cb up	1'8"	Headroom	4'
Shoal cb dn	4'10"	SA/Disp	23.6
Deep	1'11"	Disp/LWL	222
Disp	2200 lbs	Blst/Disp	23%
Ballast	500 lbs	Designer	
Sail Area			Charles Wittholz
Cat (Gaff)	250 sq ft	Price	$11,900
Auxiliary	opt		without sales
	6 hp		

LOD	17'	Hull	FRP
LWL	16'	Deck	FRP
Beam	7'4"	Spar	Alum
Draft		SA/Disp	26.3
Swing keel up	10"	Disp/LWL	119
Swing keel dn	3'	Blst/Disp	45%
Disp	1100 lbs	Builder	
Ballast	500 lbs		Dockrell, England
Sail Area		Price	$3,495
Sloop	175 sq ft		with sails
Auxiliary	opt		

LOD	17'	Hull	FRP
LWL	15'	Deck	FRP
Beam	7'6"	Spar	Alum
Draft		Pos Float	yes
cb up	5"	SA/Disp	37.5
cb dn	3'8"	Disp/LWL	74
Disp	565 lbs	1 Design	yes
Ballast	0 lbs	Price	$6,170
Sail Area			without sails
Sloop	160 sq ft		
Mast Ht	25'		

CAPE COD SHIPBUILDING CO.
Narrows Rd.
Box 152
Wareham, MA 02571
(617) 295-3550

DOCKRELL YACHTS
1839 Route 46
Parsippany, NJ 07054
(201) 226-3200

BOSTON WHALER INC.
P. O. Box 10184
Riviera Beach, FL 33404
(305) 842-5171

Holder 17

LOD	17'	Hull	FRP
LWL	15'	Deck	FRP
Beam	7'3"	Spar	Alum
Draft		Pos Float	yes
Swing keel up	1'8"	Cockpit	6'2"
Swing keel dn	4'2"	Headroom	4'6"
Disp	950 lbs	Fr. Water	7 gal
Ballast	345 lbs	SA/Disp	24.3
Sail Area		Disp/LWL	125
Sloop	147 sq ft	Blst/Disp	36%
Mast Ht	25'	Designer	Ron Holder
Auxiliary	opt	First Built	1981
	7.5 hp	1 Design	yes
		Price	na

HOBIE CAT
Box 1008, 4925 E. Oceanside Blvd.
Oceanside, CA 92054
(714) 758-9100

Holder 17 DS

LOD	17'	Hull	FRP
LWL	15'	Deck	FRP
Beam	7'3"	Spar	Alum
Draft		Pos Float	yes
Swing keel up	1'8"	Cockpit	11'
Swing keel dn	4'2"	SA/Disp	24.8
Disp	925 lbs	Disp/LWL	122
Ballast	345 lbs	Blst/Disp	37%
Sail Area		Designer	Ron Holder
Sloop	147 sq ft	First Built	1982
Mast Ht	25'	1 Design	yes
Auxiliary	opt	Price	na
	7.5 hp		

HOBIE CAT
Box 1008, 4925 E. Oceanside Blvd.
Oceanside, CA 92054
(714) 758-9100

Marsh Hen

LOD	17'	Hull	FRP
LWL	16'3"	Deck	FRP
Beam	6'	Spar	Alum
Draft		Pos Float	yes
cb up	6"	Cockpit	12'
cb dn	3'2"	SA/Disp	32
Disp	650 lbs	Disp/LWL	68
Ballast	0 lbs	Designer	Reuben Trane
Sail Area		First Built	1981
Cat	150 sq ft	No. Built	35
Mast Ht	23'	1 Design	yes
Mast	unstayed	Kit	$5,450
Auxiliary	opt	Price	$7,450
	4 hp		with sails

FLORIDA BAY BOAT CO.
270 NW 73rd St.
Miami, FL 35150
(305) 754-9022

Menger Cat

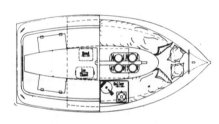

LOD . . . . 17'	Hull . . . . FRP
LWL . . . . 16'6"	Deck . . . . FRP
Beam . . . . 8'	Spar . . . . Alum
Draft	SA/Disp 23.6
cb up . . . . . . 1'8"	Disp/LWL 218
cb dn . . . . na	Designer . . A. Menger
Disp . . . . . . 2200 lbs	Price $8,700
Ballast . . . . 0 lbs	without sails
Sail Area	
Cat (Gaff) . 250 sq ft	
Auxiliary . . . . opt	
Diesel . . . . 8 hp	

MENGER ENTERPRISES INC.
77 Cedar St.
P. O. Box 141
Babylon, NY 11702
(516) 587-4930

Mobjack

LOD . . . . 17'	Hull . . . . FRP
LWL . . . . 16'9"	Deck . . . . FRP
Beam . . . . 6'	Spar . . . . Alum
Draft	Pos Float . . . . . . yes
cb up . . . . 9"	Cockpit . . . . 16'
cb dn . . . . 4'	Designer . . . Mooman
Disp . . . . na	Builder
Ballast . . . . 0 lbs	Baycraft Marine
Sail Area	First Built 1958
Sloop . . . . na	No. Built . . . . . 500+
Mast Ht . . . . . . 25'6"	1 Design . . . . yes
Auxiliary . . . . opt	Price $3,650
3 hp	with sails
outbd	

MOBJACK SALES CORP.
11521 Danville Dr.
Rockville, MD 20852
(301) 881-7411

Montgomery 17

LOA . . . . 17'2"	Hull . . . . FRP
LOD . . . . 17'	Deck . . . . FRP
LWL . . . . 15'10"	Spar . . . . Alum
Beam . . . . 7'4"	Pos Float . . . . . . yes
Draft	Cockpit . . . . 6'4"
cb up . . . . . . 1'9"	Headroom . . . . . 4'9"
cb dn . . . . . . 3'6"	Fr. Water . . . . . 9 gal
Disp . . . . . . 1600 lbs	SA/Disp 18
Ballast . . . . . 580 lbs	Disp/LWL 180
Sail Area	Blst/Disp 36%
Sloop . . . . 154 sq ft	Designer . . Lyle Hess
	First Built 1973
	No. Built 365
	1 Design . . . . no
	Price $7,477
	with sails

MONTGOMERY MARINE
935 W. 18th St.
Costa Mesa, CA 92626
(714) 548-9452

National One Design

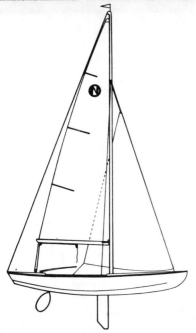

LOD . . . . 17'	Hull . . . . FRP
LWL . . . . 10'6"	Deck . . . . FRP
Beam . . . . 5'8"	Spar . . . . Alum
Draft	Pos Float . . . . yes
cb up . . . . 8"	SA/Disp 40.4
cb dn . . . . . . 3'6"	Disp/LWL 154
Disp . . . . . . 400 lbs	Designer
Ballast . . . . 0 lbs	William Crosby
Sail Area	First Built 1936
Sloop . . . . 137 sq ft	No. Built 1500
Mast Ht . . . . 26'	1 Design . . . . yes
	Price $3,950
	with sails

FIBERGLAS UNLIMITED
8133 Milmont, NW
Massillon, OH
(216) 833-1515

Noank Smuggler

LOD . . . . 17'	Hull . . . . FRP
LWL . . . . 15'6"	Spar . . . . Wood
Beam . . . . 4'10"	Pos Float . . . . yes
Draft	Cockpit . . . . 17'
Shoal . . . . 15"	SA/Disp 25
Deep . . . . 18"	Disp/LWL 65
Disp . . . . . 550 lbs	Blst/Disp 27%
Ballast . . . . . 150 lbs	First Built 1977
Sail Area	No. Built 11
Sloop (gaff) 105 sq ft	1 Design . . . . no
Mast Ht . . . . 19'	Price $5,600
Auxiliary . . . . opt	with sails
3 hp	
outbd	

GOLDEN ERA BOATS
Box 212, Marsh Rd.
Noank, CT 06340
(203) 536-1005

North River Swampscott Dory

LOD . . . . 17'	Hull . . . . Wood
LWL . . . . na	Spar . . . . Wood
Beam . . . . 4'6"	Pos Float . . . . no
Draft	Designer . . Traditional
cb up . . . . 8"	1 Design . . . . no
cb dn . . . . . . 2'6"	Price $5,000
Disp . . . . na	with sails
Ballast . . . . na	
Sail Area	
Sloop . . . . . 65 sq ft	
Sloop (sprit) 60 sq ft	
Mast Ht	
Sloop . . . . 14'	
Sloop (sprit) . . . 12'	
Mast . . . . . . unstayed	
Auxiliary . . . . opt	
2 hp	
outbd	

NORTH RIVER BOATWORKS
6 Elm Street
Albany, NY 12202
(518) 434-4414

Slipper 17

LOA	17'6"	Hull	FRP
LOD	17'	Deck	FRP
LWL	16'	Spar	Alum
Beam	8'	Pos Float	yes
Draft		Cockpit	7'
cb up	19"	Headroom	4'
cb dn	2'6"	Fr. Water	5 gal
Disp	1300 lbs	SA/Disp	21.5
Ballast	425 lbs	Disp/LWL	142
Sail Area		Blst/Disp	33%
Sloop	160 sq ft	Designer	
Mast Ht	25'		Nicholas Hake
		First Built	1979
		No. Built	370
		1 Design	yes
		Price	$4,995
			with sails

STARBOARD YACHT CO.
4550 S.E. Hampton Ct.
Stuart, FL 33494
(305) 286-7170

Sovereign 17

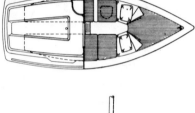

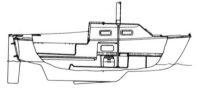

LOD	17'	Hull	FRP
LWL	14'6"	Deck	FRP
Beam	7'	Spar	Alum
Draft		Pos Float	yes
cb up	1'10"	Cockpit	5'9"
cb dn	4'10"	Headroom	4'
Disp	1350 lbs	SA/Disp	18.1
Ballast	625 lbs	Disp/LWL	198
Sail Area		Blst/Disp	46%
Sloop	138 sq ft	Price	$5,695
Mast Ht	24'		with sails

SOVEREIGN YACHT CO. INC.
233 Commerce Drive South
Largo, FL 33540
(813) 581-1382

Thistle

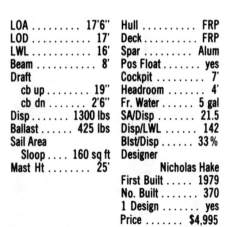

LOD	17'	Hull	Wood or Fg
LWL	17'	Spar	Wood or Alum
Beam	6'	Pos Float	yes
Draft		SA/Disp	47.6
cb up	9"	Disp/LWL	47
cb dn	4'6"	Designer	
Disp	515 lbs		Sandy Douglass
Ballast	0 lbs	First Built	1946
Sail Area		No. Built	3750
Sloop	191 sq ft	1 Design	yes
Mast Ht	24'6"	Kit	$4,425
		Price	$6,175
			with sails

GREAT MIDWEST YACHT CO.
Box 364, 140 E. Granville St.
Sunbury, OH 43074
(614) 965-4511

Vagabond 17

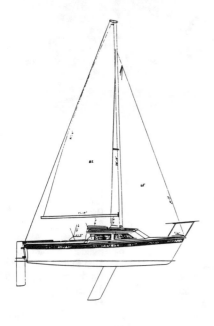

LOD . . . . 17'	Hull . . . . FRP
LWL . . . . 15'	Deck . . . . FRP
Beam . . . . 7'3"	Spar . . . . Alum
Draft	Pos Float . . . . yes
Swing keel up . 1'8"	SA/Disp 24.3
Swing keel dn . 4'2"	Disp/LWL 126
Disp . . . . 950 lbs	Blst/Disp . . . . . . 36 %
Ballast . . . . . . 345 lbs	Price . . . . na
Sail Area	
Sloop . . . . 147 sq ft	
Auxiliary . . . . opt	

VAGABOND SAILBOATS
3401 West Fordham
Santa Ana, CA 92704
(714) 979-9361

Klepper Aerius II

LOD . . . . 17'1"	Hull . Hypalon Rubber
LWL . . . . na	Deck . . . . Canvas
Beam . . . . 2'10"	First Built , ... 1951
Draft	1 Design . . . . yes
lb up . . . . na	price $1,990
lb dn . . . . na	without sails
Disp . . . . na	
Ballast . . . . na	
Sail Area	
Sloop . . . . . 55 sq ft	

HANS KLEPPER CORP.
35 Union Square W
New York, NY 10003
(212) 243-3428

Drifter 17

LOA . . . . 18'8"	Hull . . . . FRP
LOD . . . . 17'2"	Deck . . . . FRP
LWL . . . . 14'3"	Spar . . . . Alum
Beam . . . . 6'7"	Pos Float . . . . yes
Draft	Cockpit . . . . 5'1"
cb up . . . . . . 1'10"	Headroom . . . . . . 3'6"
cb dn . . . . 4'	SA/Disp 22.4
Disp . . . . . . 1100 lbs	Disp/LWL 169
Ballast . . . . . 400 lbs	Blst/Disp . . . . . 36 %
Sail Area	Designer
Sloop . . . . 149 sq ft	Michael Schallmann
Mast Ht . . . . 25'1"	First Built 1980
Auxiliary . . . . opt	No. Built 23
4 hp	1 Design . . . . no
outbd	Price $4,500
	with sails

DRIFTER MARINE ENTERPRISES
P. O. Box 11163
Phoenix, AZ 85061
(602) 246-0227

Siren

LOD . . . . 17'2"	Hull . . . . FRP
LWL . . . . 15'	Deck . . . . FRP
Beam . . . . 6'8"	Spar . . . . Alum
Draft	Pos Float . . . . yes
Swing keel up . . 8"	Cockpit . . . . 7'
Swing keel dn . 4'3"	SA/Disp 28.1
Disp . . . . . . 750 lbs	Disp/LWL 99
Ballast . . . . . . 130 lbs	Blst/Disp 17%
Sail Area	1 Design . . . . yes
Sloop . . . . 145 sq ft	Price $4,395
Auxiliary . . . . opt	with sails
7 hp	

VANDESTADT & McGRUER LTD.
Box 7, Owen Sound
Ontario, Canada N4K 5P1
(519) 376-8548

Skipper's Mate

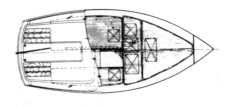

LOD . . . . 17'2"	Hull . . . . FRP
LWL . . . . 15'	Deck . . . FRP/Coremat
Beam . . . . 7'2"	Spar . . . . Alum
Draft	Pos Float . . . . no
cb up . . . . 1'	Cockpit . . . . 6'6"
cb dn . . . . . . 3'6"	Headroom . . . . . 4'6"
Disp . . . . . . 1100 lbs	SA/Disp 22.4
Ballast . . . . . . 250 lbs	Disp/LWL 146
Sail Area	Blst/Disp 23%
Sloop . . . . 149 sq ft	First Built 1982
Mast Ht . . . . 25'	No. Built 55
Auxiliary . . . . opt	1 Design . . . . no
7.5 hp	Price $5,695
	with sails

SOUTHERN SAILS INC.
4477K 122nd Ave. N.
Clearwater, FL 33520
(813) 577-7475

Renken 18

LOD . . . . 17'6"	Hull . . . . FRP
LWL . . . . . . 14'11"	Deck . . . . FRP
Beam . . . . 6'4"	Spar . . . . Alum
Draft . . . . 2'	Pos Float . . . . yes
Disp . . . . na	Builder . Renken Boats
Ballast . . . . . . 450 lbs	First Built 1982
Sail Area	No. Built 75
Sloop . . . . 150 sq ft	1 Design . . . . yes
Mast Ht . . . . 21'	Price $5,500
Auxiliary . . . . opt	with sails
3.5 hp	
outbd	

CAROLINA BOAT DISTRIBUTORS
3634 Fernandina Road
Columbia, SC 29210
(803) 772-1278

US 18

Ocean Breeze 18

Chaser Cat

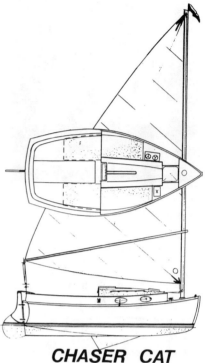

CHASER CAT

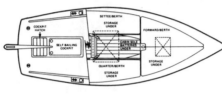

LOD	17'7"	Hull	FRP
LWL	15'7"	Deck	FRP
Beam	6'8"	Spar	Alum
Draft		SA/Disp	30.1
cb up	8"	Disp/LWL	71
cb dn	3'6"	1 Design	no
Disp	600 lbs	Price	na
Ballast	0 lbs		
Sail Area			
Sloop	134 sq ft		
Mast Ht	21'7"		

LOD	17'9"	Hull	FRP
LWL	15'	Deck	FRP
Beam	6'3"	Spar	Alum
Draft	2'	Pos Float	no
Disp	2600 lbs	Cockpit	5'
Ballast	800 lbs	Headroom	4'
Sail Area		SA/Disp	14
Sloop	165 sq ft	Disp/LWL	343
Mast Ht	25'	Blst/Disp	31%
Auxiliary	opt	First Built	1980
G.E.	2 hp	No. Built	4
Electric	inbd	1 Design	yes
Fuel Cap	2-8 hours	Price	$5,495
			with sails

LOD	18'	Hull	FRP
LWL	15'6"	Deck	FRP/Balsa
Beam	7'6"	Spar	Alum
Draft		Pos Float	no
Swing keel up	1'6"	Cockpit	6'
Swing keel dn	4'	Headroom	3'11"
Disp	1300 lbs	SA/Disp	23.5
Ballast	250 lbs	Disp/LWL	156
Sail Area		Blst/Disp	19%
Cat	175 sq ft	First Built	1982
Mast	unstayed	No. Built	7
Auxiliary	opt	Kit	$2,700
	9.5 hp	Price	$7,950
			with sails

US YACHT
P. O. Box 24467
Seattle, WA 98134

INLAND CRUISING YACHTS
Rt. 10 Box 225E
Orlando, FL 32820
(305) 568-4456

MORETTE'S
17 Sideroad
Erin, Ontario
Canada N0B 1T0
(519) 833-2263

Gloucester 18

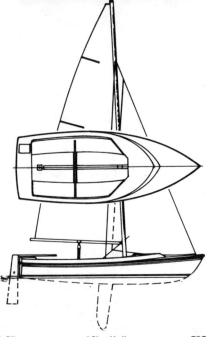

LOD	18'	Hull	FRP
LWL	16'6"	Deck	FRP
Beam	6'7"	Spar	Alum
Draft		Pos Float	yes
cb up	8"	Cockpit	9'9"
cb dn	5'	SA/Disp	34.1
Disp	750 lbs	Disp/LWL	74
Ballast	80 lbs	Blst/Disp	11%
Sail Area		Designer	
Sloop	176 sq ft		Harry R. Sindle
Mast Ht	27'6"	First Built	1977
Auxiliary	opt	No. Built	160
	4 hp	1 Design	yes
	outbd	Price	$3,895
			with sails

GLOUCESTER YACHTS
P. O. Box 307, Rte. 623
Gloucester, VA 23061
(804) 693-3818

Grand Slam 5.5

LOD	18'	Hull	FRP
LWL	16'3"	Deck	FRP/Balsa
Beam	7'8"	Spar	Alum
Draft		Pos Float	yes
cb up	6"	Cockpit	10'
cb dn	4'	SA/Disp	39.4
Disp	600 lbs	Disp/LWL	62
Ballast	0. lbs	Designer	Wennersten
Sail Area		1 Design	yes
Sloop	175 sq ft	Price	$5,800
Auxiliary	opt		with sails
	outbd		

S2 YACHTS INC.
725 E. 40th St.
Holland, MI 49423
(616) 392-7163

Island Creek 18

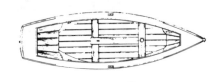

LOD	18'	Hull	FRP
LWL	16'	Deck	Wood
Beam	5'4"	Spar	Wood
Draft		Pos Float	yes
cb up	1'	SA/Disp	15.9
cb dn	2'6"	Disp/LWL	142
Disp	1300 lbs	Designer	
Ballast	0 lbs		George Surgent
Sail Area		Kit	$1,870
Sloop (sprit)	118 sq ft	Price	$5,060
Mast	unstayed		without sails

GEORGE SURGENT
Box 151, Williams Wharf Rd.
St. Leonard, MD 20685
(301) 586-1893

Laguna 18 Daysailer

Rhodes 18

Starwind 18

No Photo
or
Line Drawing
Available

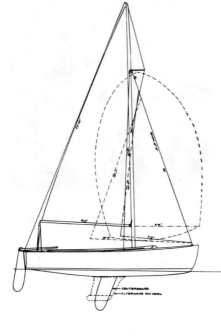

Laguna 18	
LOD . . . . 18'	Hull . . . . FRP
LWL . . . . 16'	Deck . . . . FRP
Beam . . . . 8'	Spar . . . . Alum
Draft	Pos Float . . . . no
Fixed . . . . 2'3"	SA/Disp 20.4
Swing keel up . . 12"	Disp/LWL 141
Swing keel dn . 4'6"	Blst/Disp 38%
Disp	Designer
Fixed . . . . 1300 lbs	W. Shad Turner
Swing . . . . 1240 lbs	1 Design . . . . yes
Ballast	Price $5,841
Fixed . . . . . 500 lbs	with sails
Swing . . . . . 440 lbs	
Sail Area	
Sloop . . . . 151 sq ft	
Mast Ht . . . . 23'6"	

Rhodes 18	
LOD . . . . 18'	Hull . . . . FRP
LWL . . . . 16'	Deck . . . . FRP
Beam . . . . 6'3"	Spar . . . . Alum
Draft	SA/Disp 30.1
cb up . . . . 7"	Disp/LWL 87
cb dn . . . . 4'	Designer
Fixed . . . . 2'8"	Philip Rhodes
Disp	Price $6,161
cb . . . . 800 lbs	with sails
Fixed . . . . 920 lbs	
Ballast	
cb . . . . 0 lbs	
Fixed . . . . 120 lbs	
Sail Area	
Sloop . . . . 162 sq ft	
Auxiliary . . . . opt	

Starwind 18	
LOD . . . . 18'	Hull . . . . FRP
LWL . . . . 16'8"	Deck . . . . FRP
Beam . . . . 6'	Spar . . . . Alum
Draft	SA/Disp 44.4
db up . . . . 7"	Disp/LWL 48
db dn . . . . . 3'10"	Price . . . . na
Disp . . . . . . 500 lbs	
Ballast . . . . 0 lbs	
Sail Area	
Sloop . . . . 175 sq ft	

LAGUNA YACHTS INC.
10960 Boatman
Stanton, CA 90680
(714) 527-7262

CAPE COD SHIPBUILDING CO.
Narrows Rd.
Box 152
Wareham, MA 02571
(617) 295-3550

STARWIND
8151 Bradenton Road
Sarasota, FL 33580
(813) 756-1811

Volant

LOD	18'	Hull	FRP
LWL	na	Deck	FRP
Beam	na	Spar	Alum
Draft		Pos Float	yes
cb up	na	SA/Disp	50.2
cb dn	na	Designer	
Disp	410 lbs		Harken/Vanguard
Ballast	0 lbs	Price	$5,610
Sail Area			with sails
Sloop	173 sq ft		

VANGUARD
1251 E. Wisconsin Ave.
Pewaukee, WI 53072
(414) 691-3320

Windrose 5.5

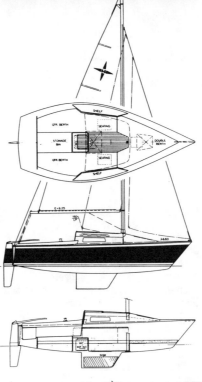

LOD	18'	Hull	FRP
LWL	16'	Deck	FRP
Beam	8'	Spar	Alum
Draft	2'3"	Pos Float	no
Disp	1500 lbs	SA/Disp	18.5
Ballast	500 lbs	Disp/LWL	163
Sail Area		Blst/Disp	33%
Sloop	151 sq ft	Designer	
Mast Ht	23'6"		W. Shad Turner
Auxiliary	opt	1 Design	yes
	6 hp	Price	$5,841
	outbd		with sails

LAGUNA YACHTS INC.
10960 Boatman
Stanton, CA 90680
(714) 527-7262

Y–Flyer

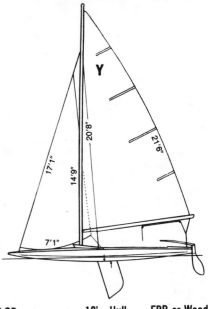

LOD	18'	Hull	FRP or Wood
LWL	14'6"	Deck	FRP or Wood
Beam	5'8"	Spar	Alum
Draft		Pos Float	yes
cb up	6"	SA/Disp	40.9
cb dn	4'	disp/LWL	73
Disp	500 lbs	Designer	
Ballast	0 lbs		Alvin Youngquist
Sail Area		First Built	1942
Sloop	161 sq ft	No. Built	2100
Mast Ht	24'	1 Design	yes
		Kit	$5,500
		Price	$7,500
			with sails

JACK A. HELMS CO.
Hwy. 60, P. O. Drawer A
Irmo, SC 29063
(803) 781-5133

Y—Flyer

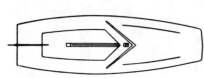

LOD	18'	Hull	FRP
LWL	14'6"	Deck	FRP
Beam	5'8"	Spar	Alum
Draft		Pos Float	yes
cb up	6"	SA/Disp	40.9
cb dn	4'	Disp/LWL	73
Disp	500 lbs	Designer	
Ballast	0 lbs		Alvin Youngquist
Sail Area		First Built	1941
Sloop	161 sq ft	No. Built	2600
Mast Ht	23'6"	1 Design	yes
		Price	$5,000
			without sails

TURNER MARINE
RR 1, Lake Mattoon
Neoga, IL 62447
(217) 895-3395

"O" Boat

LOD	18'1"	Hull	Wood
LWL	16'	Deck	Canvas/Wood
Beam	6'8"	Spar	Wood
Draft		Pos Float	no
cb up	1'	Cockpit	8'
cb dn	4'	SA/Disp	27.2
Disp	1200 lbs	Disp/LWL	130
Ballast	300 lbs	Blst/Disp	25%
Sail Area		Designer	John Alden
Sloop	192 sq ft	First Built	1980
Mast Ht	22'	No. Built	3
Auxiliary	opt	1 Design	yes
	4 hp	Price	$7,500
			with sails

THE LANDING BOATSHOP
P. O. Box 461
Kennebunkport, ME 04046
(207) 985-7976

Ranger 18

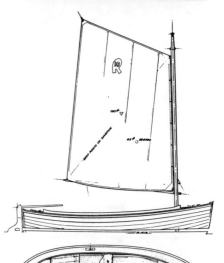

LOD	18'2"	Hull	FRP
LWL	na	Deck	FRP
Beam	6'8"	Spar	Alum
Draft		Pos Float	no
cb up	1'2"	SA/Disp	23
cb dn	3'	Blst/Disp	17%
Disp	1700 lbs	Designer	
Ballast	288 lbs		Raymond Richards
Sail Area		First Built	1980
Sloop	205 sq ft	No. Built	35
Sprit	130 sq ft	Price	$5,400
Auxiliary	opt		with sails
	10 hp		
	inbd		

RANGER BOAT CO.
25802 Pacific Hwy. S.
Kent, WA 98031
(206) 839-5213

Sanderling

LOD	18'2''	Hull	FRP
LWL	na	Deck	FRP
Beam	8'6''	Spar	Alum
Draft		Pos Float	yes
cb up	1'7''	SA/Disp	23.9
cb dn	4'4''	Blst/Disp	23%
Disp	2200 lbs	First Built	1962
Ballast	500 lbs	No. Built	500+
Sail Area		Price	$9,850
Cat (gaff)	253 sq ft		without sails
Auxiliary	opt		
Yanmar			
Diesel			

MARSHALL MARINE CORP.
P. O. Box P-266
S. Dartmouth, MA 02748
(617) 994-0414

Goldeneye

LOD	18'3''	Hull	FRP
LWL	15'10''	Deck	FRP
Beam	6'4''	Spar	Alum
Draft	3'	SA/Disp	16.8
Disp	2500 lbs	Disp/LWL	281
Ballast	1320 lbs	Blst/Disp	53%
Sail Area		Designer	
Sloop	193 sq ft		N. Herreshoff
Auxiliary	opt	Price	$11,865
			with sails

CAPE COD SHIPBUILDING CO.
Narrows Rd.
Box 152
Wareham, MA 02571
(617) 295-3550

Beachcomber Dory

LOD	18'4''	Hull	FRP
LWL	15'3''	Spar	Alum
Beam	6'	Pos Float	yes
Draft		SA/Disp	29.2
Swing keel up	6''	Disp/LWL	75
Swing keel dn	3'6''	Blst/Disp	10%
Disp	600 lbs	Designer	
Ballast	60 lbs		John Blanchard
Sail Area		First Built	1978
Sloop	130 sq ft	No. Built	43
Sprit	135 sq ft	1 Design	yes
Mast Ht		Kit	$1,390
Sloop	18'4''	Price	$6,200
Sprit	16'4''		with sails
Auxiliary	opt		
	9 hp		

**BEACHCOMBER
BOAT BUILDING**
P. O. Box 206
Port Salerno, FL 33492

Victoria 18

LOD	18'5"	Hull	FRP
LWL	12'10"	Deck	FRP
Beam	5'6"	Spar	Alum
Draft	2'	Cockpit	6'
Disp	1200 lbs	SA/Disp	19
Ballast	550 lbs	Disp/LWL	253
Sail Area		Blst/Disp	46%
Sloop	134 sq ft	Designer	Bill McVay
		Price	na

Sandpiper 565

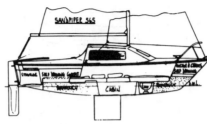

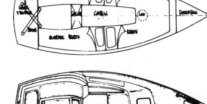

LOD	18'6"	Hull	FRP
LWL	15'	Deck	FRP
Beam	7'1"	Spar	Alum
Draft		SA/Disp	20.4
Shoal	10"	Disp/LWL	158
Deep	2'9"	Blst/Disp	25%
Disp	1200 lbs	Price	na
Ballast	300 lbs		
Sail Area			
Sloop	144 sq ft		
Auxiliary	opt		
	7.5 hp		

Pierce Arrow 18

LOD	18'7"	Hull	FRP/Balsa
LWL	16'8"	Deck	FRP/Balsa
Beam	8'	Spar	Alum
Draft		Pos Float	opt
Ver ret keel up	9"	Cockpit	7'6"
Ver ret keel dn	4'	Headroom	4'4"
Disp	1100 lbs	Fr. Water	11 gal
Ballast	400 lbs	SA/Disp	27.8
Sail Area		Disp/LWL	106
Sloop	185 sq ft	Blst/Disp	36%
Mast Ht	30'10"	Designer	
Auxiliary	opt		Mark S. Leonard
	4.5 hp	First Built	1982
		1 Design	no
		Kit	$2,995
		Price	$7,620
			with sails

VICTORIA YACHTS INC.
203 Benson Junction Rd.
Debary, FL 32713
(305) 668-8607

C&L BOAT WORKS
884 Dillingham Rd.
Pickering, Ontario
Canada L1W 1Z6
(416) 839-7991

PIERCE ARROW MARINE INC.
10502 Product Dr.
Rockford, IL 61111
(815) 654-1229

Starwind 19

Lugger

Appledore 19

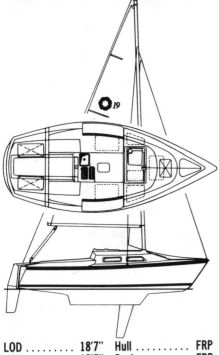

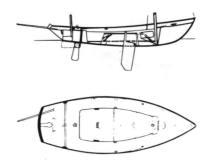

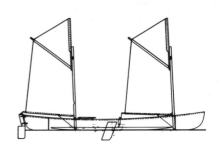

LOD	18'7"	Hull	FRP
LWL	15'7"	Deck	FRP
Beam	7'6"	Spar	Alum
Draft		Pos Float	yes
cb up	1'6"	Headroom	sitting
cb dn	4'6"	Fr. Water	2.5 gal
Disp	1350 lbs	SA/Disp	20
Ballast	395 lbs	Disp/LWL	159
Sail Area		Blst/Disp	29%
Sloop	153 sq ft	Designer	Jim Taylor
Mast Ht	27'	First Built	1982
Auxiliary	opt	1 Design	yes
	7.5 hp	Price	$6,995
	outbd		with sails

LOD	18'9"	Hull	FRP
LWL	15'	Deck	FRP
Beam	6'3"	Spar	Wood
Draft		Pos Float	yes
cb up	10"	SA/Disp	23.5
cb dn	4'	Disp/LWL	112
Disp	850 lbs	Designer	
Ballast	0 lbs		John Watkinson
Sail Area		Price	$7,146
Gunter yawl 132 sq ft			with sails
Auxiliary	opt		
	6 hp		

LOD	19'	Hull	FRP
LWL	18'	Deck	Wood
Beam	3'3"	Spar	Alum
Draft		Pos Float	yes
db up	na	Price	$2,915
db dn	na		with sails
Disp	na		
Ballast	na		
Sail Area			
Scnr (gaff)	80 sq ft		

STARWIND
8151 Bradenton Road
Sarasota, FL 33580
(813) 756-1811

MAINE MARINE CORP.
Rte. 32
Waldoboro, ME 04572
(207) 832-5323

MARTIN MARINE CO. INC.
Box 251
Kittery Point, ME 03905
(207) 439-1507

West Wight Potter 19

DESIGNED BY
Herb Stewart

The world famous Wight Potter cruisers are now in their 19th year of production with thousands sailing the waters of the USA and world-over. The Potter represents the original of the easily trailerable ocean cruisers and remains the best sailboat value available anywhere. The West Wight Potter 19—the newest in the Potter line—incorporates advance space age foam core construction with traditional quality hand laid fiberglass to provide an extremely light weight high performance cruiser design which may be easily trailered behind a compact car. With the wide bottom unique to the Potter, excellent stability is achieved while providing an enormous interior usually found only in far larger cruisers. The Potter's advanced spade keel design retracts vertically into the hull eliminating the usual interior keel trunk protrusion and keel slot drag. The keel retracts flush with the bottom of the hull allowing the Potter to be the only completely beachable cruiser of her size—great for going ashore in remote areas.

The Potter is self-righting and non-sinkable (closed cell foam floatation) and is extremely stable under sail. Even in strong winds the Potter sails more level than comparable boats. Her high dry self-bailing cockpit and stability under sail is one of the Potter's most impressive attributes. The West Wight Potter 19 has a combination of important design features not found in any other trailerable cruiser.

The roomy interior has four wide 6'6" long bunks, a complete galley sink, fresh water system, and enclosed head compartment. Mahogany trim is used extensively to compliment designer cushion fabrics. Two dinette seats with comfortable seat backs allow seating for four without restricting the use of the sleeping berths. Storage is extensive. With its carefully laid-out design, THE POTTER 19 OFFERS MORE USABLE SPACE THAN MANY BOATS 25 FEET IN LENGTH.

The West Wight Potter 19 represents a beautifully finished ocean cruiser with accommodations and features found only in far larger yachts. Yet the cruiser's practical size allows ease of trailering and launching not possible with heavier boats. As one of the nation's oldest and most respected sailboat manufacturers, the West Wight Potter 19 is presented as the ultimate answer in an easy to use luxury cruiser.

LOD	18'9"	Hull	FRP/Foam
LWL	16'	Deck	FRP
Beam	7'6"	Spar	Alum
Draft		Pos Float	yes
Ver ret keel up	8"	Cockpit	5'6"
Ver ret keel dn	3'7"	Headroom	5'
Disp	1100 lbs	Fr. Water	2.5 gal
Ballast	340 lbs	SA/Disp	27.2
Sail Area		Disp/LWL	119
Sloop	181 sq ft	Blst/Disp	31%
Mast Ht	27'	First Built	1976
Auxiliary	opt	No. Built	214
	6 hp	1 Design	yes
	outbd	Price	$6,495
			with sails

HMS MARINE
904 W. Hyde Park Blvd.
Inglewood, CA 90302
(213) 674-4540

Com—Pac 19

LOD . . . . 19'	Hull . . . . FRP
LWL . . . . 16'4"	Deck . . . . FRP
Beam . . . . 7'	Spar . . . . Alum
Draft . . . . 2'	Pos Float . . . . . . no
Disp . . . . . . 2000 lbs	Cockpit . . . . 6'8"
Ballast . . . . . 800 lbs	Fr. Water . . . . 5 gal
Sail Area	SA/Disp 18.9
Sloop . . . . 188 sq ft	Disp/LWL 205
Mast Ht . . . . 25'	Blst/Disp 40%
Auxiliary . . . . opt	Designer Bob Johnson
6 hp	First Built 1981
outbd	No. Built 108
	1 Design . . . . . . yes
	Price $7,995
	with sails

HUTCHINS CO. INC.
1195 Kapp Dr.
Clearwater, FL 33515
(813)443-4408

Flying Scot

LOD . . . . 19'	Hull . . . . . FRP/Balsa
LWL . . . . 18'6"	Deck . . . . . FRP/Balsa
Beam . . . . 6'9"	Spar . . . . Alum
Draft	Pos Float . . . . . . yes
cb up . . . . 8"	Cockpit . . . . 8'
cb dn . . . . 4'	SA/Disp 34.1
Disp . . . . . 850 lbs	Disp/LWL 59
Ballast . . . . . . 0 lbs	Designer
Sail Area	Gordon K. Douglass
Sloop . . . . 191 sq ft	First Built 1957
Mast Ht . . . . 29'	No. Built 3855
Auxiliary . . . . opt	1 Design . . . . . . yes
outbd	Price $5,985
	without sails

GORDON DOUGLASS BOAT CO.
Cemetery Street
Deer Park, MD 21550
(301) 334-4848

Flying Scot

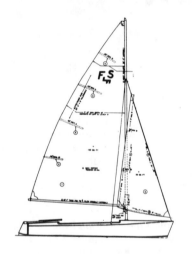

LOD . . . . 19'	Hull . . . . FRP
LWL . . . . 18'6"	Deck . . . . FRP
Beam . . . . 6'9"	Spar . . . . Alum
Draft	Pos Float . . . . . . yes
cb up . . . . 8"	SA/Disp 39.7
cb dn . . . . 4'	Disp/LWL 48
Disp . . . . . 675 lbs	Blst/Disp 16%
Ballast . . . . . 105 lbs	Designer
Sail Area	Gordon Douglass
Sloop . . . . 191 sq ft	First Built 1983
Mast Ht . . . . . . 27'7"	1 Design . . . . . . yes
	Price $5,800
	without sails

SOUTHERN YACHTS
3550 South East Blvd.
Wichita, KS 67216

Johnson Daysailer 19

LOD	19'	Hull	FRP
LWL	na	Deck	FRP
Beam	6'7"	Spar	Alum
Draft		Price	$4,650
cb up	na		without sails
cb dn	na		
Disp	na		
Ballast	na		
Sail Area			
Sloop	160 sq ft		

JOHNSON BOAT WORKS
323 S. Lake Ave.
White Bear Lake, MN 55110

Lightning

LOD	19'	Hull	FRP
LWL	15'3"	Deck	FRP
Beam	6'6"	Spar	Alum
Draft		Pos Float	yes
cb up	6"	SA/Disp	35.9
cb dn	5'	Disp/LWL	88
Disp	700 lbs	Designer	
Ballast	0 lbs		Sparkman Stephens
Sail Area		First Built	1938
Sloop	177 sq ft	No. Built	13,500
Mast Ht	28'	1 Design	yes
		Price	$4,995
			without sails

ALLEN BOAT CO.
655 Fuhrman Blvd.
Buffalo, NY 14203

O'Day 19

LOD	19'	Hull	FRP
LWL	16'8"	Deck	FRP
Beam	7'9"	Spar	Alum
Draft		Pos Float	yes
cb up	1'	Cockpit	7'6"
cb dn	4'4"	Headroom	46"
Disp	1400 lbs	SA/Disp	21.1
Ballast	300 lbs	Disp/LWL	134
Sail Area		Blst/Disp	21%
Sloop	165 sq ft	Designer	
Mast Ht	29'4"		C. R. Hunt Assoc.
Auxiliary	opt	First Built	1979
	8 hp	No. Built	444
	outbd	1 Design	yes
		Price	na

BANGOR PUNTA MARINE
848 Airport Rd.
Box 991
Fall River, MA 02722
(617) 678-5291

Mariner

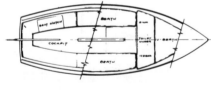

LOD .... 19'2"	Hull .... FRP
LWL .... 17'9"	Deck .... FRP
Beam .... 7'	Spar .... Alum
Draft	Pos Float .... yes
cb up .... 10"	Cockpit .... 8'6"
cb dn ..... 4'11"	Headroom ..... 3'8"
Disp ...... 1200 lbs	SA/Disp 24.5
Ballast .... 200 lbs	Disp/LWL 96
Sail Area	Blst/Disp 17%
Sloop .... 173 sq ft	Designer . O'Day Corp.
Mast Ht .... 29'	First Built 1962
Auxiliary .... opt	No. Built 4020
	1 Design .... yes
	Price $6,995
	with sails

SPINDRIFT ONE DESIGNS
1220 Tallevast Rd.
Tallevast, FL 33588
(813) 355-8455

Rhodes 19

LOD .... 19'2"	Hull .... FRP
LWL .... 17'8"	Deck .... FRP
Beam .... 7'	Spar .... Alum
Draft	Pos Float .... yes
Fixed ...... 3'3"	Cockpit .... 7'10"
No keel cb up .. 10"	SA/Disp 24.7
No keel cb dn 4'11"	Disp/LWL 100
Disp ...... 1240 lbs	Blst/Disp 33%
Ballast .... 410 lbs	Designer
Sail Area	Philip Rhodes
Sloop .... 178 sq ft	First Built 1960
Mast Ht .... 26'	No. Built 3020
Auxiliary .... opt	1 Design .... yes
	Price $6,595
	with sails

SPINDRIFT ONE DESIGNS
1220 Tallevast Rd.
Tallevast, FL 33588
(813) 355-8455

Montego 19

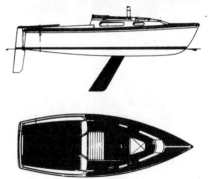

LOD .... 19'3"	Hull .... FRP
LWL .... 17'8"	Deck .... FRP
Beam .... 7'2"	Spar .... Alum
Draft	Pos Float .... yes
Swing keel up . 1'2"	Cockpit .... 7'
Swing keel dn . 4'6"	Headroom ..... 4'6"
Disp ...... 2150 lbs	Fr. Water ..... 3 gal
Ballast ..... 450 lbs	SA/Disp 18.2
Sail Area	Disp/LWL 174
Sloop .... 189 sq ft	Blst/Disp 21%
Mast Ht ...... 27'3"	Designer
Auxiliary .... opt	J. Jopie Helsen
7.5 hp	First Built 1976
outbd	No. Built 306
	1 Design .... yes
	Price .... na

UNIVERSAL MARINE CORP.
1421 Bay St. S.E.
St. Petersburg, FL 33701
(813) 823-1155

Gloucester 20

LOD .... 19'6"	Hull .... FRP
LWL .... 16'6"	Deck .... FRP
Beam .... 7'6"	Spar .... Alum
Draft	Pos Float ...... no
Fixed .... 3'	Cockpit ...... 6'6"
Swing keel up ... 1'	Headroom ..... 4'2"
Swing keel dn . 4'6"	Fr. Water ... 10 gal
Disp ...... 1650 lbs	SA/Disp 20.2
Ballast ...... 550 lbs	Disp/LWL 164
Sail Area	Blst/Disp 33%
Sloop .... 176 sq ft	Designer .. S. Windley
Mast Ht .... 28'3"	First Built 1980
Auxiliary .... opt	No. Built 85
4 hp	1 Design .... yes
outbd	Price $6,295
	without sails

GLOUCESTER YACHTS
P. O. Box 307, Rte. 623
Gloucester, VA 23061
(804) 693-3818

Montego 20

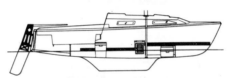

LOD .... 19'6"	Hull .... FRP
LWL .... 17'9"	Deck .... FRP
Beam .... 7'2"	Spar .... Alum
Draft .... 2'	Pos Float ...... yes
Disp ...... 2300 lbs	Cockpit .... 7'
Ballast ...... 600 lbs	Headroom ..... 4'6"
Sail Area	Fr. Water ..... 3 gal
Sloop .... 189 sq ft	SA/Disp 17.4
Mast Ht .... 27'3"	Disp/LWL 184
Auxiliary .... opt	Blst/Disp 26%
7.5 hp	Designer
outbd	J. "Jopie" Helsen
	First Built 1982
	No. Built 135
	1 Design ...... yes
	Price .... na

UNIVERSAL MARINE CORP.
1421 Bay St. S.E.
St. Petersburg, FL 33701
(813) 823-1155

Nordica 20

LOD .... 19'6"	Hull .... FRP
LWL .... 16'6"	Deck .... FRP
Beam .... 7'8"	Spar .... Alum
Draft .... 3'3"	Fr. Water ... 10 gal
Disp ...... 2520 lbs	SA/Disp 16.2
Ballast .... 1020 lbs	Disp/LWL 250
Sail Area	Blst/Disp 40%
Sloop .... 188 sq ft	Price $9,700
Mast Ht .... 30'	with sails
Auxiliary ..... std	
BMW .... 7 hp	
Diesel	

EXE FIBRECRAFT LTD.
London Rd. S
Exeter, Ontario
Canada Nom 1S0
(519) 235-0610

Halman 20

LOA	19'8"	Hull	FRP
LOD	18'6"	Deck	FRP
LWL	16'6"	Spar	Alum
Beam	7'9"	Pos Float	no
Draft	2'10"	Cockpit	4'6"
Disp	2500 lbs	Headroom	5'
Ballast	1000 lbs	Fr. Water	10 gal
Sail Area		SA/Disp	17.4
Sloop	200 sq ft	Disp/LWL	248
Mast Ht	30'	Blst/Disp	40%
Auxiliary	opt	Designer	
	7.5 hp		Nisket/Navin
	outbd	First Built	1977
		No. Built	400
		1 Design	yes
		Price	$9,995
			with sails

HALMAN MFG.
Durham Rd., P. O. Box 659
Beamsville, Ontario
Canada L0R 1B0
(416) 945-6666

Hunter 20

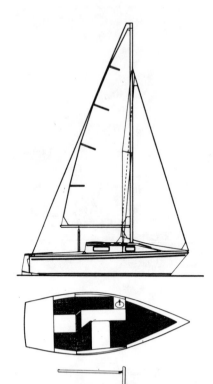

LOD	19'8"	Hull	FRP
LWL	15'6"	Deck	FRP
Beam	7'6"	Spar	Alum
Draft		Fr. Water	5 gal
Swing keel up	1'3"	SA/Disp	19.1
Swing keel dn	4'	Disp/LWL	203
Disp	1700 lbs	Blst/Disp	24%
Ballast	400 lbs	Price	$6,899
Sail Area			with sails
Sloop	170 sq ft		
Mast Ht	19'6"		
Auxiliary	opt		
	outbd		

HUNTER MARINE
Box 1030, Hwy 441
Alachua, FL 32601
(904) 462-3077

Flying Dutchman

LOD	19'10"	Hull	FRP
LWL	18'8"	Deck	FRP or Wood
Beam	5'8"	Spar	Alum
Draft		Pos Float	yes
cb up	8"	Cockpit	8'
cb dn	3'	SA/Disp	62.7
Disp	365 lbs	Disp/LWL	25
Ballast	0 lbs	Designer U. Van Esson
Sail Area		First Built	1964
Sloop	200 sq ft	No. Built	3000
Mast Ht	26'	1 Design	yes
		Kit	available
		Price	$7,200
			without sails

DYNAMIC PLASTICS
Route 1, Box 6
New Paris, OH 45347
(513) 437-7261

C Scow

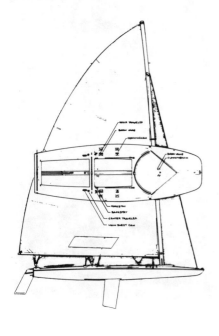

LOD	20'	Hull	FRP
LWL	na	Deck	FRP
Beam	7'	Spar	Alum
Draft		Pos Float	yes
lb up	3"	SA/Disp	46.1
lb dn	3'3"	First Built	1903
Disp	650 lbs	1 Design	yes
Ballast	0 lbs	Price	$6,795
Sail Area			without sails
Cat	216 sq ft		
Mast Ht	29'		

Flica

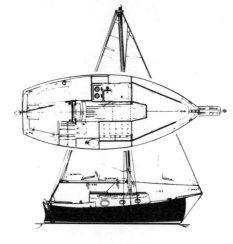

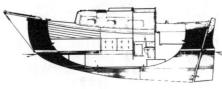

LOA	24'	Hull	FRP
LOD	20'	Deck	FRP/Plywood
LWL	18'2"	Spar	Alum
Beam	8'	Pos Float	no
Draft	3'3"	Cockpit	5'3"
Disp	4500 lbs	Headroom	6'
Ballast	1750 lbs	Fr. Water	25 gal
Sail Area		SA/Disp	14.7
Sloop	250 sq ft	Disp/LWL	335
Mast Ht	30'11"	Blst/Disp	39%
Auxiliary	opt	Designer	
Diesel	7.5 hp		Bruce Bingham
		No. Built	300
		1 Design	no
		Kit	$7,920
		Price	$19,200
			with sails

Grampian 20

LOD	20'	Hull	FRP
LWL	18'7"	Deck	FRP/Balsa
Beam	7'6"	Spar	Alum
Draft		SA/Disp	20.9
Swing keel up	1'8"	Disp/LWL	132
Swing keel dn	6'	Blst/Disp	29%
Disp	1900 lbs	Price	$12,995
Ballast	550 lbs		with sails
Sail Area			
Sloop	200 sq ft		
Auxiliary	opt		

Heritage Cat Boat　M-20　Mirador

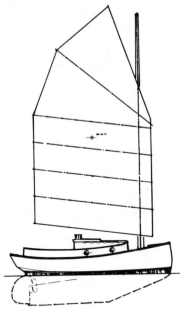

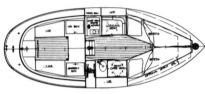

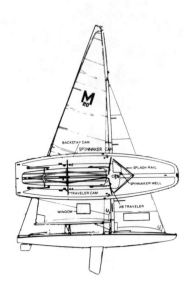

LOD	20'	Hull	FRP
LWL	18'	Deck	FRP/Wood
Beam	8'	Spar	Wood
Draft		Pos Float	no
Shoal	2'6"	Cockpit	6'
Deep	3'6"	Headroom	5'4"
Disp	5260 lbs	Fr. Water	14 gal
Ballast	1600 lbs	SA/Disp	16.4
Sail Area		Disp/LWL	402
Sloop	310 sq ft	Blst/Disp	30%
Cat (Gaff)	310 sq ft	Designer	
Lug	310 sq ft		Jay R. Benford
Mast Ht	33'	First Built	1976
Auxiliary	std	No. Built	16
BMW	12 hp	1 Design	no
Diesel		Kit	$3,500
		Price	$40,000
			with sails

LOD	20'	Hull	FRP
LWL	na	Deck	FRP
Beam	na	Spar	Alum
Draft		Pos Float	yes
lb up	3"	Designer	
lb dn	3'6"		Henry Melges Sr.
Disp	595 lbs	First Built	1964
Ballast	0 lbs	No. Built	650
Sail Area		1 Design	yes
Sloop	na	Price	$5,910
			without sails

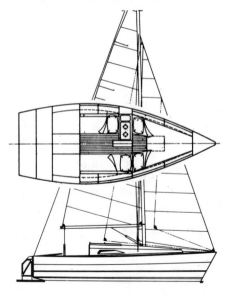

LOD	20'	Hull	Wood Epoxy
LWL	16'	Deck	Wood Epoxy
Beam	8'2"	Spar	Alum
Draft		Designer	
cb up	9"		Julian Everitt
cb dn	4'	Kit	$7,560
Disp	na	Price	$11,160
Ballast	na		with sails
Sail Area			
Sloop	179 sq ft		

HERITAGE BOAT WORKS
1331 Country Club Rd.
Hood River, OR 97031
(503) 386-1526

MELGES BOAT WORKS
Zenda, WI 53195

A & T MARINE SERVICES
P. O. Box 1423
Tacoma, WA 98401
(206) 584-8563

Mystic 20

Ranger 20

20' Sailing Surf Dory

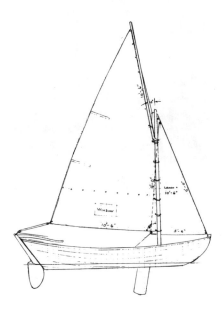

LOD . . . . 20'	Hull . . . . FRP
LWL . . . . na	Deck . . . . FRP
Beam . . . . 8'	Spar . . . . Wood
Draft	Cockpit . . . . 7'7"
cb up . . . . . . 2'1"	SA/Disp 21
cb dn . . . . . . 4'3"	Price $16,750
Disp . . . . . . 3000 lbs	without sails
Ballast . . . . na	
Sail Area	
Sloop (Gaff) 273 sq ft	
Cat (Gaff) . 282 sq ft	
Auxiliary . . . . opt	
Diesel	

LOD . . . . 20'	Hull . . . . FRP
LWL . . . . 15'10"	Deck . . . . FRP
Beam . . . . 7'10"	Spar . . . . Alum
Draft	Pos Float . . . . . . yes
cb up . . . . . . 1'9"	SA/Disp 24.6
cb dn . . . . . . 3'1"	Disp/LWL 174
Disp . . . . . . 1550 lbs	Blst/Disp 35%
Ballast . . . . . . 550 lbs	Designer
Sail Area	Raymond Richards
Sloop . . . . 206 sq ft	First Built 1972
Mast Ht . . . . 28'6"	No. Built 520
Auxiliary . . . . opt	1 Design . . . . . . yes
6 hp	Price $7,445
	with sails

LOD . . . . 20'	Hull . . . . Wood
LWL . . . . 17'	Spar . . . . Wood
Beam . . . . 6'4"	Pos Float . . . . . . yes
Draft	First Built 1793
cb up . . . . . . 4"	No. Built 10,000
cb dn . . . . . . 38"	1 Design . . . . . . yes
Disp . . . . na	Kit . . . . available
Ballast . . . . . . 200 lbs	Price $7,800
Sail Area	with sails
Sloop (Gaff) 138 sq ft	
Spirit . . . . 110 sq ft	
Mast Ht . . . . . . 15'6"	
Mast . . . . . . unstayed	
Auxiliary . . . . opt	
7.5 hp	

LEGNOS BOAT BUILDING CO.
973 North Rd.
Groton, CT 06340
(203) 446-8058

RANGER BOAT CO.
25802 Pacific Hwy. S.
Kent, WA 98031
(206) 839-5213

LOWELL'S BOAT SHOP INC.
459 Main Street
Amesbury, MA 01913

Skipper 20

LOD	20'	Hull	FRP
LWL	15'	Deck	FRP
Beam	6'8"	Spar	Alum
Draft	2'	Headroom	4'6"
Disp	2000 lbs	SA/Disp	14.4
Ballast	800 lbs	Disp/LWL	265
Sail Area		Blst/Disp	40%
Sloop	143 sq ft	Price	$7,395
Auxiliary	opt		with sails

Wild Wind

LOD	20'	Hull	FRP
LWL	18'	Deck	FRP
Beam	7'11"	Spar	Alum
Draft		Pos Float	yes
Swing keel up	2'	SA/Disp	18.3
Swing keel dn	5'8"	Disp/LWL	168
Disp	2200 lbs	Blst/Disp	36%
Ballast	800 lbs	Price	na
Sail Area			
Sloop	193 sq ft		
Auxiliary	opt		

Gauntlet

No Photo
or
Line Drawing
Available

LOD	20'1"	Hull	FRP
LWL	18'4"	Deck	FRP
Beam	6'6"	Spar	Alum
Draft	3'9"	SA/Disp	34.8
Disp	950 lbs	Disp/LWL	68
Ballast	370 lb	Blst/Disp	39%
Sail Area		Designer	
Sloop	210 sq ft		Sidney Herreshoff
		Price	$7,534
			with sails

SOUTHERN SAILS INC.
4477K 122nd Ave. N.
Clearwater, FL 33520
(813) 577-7475

RINKERBUILT BOAT CO.
207 Chicago St.
Syracuse, IN 46567
(219) 457-5731

CAPE COD SHIPBUILDING CO.
Narrows Rd.
Box 152
Wareham, MA 02571
(617) 295-3550

Santana 20

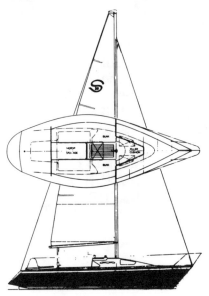

LOD	20'2"	Hull	FRP
LWL	16'	Deck	FRP
Beam	8'	Spar	Alum
Draft	4'	SA/Disp	24.4
Disp	1350 lbs	Disp/LWL	147
Ballast	550 lbs	Blst/Disp	41%
Sail Area		Price	$8,895
Sloop	186 sq ft		with sails

W. D. SCHOCK CORP.
3502 S. Greenville St.
Santa Ana, CA 92704
(714) 549-2277

Holder 20

LOA	20'4"	Hull	FRP
LOD	20'3"	Deck	FRP
LWL	18'5"	Spar	Alum
Beam	7'10"	Pos Float	yes
Draft		Cockpit	9'6"
Ver ret keel up	1'2"	Headroom	4'2"
Ver ret keel dn	4'2"	SA/Disp	28.7
Disp	1160 lbs	Disp/LWL	82
Ballast	335 lbs	Blst/Disp	29%
Sail Area		Designer	Ron Holder
Sloop	198 sq ft	First Built	1981
Mast Ht	29'	1 Design	yes
Auxiliary	opt	Price	$8,495
	4 hp		with sails
	outbd		

HOBIE CAT
Box 1008, 4925 E. Oceanside Blvd.
Oceanside, CA 92054
(714) 758-9100

Harpoon 6.2

LOD	20'4"	Hull	FRP
LWL	15'10"	Deck	FRP
Beam	8'	Spar	Alum
Draft	3'6"	Pos Float	yes
Disp	1700 lbs	SA/Disp	24.7
Ballast	550 lbs	Disp/LWL	191
Sail Area		Blst/Disp	32%
Sloop	220 sq ft	Price	$11,960
			without sails

BOSTON WHALER INC.
P. O. Box 10184
Riviera Beach, FL 33404
(305) 842-5171

Companion

**Sail with
a Companion**

**She is:
WHOLESOME
AND
HANDSOME
AND
FUN!**

**1982
Design**

**Check
out
the
Bottom
Line**

**SAFETY!
COMFORT!
VALUE!**

LOD	20'6"	Hull	FRP
LWL	16'	Deck	FRP
Beam	7'1"	Spar	Alum
Draft	2'9"	Cockpit	8'
Disp	3000 lbs	Headroom	4'11"
Ballast	1000 lbs	SA/Disp	16.8
Sail Area		Disp/LWL	327
Sloop	218 sq ft	Blst/Disp	33%
Sloop (tall)	240 sq ft	Designer	Aborn Smith
Mast Ht		First Built	1983
Sloop	28'9"	1 Design	yes
Sloop (tall)	31'3"	Price	$12,500
Auxiliary	opt		with sails
	9 hp		
	outbd		

COMPANION SLOOP
Sug. List $12,500 with sails

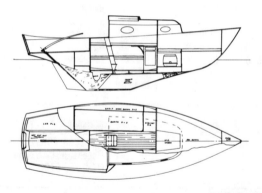

TRUMP YACHTS
P. O. Box 361
Stonington, CT 06378
(203) 535-2921

Antrim 20

LOD	20'5"	Hull	FRP/Foam
LWL	17'6"	Deck	FRP/Foam
Beam	8'	Spar	Alum
Draft	4'	Pos Float	no
Disp	1850 lbs	Cockpit	6'11"
Ballast	750 lbs	Headroom	4'4"
Sail Area		SA/Disp	29.7
Sloop	280 sq ft	Disp/LWL	154
Mast Ht	32'7"	Blst/Disp	41%
Auxiliary	opt	Designer	Jim Antrim
	10 hp	First Built	1982
	Outbd	1 Design	yes
		Price	$13,500
			with sails

ANTRIM MARINE
287 Nahant Rd.
Nahant, MA 01908

San Juan 21

LOD	20'6"	Hull	FRP
LWL	17'	Deck	FRP
Beam	7'	Spar	Alum
Draft		Pos Float	no
Swing keel up	1'	Cockpit	6'9"
Swing Keel dn	4'	Headroom	4'
Disp	1250 lbs	Fr. Water	5 gal
Ballast	400 lbs	SA/Disp	26.2
Sail Area		Disp/LWL	113
Sloop	190 sq ft	Blst/Disp	32%
Auxiliary	opt	Designer	Don Clark
		First Built	1969
		No. Built	2500
		1 Design	yes
		Kit	available
		Price	$7,995
			with sails

CLARK BOAT CO.
25-37th St. NE
Auburn, WA 98002
(206) 854-5400

Sea Pearl 21

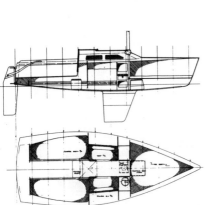

LOA	21'	Hull	FRP/Balsa
LOD	20'6"	Deck	FRP/Balsa
LWL	19'	Spar	Wood or al
Beam	5'6"	Pos Float	yes
Draft		Cockpit	6'6"
lb up	6"	SA/Disp	34.1
lb dn	2'6"	Disp/LWL	35
Disp	550 lbs	First Built	1981
Ballast	0 lbs	No. Built	33
Sail Area		Kit	available
Cat ketch	143 sq ft	Price	$6,400
Cat ketch lug			with sails
	138 sq ft		
Mast Ht			
Cat ketch	19'		
Cat ketch lug	15'		
Mast	unstayed		
Auxiliary	opt		
	4.5 hp		
	outbd		

MARINE CONCEPTS
159 Oakwood St. East
Tarpon Springs, FL 33589
(813) 937-0166

Seaforth Coastal Cruiser

Northstar 21

Petrel

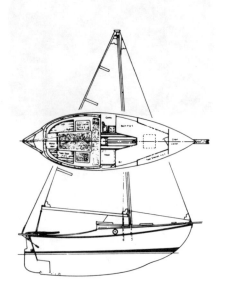

LOA	24'	Hull	FRP
LOD	20'6"	Deck	FRP
LWL	17'	Spar	Alum
Beam	7'4"	SA/Disp	13.8
Draft	2'6"	Disp/LWL	363
Disp	4000 lbs	Blst/Disp	40%
Ballast	1600 lbs	Designer	Steve Seaton
Sail Area		Builder	
Sloop	217 sq ft		Precision Boat Works
Mast Ht	30'	Price	$16,300
Auxiliary	std		with sails
Diesel	8 hp		

LOD	20'9"	Hull	FRP
LWL	17'6"	Deck	FRP
Beam	6'10"	Spar	Alum
Draft	3'9"	Headroom	4'6"
Disp	2000 lbs	SA/Disp	20.2
Ballast	900 lbs	Disp/LWL	167
Sail Area		Blst/Disp	45%
Sloop	200 sq ft	Kit	$4,200 Can
Auxiliary	opt	Price	$8,995 Can
			without sails

LOD	20'9"	Hull	FRP/Airex
LWL	16'	Deck	FRP/Plywood
Beam	7'1"	Spar	Wood
Draft	3'1"	Pos Float	yes
Disp	2900 lbs	Cockpit	10'5"
Ballast	1400 lbs	Headroom	sitting
Sail Area		SA/Disp	20.8
Sloop	265 sq ft	Disp/LWL	316
Sloop (gaff)	265 sq ft	Blst/Disp	48%
Mast Ht	31'	Designer	
Auxiliary	opt		N. Herreshoff
	7 hp	First Built	1977
		No. Built	20
		1 Design	yes
		Price	$19,500
			with sails

BUCK THOMAS & ASSOC.
1195 Kapp Drive
Clearwater, FL 33515
(813) 443-4408

J & C FIBERCRAFT
P. O. Box 263
Barrie, Ontario
Canada L4M 4T2
(705) 326-8880

GOLDEN ERA BOATS
Box 212, Marsh Rd.
Noank, CT 06340
(203) 536-1005

Yngling

LOD	20'9"	Hull	FRP
LWL	15'5"	Deck	FRP
Beam	5'8"	Spar	Alum
Draft	3'6"	Pos Float	yes
Disp	1380 lbs	SA/Disp	19.4
Ballast	690 lbs	Disp/LWL	168
Sail Area		Blst/Disp	50%
Sloop	150 sq ft	Designer	
Auxiliary	opt		Jan Herman Linge
	4 hp	First Built	1967
		No. Built	2500
		1 Design	yes
		Kit	available
		Price	$8400 Can
			with sails

SCANDIA PLAST BOAT WORKS
P. O. Box 58274 Station L
Vancouver, B.C.
Canada V6P 6E3
(604) 270-7445

Kiwi 21

LOD	20'10"	Hull	FRP
LWL	16'6"	Deck	FRP
Beam	8'	Spar	Alum
Draft		Disp/LWL	139
db up	na	Blst/Disp	29%
db dn	4'5"	Designer	Ron Holland
Disp	1400 lbs	Price	$15,397
Ballast	400 lbs		with sails
Sail Area			
Sloop	na		

KIWI BOATS
12025 66nd St. N.
Largo, FL 33543
(813) 531-5874

MacGregor 21

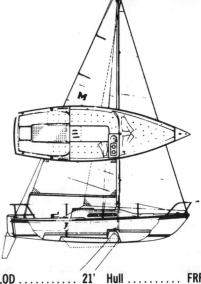

LOD	21'	Hull	FRP
LWL	18'6"	Deck	FRP
Beam	6'10"	Spar	Alum
Draft		Pos Float	yes
Swing keel up	1'	Cockpit	6'
Swing keel dn	5'6"	Headroom	4'
Disp	1175 lbs	Fr. Water	2 gal
Ballast	400 lbs	SA/Disp	25.1
Sail Area		Disp/LWL	82
Sloop	175 sq ft	Blst/Disp	34%
Mast Ht	28'	Designer	
Auxiliary	opt		R. N. MacGregor
	10 hp	First Built	1967
	outbd	No. Built	4200
		1 Design	yes
		Price	$5,396
			with sails

MacGREGOR
1631 Placentia
Costa Mesa, CA 92627
(714) 642-6830

Mistral T—21

LOD	21'	Hull	FRP
LWL	18'8"	Deck	FRP
Beam	8'2"	Spar	Alum
Draft		Headroom	4'7"
Ver ret keel up	1'2"	Fr. Water	12 gal
Ver ret keel dn	5'1"	SA/Disp	19.6
Disp	2700 lbs	Disp/LWL	185
Ballast	220 lbs	Blst/Disp	8%
Sail Area		Price	na
Sloop	237 sq ft		
Auxiliary	opt		

MISTRAL INC.
2187 De La Province
Longueuil, Quebec
Canada J4G 1R2
(514) 679-6221

Southwind 21

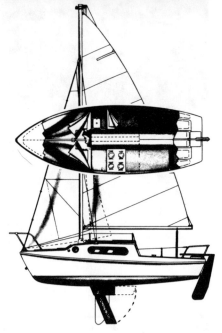

LOD	21'	Hull	FRP
LWL	17'6"	Deck	FRP
Beam	7'	Spar	Alum
Draft		Pos Float	no
Swing keel up	1'10"	Cockpit	6'
Swing keel dn	5'1"	Headroom	4'8"
Disp	1850 lbs	Fr. Water	5 gal
Ballast	440 lbs	SA/Disp	21.2
Sail Area		Disp/LWL	154
Sloop	200 sq ft	Blst/Disp	24%
Mast Ht	28'	Designer	Luger
Auxiliary	opt	1 Design	no
	9 hp	Kit	$3,647
	outbd		

LUGER INDUSTRIES INC.
3800 West Hwy 13
Burnsville, MN 55337
(612) 890-3000

Victory 21

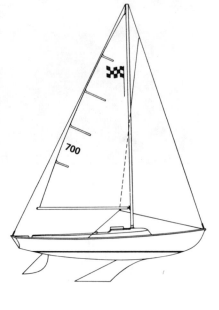

LOD	21'	Hull	FRP
LWL	15'	Deck	FRP
Beam	6'3"	Spar	Alum
Draft	3'	Pos Float	yes
Disp	1350 lbs	SA/Disp	24.2
Ballast	500 lbs	Disp/LWL	178
Sail Area		Blst/Disp	37%
Sloop	185 sq ft	Designer	Frank Butler
Auxiliary	opt	First Built	1959
	6 hp	No. Built	690
	outbd	1 Design	yes
		Price	$3950
			without sails

CATALINA YACHTS
21200 Victory Blvd.
Woodland Hills, CA 91367
(213) 884-7700

Poacher

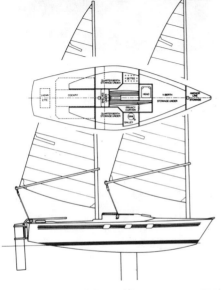

LOD	21'1"	Hull	FRP
LWL	17'9"	Deck	FRP
Beam	7'6"	Spar	FRP
Draft		Pos Float	yes
db up	1'	Cockpit	6'
db dn	4'6"	Headroom	4'
Disp	1792 lbs	Fr. Water	15 gal
Ballast	550 lbs	SA/Disp	24.7
Sail Area		Disp/LWL	143
Cat Ketch	228 sq ft	Blst/Disp	31%
Mast Ht	27'7"	Designer	
Mast	unstayed		W. Richardson
Auxiliary	opt	First Built	1979
	7.5 hp	No. Built	50
		1 Design	yes
		Price	$13,450
			with sails

PARKER/DAWSON YACHTS
55 Park Road
South Shore Park
Hingham, MA 02043
(617) 749-6444

Indian

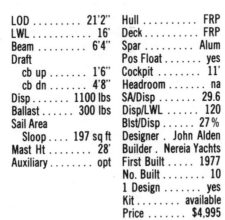

LOD	21'2"	Hull	FRP
LWL	16'	Deck	FRP
Beam	6'4"	Spar	Alum
Draft		Pos Float	yes
cb up	1'6"	Cockpit	11'
cb dn	4'8"	Headroom	na
Disp	1100 lbs	SA/Disp	29.6
Ballast	300 lbs	Disp/LWL	120
Sail Area		Blst/Disp	27%
Sloop	197 sq ft	Designer	John Alden
Mast Ht	28'	Builder	Nereia Yachts
Auxiliary	opt	First Built	1977
		No. Built	10
		1 Design	yes
		Kit	available
		Price	$4,995
			with sails

NEREIA YACHTS
5316 Denee Dr.
Wilmington, NC 28405
(919) 675-0923

Sirius

LOD	21'2"	Hull	FRP
LWL	18'9"	Deck	FRP
Beam	7'11"	Spar	Alum
Draft		Pos Float	yes
Swing keel up	1'4"	SA/Disp	20.5
Swing keel dn	5'	Disp/LWL	135
Disp	2000 lbs	Blst/Disp	26%
Ballast	525 lbs	1 Design	yes
Sail Area		Price	$10,250
Sloop	203 sq ft		with sails
Auxiliary	opt		

VANDESTADT & McGRUER LTD.
Box 7, Owen Sound
Ontario, Canada N4K 5P1
(519) 376-8548

Atlantic City Kitty   Ocean Breeze 21   US 21

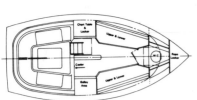

The Ocean Breeze 21 will be introduced in the fall of 1983 and will fill the need for a sensible low-priced cruising yacht for inland and coastal areas.

LOD . . . . 21'3"	Hull . . . . FRP
LWL . . . . 18'	Deck . . . . FRP
Beam . . . . 7'3"	Spar . . . . Alum
Draft . . . . 2'6"	Pos Float . . . . . . yes
Disp . . . . . . 3200 lbs	Cockpit . . . . 6'
Ballast . . . . . 1200 lbs	Headroom . . . . . 4'6"
Sail Area	Fr. Water . . . . 10 gal
Sloop . . . . 220 sq ft	SA/Disp 16.2
Mast Ht . . . . 28'	Disp/LWL 244
Auxiliary . . . . opt	Blst/Disp 38%
Yanmaz . . . . 7.5 hp	First Built . . Fall 1983
Diesel	1 Design . . . . no
Fuel Cap . . . . . . 10 gal	Price $12,000
	with sails

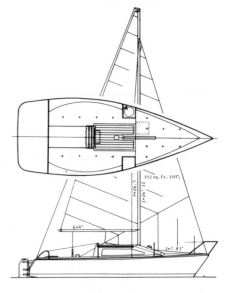

LOD . . . . 21'3"	Hull . . . . FRP
LWL . . . . 17'10"	Deck . . . . FRP
Beam . . . . 9'6"	Spar . . . . Alum
Draft	Pos Float . . . . no
cb up . . . . 2'	Cockpit . . . . 7'
cb dn . . . . 5'	Headroom . . . . . 5'3"
Disp . . . . . . 5300 lbs	Fr. Water . . . . 15 gal
Ballast . . . . . 1800 lbs	SA/Disp 18.4
Sail Area	Disp/LWL 417
Cat (Gaff) . 350 sq ft	Blst/Disp 34%
Mast Ht . . . . 28'	Designer
Auxiliary . . . . opt	Bob O'Donnell
12 hp	Builder Mark-O Custom
outbd	First Built 1982
	1 Design . . . . yes
	Price $16,900
	with sails

LOD . . . . 21'3"	Hull . . . . FRP
LWL . . . . 18'	Deck . . . . FRP
Beam . . . . 8'	Spar . . . . Alum
Draft	Pos Float . . . . no
db up . . . . . . 1'4"	Fr. Water . . . . 5 gal
db dn . . . . . . 4'7"	SA/Disp 25.8
Disp . . . . . . 1600 lbs	Disp/LWL 122
Ballast . . . . . . 200 lbs	Blst/Disp 13%
Sail Area	First Built 1983
Sloop . . . . 221 sq ft	1 Design . . . . yes
Mast Ht . . . . . . 32'6"	Price . . . . na
Auxiliary . . . . opt	

Dovekie

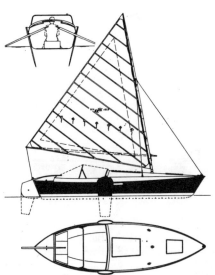

LOD	21'5"	Hull	FRP/Foam
LWL	19'	Deck	FRP/Foam
Beam	6'8"	Spar	Wood
Draft		Pos Float	yes
lb up	4"	Cockpit	4'
lb dn	2'6"	Headroom	5'
Disp	600 lbs	SA/Disp	32.2
Ballast	0 lbs	Disp/LWL	39
Sail Area		Designer	
Cat	143 sq ft		Philip Bolger
Mast Ht	24'	First Built	1976
Auxiliary	opt	No. Built	60
	2 hp	Price	$6,190
	outbd		with sails

EDEY & DUFF INC.
15 Harbor Rd.
Mattapoisett, MA 02739
(617) 758-2743

Catalina 22

LOD	21'6"	Hull	FRP
LWL	19'4"	Deck	FRP
Beam	7'8"	Spar	Alum
Draft		Pos Float	no
Swing keel up	2'	SA/Disp	19.8
Swing keel dn	5'	Disp/LWL	138
Fixed	3'6"	Blst/Disp	24%
Disp		Designer	Frank Butler
Swing	2250 lbs	First Built	1969
Fixed	2490 lbs	No. Built	11,493
Ballast		1 Design	yes
Swing	550 lbs	Price	$5295
Fixed	800 lbs		without sails
Sail Area			
Sloop	212 sq ft		
Mast Ht	29'1"		
Auxiliary	opt		
	6 hp		
	outbd		

CATALINA YACHTS
21200 Victory Blvd.
Woodland Hills, CA 91367
(213) 884-7700

Drifter

LOD	21'6"	Hull	FRP
LWL	18'4"	Deck	FRP
Beam	7'3"	Spar	Wood
Draft	2'	Pos Float	yes
Disp	2000 lbs	SA/Disp	21.2
Ballast	0 lbs	Disp/LWL	144
Sail Area		Designer	
Yawl (Gaff)	210 sq ft		John Watkinson
Auxiliary	opt	Price	$16,704
	10 hp		with sails

MAINE MARINE CORP.
Rte. 32
Waldoboro, ME 04572
(207) 832-5323

Spindrift 22

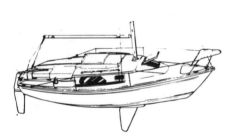

LOD . . . . 21'6"	Hull . . . . FRP
LWL . . . . 19'1"	Deck . . . . FRP
Beam . . . . 8'	Spar . . . . Alum
Draft	Pos Float . . . . no
cb up . . . . 1'6"	Cockpit . . . . 7'4"
cb dn . . . . 4'8"	Headroom . . 5'8" pop
Disp . . . . 1990 lbs	Fr. Water . . . . . 5 gal
Ballast . . . . . . 600 lbs	SA/Disp 19.6
Sail Area	Disp/LWL 128
Sloop . . . . 194 sq ft	Blst/Disp 30%
Auxiliary . . . . opt	Designer James Taylor
	First Built 1982
	No. Built 26
	1 Design . . . . yes
	Price $9,995
	with sails

SPINDRIFT ONE DESIGNS
1220 Tallevast Rd.
Tallevast, FL 33588
(813) 355-8455

Balboa 22

LOD . . . . 21'7"	Hull . . . . FRP
LWL . . . . 19'	Deck . . . . FRP
Beam . . . . 8'	Spar . . . . Alum
Draft	Pos Float . . . . no
Fixed . . . . . . 2'11"	Headroom . . . . . . 6'
Swing keel up . 1'3"	SA/Disp 19
Swing keel dn . 5'6"	Disp/LWL 148
Disp	Blst/Disp 39%
Fixed . . . . 2280 lbs	Designer
Swing . . . . 1980 lbs	Turner/Downing
Ballast	First Built 1978
Fixed . . . . . 900 lbs	1 Design . . . . yes
Swing . . . . . 600 lbs	Price $9,391
Sail Area	with sails
Sloop . . . . 206 sq ft	
Mast Ht . . . . 26'6"	
Auxiliary . . . . opt	
10 hp	
outbd	

LAGUNA YACHTS INC.
10960 Boatman
Stanton, CA 90680
(714) 527-7262

Windrose 22

LOD . . . . 21'7"	Hull . . . . FRP
LWL . . . . 19'	Deck . . . . FRP
Beam . . . . 8'	Spar . . . . Alum
Draft	Pos Float . . . . no
Fixed . . . . . . 2'11"	SA/Disp 19
Swing keel up . 1'3"	Disp/LWL 148
Swing keel dn . 5'6"	Blst/Disp 39%
Disp	Designer
Fixed . . . . 2280 lbs	W. Shad Turner
Swing . . . . 1980 lbs	1 Design . . . . yes
Ballast	Price $8,798
Fixed . . . . . 900 lbs	with sails
Swing . . . . . 600 lbs	
Sail Area	
Sloop . . . . 206 sq ft	
Mast Ht . . . . 26'6"	
Auxiliary . . . . opt	
10 hp	
outbd	

LAGUNA YACHTS INC.
10960 Boatman
Stanton, CA 90680
(714) 527-7262

660   Freedom 21   O'Day 22

660	
LOD .... 21'8"	Hull ... FRP/Klegecell
LWL .... 18'1"	Deck .. FRP/Klegecell
Beam .... 6'2"	Spar .... Alum
Draft .... 3'9"	Disp/LWL 64
Disp ...... 850 lbs	Blst/Disp 47%
Ballast ...... 400 lbs	Designer
Sail Area	Carl Schumacher
Sloop .... na	1 Design .... yes
	Price $8,900
	without sails

Freedom 21	
LOD .... 21'8"	Hull ..... FRP/Balsa
LWL .... 15'8"	Deck .... FRP/Balsa
Beam .... 8'	Spar ... Carbon Fiber
Draft	Pos Float .... no
Shoal .... 2'	Cockpit ..... 6'3"
Deep ...... 3'9"	SA/Disp 16.5
Disp	Disp/LWL 232
Shoal .... 2000 lbs	Blst/Disp 35%
Deep .... 1800 lbs	Builder
Ballast	Tillotson-Pearson
Shoal .... 700 lbs	First Built 1982
Deep .... 500 lbs	No. Built 44
Sail Area	1 Design .... yes
Cat ...... 164 sq ft	Price $10,900
Mast Ht .... 32"	with sails
Mast ...... unstayed	

O'Day 22	
LOD .... 21'8"	Hull .... FRP
LWL .... 18'11"	Deck .... FRP
Beam .... 7'2"	Spar .... Alum
Draft	Pos Float .... no
cb up .... 1'3"	Cockpit ..... 5'10"
cb dn .... 4'3"	Headroom ..... 4'3"
Disp .... 2623 lbs	Fr. Water ..... 15 gal
Ballast .... 800 lbs	SA/Disp 16.7
Sail Area	Disp/LWL 172
Sloop .... 198 sq ft	Blst/Disp 30%
Mast Ht .... 31'	Designer
Auxiliary .... opt	C. R. Hunt Assoc.
15 hp	First Built 1972
10	No. Built 2595
	1 Design .... yes
	Price .... na

PYRAMID BOATWORKS
2429 Pratt Ave.
Hayward, CA 94544
(415) 489-8025

FREEDOM YACHTS
49 America's Cup Ave.
Newport, RI 02840
(401) 847-7475

BANGOR PUNTA MARINE
848 Airport Rd.
Box 991
Fall River, MA 02722
(617) 678-5291

Seafarer 22

LOD . . . . 21'8"	Hull . . . . FRP
LWL . . . . 18'4"	Deck . . . . FRP
Beam . . . . 7'5"	Spar . . . . Alum
Draft	Pos Float . . . . no
Shoal . . . . 2'1"	Cockpit . . . . 6'1"
Deep . . . . . . 2'10"	Headroom . . . . . 4'9"
Disp . . . . . . 2400 lbs	Fr. Water . . 12 gal
Ballast . . . . . 1010 lbs	SA/Disp 19.5
Sail Area	Disp/LWL 174
Sloop . . . . 219 sq ft	Blst/Disp 42%
Mast Ht . . . . 28'9"	Designer
Auxiliary . . . . opt	McCurdy/Rhodes
7.5 hp	First Built 1975
	No. Built 275
	1 Design . . . . no
	Price $12,600
	with sails

SEAFARER YACHTS INC.
760 Park Ave.
Huntington, NY 11743
(516) 427-6670

Coaster

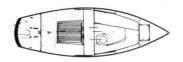

LOD . . . . 21'9"	Hull . . . . FRP
LWL . . . . 18'	Spar . . . . Wood
Beam . . . . 6'7"	Pos Float . . . . yes
Draft	SA/Disp 25.2
cb up . . . . 1'	Disp/LWL 81
cb dn . . . . . 3'10"	Designer
Disp . . . . . . 1060 lbs	John Watkinson
Ballast . . . . 0 lbs	Price $11,930
Sail Area	with sails
Gunter yawl 164 sq ft	
Auxiliary . . . . opt	
8 hp	

MAINE MARINE CORP.
Rte. 32
Waldoboro, ME 04572
(207) 832-5323

Longboat

LOD . . . . 21'9"	Hull . . . . FRP
LWL . . . . 18'	Spar . . . . Wood
Beam . . . . 6'7"	Pos Float . . . . yes
Draft	SA/Disp 30
cb up . . . . 1'	Disp/LWL 67
cb dn . . . . . . 4'2"	Designer
Disp . . . . 880 lbs	John Watkinson
Ballast . . . . 0 lbs	Price $8,846
Sail Area	with sails
Gunter yawl 172 sq ft	
Auxiliary . . . . opt	
8 hp	

MAINE MARINE CORP.
Rte. 32
Waldoboro, ME 04572
(207) 832-5323

Abbott 22

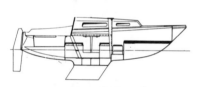

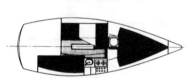

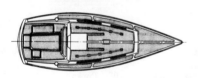

LOD	22"	Hull	FRP
LWL	18'9"	Deck	FRP
Beam	7'6"	Spar	Alum
Draft	3'10"	SA/Disp	17
Disp	3100 lbs	Disp/LWL	209
Ballast	1550 lbs	Blst/Disp	50%
Sail Area		Price	$12,500
Sloop	226 sq ft		with sails

ABBOTT BOATS LTD.
1458 London Rd.
Sarnia, Ontario
Canada N7S 1P7
(519) 542-2771

Alberg 22

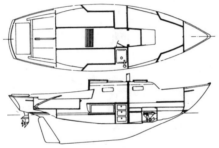

LOD	22'	Hull	FRP
LWL	16'	Deck	FRP
Beam	7'	Spar	Alum
Draft	3'1"	Pos Float	no
Disp	3200 lbs	Cockpit	8'6"
Ballast	1540 lbs	Headroom	4'6"
Sail Area		Fr. Water	5 gal
Sloop	236 sq ft	SA/Disp	17.4
		Disp/LWL	349
		Blst/Disp	48%
		Designer	
			Carl A. Alberg
		First Built	1974
		No. Built	200
		1 Design	yes
		Kit	$4,345
		Price	$14,500
			with sails

NYE YACHTS
25 Dundas St. W.
Belleville, Ontario
Canada K8P 3M7

Benford 22

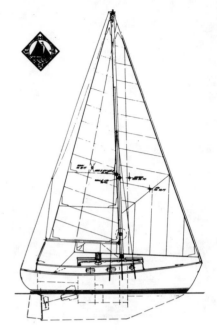

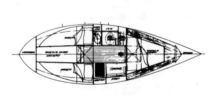

LOD	22'	Hull	FRP
LWL	18'	Deck	Wood
Beam	7'	Spar	alum or Wood
Draft		Pos Float	no
Shoal	3'1"	Cockpit	5'
Deep	3'9"	Headroom	5'3"
Disp	4000 lbs	Fr. Water	14 gal
Ballast	1400 lbs	SA/Disp	19.7
Sail Area		Disp/LWL	306
Sloop	310 sq ft	Blst/Disp	35%
Lug	310 sq ft	Designer	
Mast Ht	34'		Jay R. Benford
Auxiliary	opt	1 Design	no
BMW	7 hp	Kit	$2,500
Diesel		Price	$24,000
Fuel Cap	15 gal		without sails

HERITAGE BOAT WORKS
1331 Country Club Rd.
Hood River, OR 97031
(503) 386-1526

Dockrell 22

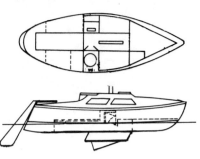

LOD	22'	Hull	FRP
LWL	19'	Deck	FRP
Beam	7'6"	Spar	Alum
Draft		Headroom	5'
cb up	1'4"	Fr. Water	6 gal
cb dn	4'	SA/Disp	16.3
Disp	2150 lbs	Disp/LWL	140
Ballast	1000 lbs	Blst/Disp	47%
Sail Area		Builder	
Sloop	170 sq ft	Dockrell Yachts, England	
Auxiliary	opt	Price	$5,995
	5.5 hp		with sails

DOCKRELL YACHTS
1839 Route 46
Parsippany, NJ 07054
(201) 226-3200

Falmouth Cutter

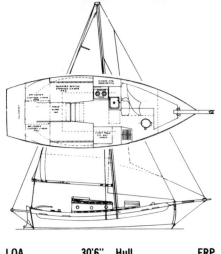

LOA	30'6"	Hull	FRP
LOD	22'	Deck	FRP
LWL	20'10"	Spar	Alum
Beam	8'	Pos Float	no
Draft	3'6"	Cockpit	3'
Disp	7400 lbs	Headroom	5'11"
Ballast	2500 lbs	Fr. Water	19 gal
Sail Area		SA/Disp	15
Cutter	357 sq ft	Disp/LWL	365
Mast Ht	33'6"	Blst/Disp	34%
Auxiliary	opt	Designer	L. C. Hass
Diesel	12 hp	First Built	1980
Fuel Cap	23 gal	No. Built	20
		1 Design	no
		Kit	available
		Price	$33,709
			without sails

SAM L. MORSE CO.
1626 Placentia Ave.
Costa Mesa, CA 92627
(714) 645-1843

Grand Slam 6.7

LOD	22'	Hull	FRP/Balsa
LWL	18'9"	Deck	FRP/Balsa
Beam	8'	Spar	Alum
Draft		Pos Float	no
Ver ret keel up	10"	Cockpit	8'
Ver ret keel dn	4'3"	Headroom	4'
Disp	2200 lbs	SA/Disp	22.2
Ballast	775 lbs	Disp/LWL	149
Sail Area		Blst/Disp	35%
Sloop	235 sq ft	Designer	Wennersten
Auxiliary	opt	1 Design	yes
	outbd	Price	$11,125
			with sails

S2 YACHTS INC.
725 E. 40th St.
Holland, MI 49423
(616) 392-7163

MacGregor 22

Merit 22

Rhodes 22

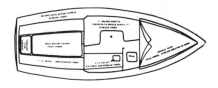

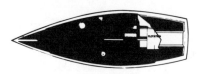

LOD	22'	Hull	FRP
LWL	19'	Deck	FRP
Beam	7'4''	Spar	Alum
Draft		Pos Float	yes
Swing keel up	1'	Cockpit	6'5''
Swing keel dn	5'6''	Headroom	4'3''
Disp	1800 lbs	SA/Disp	19.1
Ballast	500 lbs	Disp/LWL	117
Sail Area		Blst/Disp	28%
Sloop	177 sq ft	Designer	
Mast Ht	28'		R. N. MacGregor
Auxiliary	opt	First Built	1972
	10 hp	No. Built	4300
	outbd	1 Design	yes
		Price	$6,415
			with sails

LOD	22'	Hull	FRP
LWL	18'	Deck	FRP
Beam	8'	Spar	Alum
Draft		Pos Float	yes
Ver ret keel up	1'6''	Cockpit	7'6''
Ver ret keel dn	4'	Fr. Water	8 gal
Disp	2000 lbs	SA/Disp	22.7
Ballast	500 lbs	Disp/LWL	153
Sail Area		Blst/Disp	25%
Sloop	225 sq ft	Designer	Paul Yates
		First Built	1982
		1 Design	yes
		Price	$9,595
			with sails

LOD	22'	Hull	FRP
LWL	20'	Deck	FRP
Beam	8'	Spar	Alum
Draft		Pos Float	yes
cb up	1'10''	Cockpit	7'6''
cb dn	4'6''	Headroom	6'5'' pop
Disp	2500 lbs	Fr. Water	15 gal
Ballast	650 lbs	SA/Disp	23.9
Sail Area		Disp/LWL	139
Sloop	275 sq ft	Blst/Disp	26%
Mast Ht	30'	Designer	
Auxiliary	opt		Phillip Rhodes
	20 hp	First Built	1970
	outbd	No. Built	1000
		Kit	available
		Price	$9,995
			with sails

MacGREGOR
1631 Placentia
Costa Mesa, CA 92627
(714) 642-6830

MERIT MARINE
13541 Desmond St.
Pacoima, CA 91331
(213) 897-1271

GENERAL BOATS CORP.
336 Governor Ave.
North Babylon, NY 11704
(516) 842-7216

Starwind 22

LOD	22'	Hull	FRP
LWL	19'	Deck	FRP
Beam	7'9"	Spar	Alum
Draft		Fr. Water	5 gal
Swing keel up	1'11"	SA/Disp	18.8
Swing keel dn	6'	Disp/LWL	169
Disp	2600 lbs	Blst/Disp	30%
Ballast	775 lbs	Price	na
Sail Area			
Sloop	222 sq ft		
Auxiliary	opt		

STARWIND
8151 Bradenton Road
Sarasota, FL 33580
(813) 756-1811

US 22

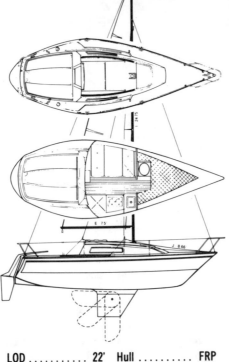

LOD	22'	Hull	FRP
LWL	19'11"	Deck	FRP
Beam	7'11"	Spar	Alum
Draft		Pos Float	no
Swing keel up	2'5"	Fr. Water	4 gal
Swing keel dn	5'9"	SA/Disp	17.8
Fixed	4'1"	Disp/LWL	138
Disp	2450 lbs	Blst/Disp	39%
Ballast	950 lbs	1 Design	no
Sail Area		Price	na
Sloop	202 sq ft		
Mast Ht	31'3"		
Auxiliary	opt		
	outbd		

US YACHT
P. O. Box 24467
Seattle, WA 98134

Sun Star 22

LOD	22'1"	Spar	Alum
LWL	18'3"	SA/Disp	26.5
Beam	7'5"	Disp/LWL	161
Draft		Blst/Disp	28%
Swing Keel up	1'2"	Price	$10,400
Swing keel dn	4'8"		with sails
Disp	2200 lbs		
Ballast	610 lbs		
Sail Area			
Sloop	280 sq ft		
Auxiliary	opt		

FIBER FOAM
P. O. Box 25
Onekama, MI 49675
(616) 889-5731

Marshall 22

LOD	22'2"	Hull	FRP
LWL	21'4"	Deck	FRP
Beam	10'2"	Spar	Alum
Draft		Pos Float	no
cb up	2'	Fr. Water	20 gal
cb dn	5'5"	SA/Disp	19.5
Disp	5660 lbs	Disp/LWL	260
Ballast	850 lbs	Blst/Disp	15%
Sail Area		First Built	1965
Cat (gaff)	388 sq ft	Price	$25,800
Sloop (gaff)	488 sq ft		with sails
Auxiliary	std		
Yanmar			
Diesel			
Fuel Cap	19 gal		

MARSHALL MARINE CORP.
P. O. Box P-266
S. Dartmouth, MA 02748
(617) 994-0414

Gazelle

LOD	22'3"	Hull	FRP
LWL	17'6"	Deck	FRP
Beam	7'3"	Spar	Alum
Draft	3'8"	Disp/LWL	168
Disp	2018 lbs	Price	$10,870 Can
Ballast	na		with sails
Sail Area			
Sloop	na		
Auxiliary	opt		

ONTARIO YACHTS CO. LTD.
243 Speers Rd.
Oakville, Ontario
Canada L6K 2EB
(416) 845-1153

Hunter 22

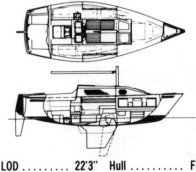

LOD	22'3"	Hull	FRP
LWL	18'4"	Deck	FRP
Beam	7'11"	Spar	Alum
Draft		Fr. Water	12 gal
Fixed	3'2"	SA/Disp	15.6
Swing keel up	1'11"	Disp/LWL	246
Swing Keel dn	5'	Blst/Disp	41%
Disp		Designer	
Fixed	3400 lbs		Cortland Steck
Swing	3200 lbs	Price	$11,690
Ballast			with sails
Fixed	1400 lbs		
Swing	1300 lbs		
Sail Area			
Sloop	220 sq ft		
Mast Ht	30'3"		
Auxiliary	opt		
	outbd		

HUNTER MARINE
Box 1030, Hwy 441
Alachua, FL. 32601
(904) 462-3077

J—22

LOD	22'6"	Hull	FRP
LWL	19'	Deck	FRP
Beam	8'	Spar	Alum
Draft	3'9"	SA/Disp	26.2
Disp	1700 lbs	Disp/LWL	111
Ballast	750 lbs	Blst/Disp	44%
Sail Area		First Built	1983
Sloop	233 sq ft	1 Design	yes
Auxiliary	opt	Price	$8,950
			with sails

J BOATS INC.
24 Mill St.
Newport, RI 02840
(401) 846-8410

Oysterman 23

LOA	31'3"	Hull	FRP
LOD	22'6"	Deck	FRP
LWL	21'1"	Spar	Alum
Beam	8'	Cockpit	7'4"
Draft		SA/Disp	30
cb up	1'8"	Disp/LWL	123
cb dn	6'	Blst/Disp	27%
Disp	2600 lbs	Kit	$4,800
Ballast	700 lbs	Price	$16,500
Sail Area			with sails
Sloop	355 sq ft		
Ketch	309 sq ft		
Auxiliary	opt		
Diesel			

MENGER ENTERPRISES INC.
77 Cedar St.
P. O. Box 141
Babylon, NY 11702
(516) 587-4930

Pearson Ensign

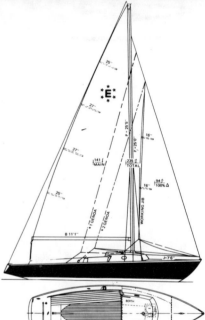

LOD	22'6"	Hull	FRP
LWL	16'9"	Deck	FRP/Balsa
Beam	7'	Spar	Alum
Draft	3'	Cockpit	8'8"
Disp	3000 lbs	Headroom	3'10"
Ballast	1200 lbs	SA/Disp	18.1
Sail Area		Disp/LWL	285
Sloop	235 sq ft	Blst/Disp	40%
		1 Design	yes
		Price	na

PEARSON YACHTS
West Shore Rd.
Portsmouth, RI 02871
(401) 683-0100

Sea Sprite 23

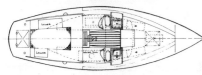

LOD	22'6"	Hull	FRP
LWL	16'3"	Deck	FRP/Balsa
Beam	7'	Spar	Alum
Draft	3'	Pos Float	no
Disp	3350 lbs	Cockpit	6'
Ballast	1400 lbs	Headroom	4'3"
Sail Area		Fr. Water	5 gal
Sloop	247 sq ft	SA/Disp	17.7
Mast Ht	22'2"	Disp/LWL	349
Auxiliary	opt	Blst/Disp	42%
Yanmar	7.5 hp	Designer	Carl Alberg
Diesel		First Built	1976
		No. Built	766
		1 Design	no
		Kit	available
		Price	na

C. E. RYDER CORP.
47 Gooding Ave.
Bristol, RI 02809
(401) 253-8554

Tanzer 22

LOD	22'6"	Hull	FRP
LWL	19'9"	Deck	FRP
Beam	7'10"	Spar	Alum
Draft		Pos Float	no
Shoal cb up	2'	Cockpit	7'9"
Shoal cb dn	4'	Headroom	4'0"
Deep	3'5"	Fr. Water	10 gal
Disp		SA/Disp	16.7
Shoal	3100 lbs	Disp/LWL	180
Deep	2900 lbs	Blst/Disp	48%
Ballast		Designer	
Shoal	1500 lbs		Johann Tanzer
Deep	1250 lbs	First Built	1970
Sail Area		No. Built	2113
Sloop	222 sq ft	1 Design	yes
Mast Ht	31'	Price	$12,200
Auxiliary	opt		with sails
	6 hp		
	outbd		

TANZER
Box 670, Cape Colony
Edenton, NC 27932
(919) 482-7404

- -

P. O. Box 67
Dorion, PQ Canada J7V 5V8
(514) 455-5681

Rob Roy 23

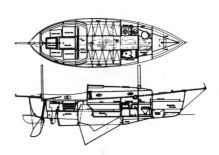

LOA	29'8"	Hull	FRP
LOD	22'8"	Deck	FRP
LWL	20'10"	Spar	Alum
Beam	6'11"	Cockpit	6'6"
Draft		Fr. Water	25 gal
cb up	1'6"	SA/Disp	25
cb dn	na	Disp/LWL	109
Disp	2200 lbs	Blst/Disp	30%
Ballast	650 lbs	Designer	Ted Brewer
Sail Area		Builder	
Yawl	264 sq ft		Marine Concepts
Auxiliary	opt	Price	$15,000
			with sails

ROB—ROY BOAT COMPANY
1230 East Rock Springs Road NE
Atlanta, GA 30306
(404) 875-2165

Sea Gypsy

Seafarer 23

Com—Pac 23

LOD .... 22'8"	Hull .... FRP
LWL .... na	Deck .... FRP
Beam .... na	Spar .... Alum
Draft	Kit $2,950
cb up .... 2'	Price $15,450
cb dn ...... 3'10"	with sails
Disp .... na	
Ballast .... na	
Sail Area	
Sloop (Gaff) 220 sq ft	
Auxiliary .... std	
Volvo ...... 15 hp	
Diesel	

LOD .... 22'8"	Hull .... FRP
LWL .... 20'	Deck .... FRP
Beam .... 7'7"	Spar .... Alum
Draft	Pos Float .... no
Shoal .... 2'4"	Cockpit .... 5'7"
Deep .... 3'3"	Headroom ..... 5'1"
Disp ..... 2750 lbs	Fr. Water ... 12 gal
Ballast .... 1020 lbs	SA/Disp 17.9
Sail Area	Disp/LWL 153
Sloop .... 219 sq ft	Blst/Disp 37%
Mast Ht ..... 28'11"	Designer
Auxiliary .... opt	McCurdy/Rhodes
9.9 hp	First Built 1977
	No. Built 150
	1 Design .... no
	Price $14,950
	with sails

LOD .... 22'9"	Hull .... FRP
LWL .... 20'2"	Deck .... FRP
Beam .... 7'10"	Spar .... Alum
Draft .... 2'3"	Pos Float .... no
Disp ..... 3000 lbs	Cockpit .... 7'2"
Ballast .... 1340 lbs	Fr. Water ... 5 gal
Sail Area	SA/Disp 17.8
Sloop .... 232 sq ft	Disp/LWL 163
Mast Ht .... 30'	Blst/Disp 45%
Auxiliary .... opt	Designer .. Clark Mills
8 hp	First Built 1979
outbd	No. Built 228
	1 Design .... yes
	Price $10,950
	with sails

O'Day 23

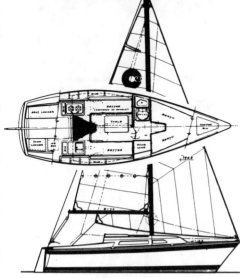

LOD	22'9"	Hull	FRP
LWL	19'6"	Deck	FRP
Beam	7'11"	Spar	Alum
Draft		Pos Float	no
cb up	2'3"	Cockpit	6'
cb dn	5'4"	Headroom	4'9"
Disp	3085 lbs	Fr. Water	15 gal
Ballast	1200 lbs	SA/Disp	18.6
Sail Area		Disp/LWL	185
Sloop	246 sq ft	Blst/Disp	39%
Mast Ht	32'	Designer	
Auxiliary	opt		C. R. Hunt Assoc.
	15 hp	First Built	1977
	10	No. Built	929
		1 Design	yes
		Price	na

BANGOR PUNTA MARINE
848 Airport Rd.
Box 991
Fall River, MA 02722
(617) 678-5291

Gloucester 23

LOD	22'10"	Hull	FRP
LWL	20'	Deck	FRP
Beam	8'	Spar	Alum
Draft		Pos Float	no
cb up	1'11"	Cockpit	6'6"
cb dn	5'6"	Headroom	5'
Disp	2700 lbs	Fr. Water	15 gal
Ballast	1000 lbs	SA/Disp	19.4
Sail Area		Disp/LWL	150
Sloop	235 sq ft	Blst/Disp	37%
Mast Ht	32'6"	Designer	S. Windley
Auxiliary	opt	First Built	1978
	6 hp	No. Built	82
	outbd	1 Design	no
		Price	$10,995
			without sails

GLOUCESTER YACHTS
P. O. Box 307, Rte. 623
Glouc·ster, VA 23061
(804) 693-3818

Windsong 23

LOA	22'10"	Hull	FRP
LOD	22'0"	Deck	FRP
LWL	20'4"	Spar	Alum
Beam	8'	Pos Float	no
Draft	1'11"	Cockpit	6'
Disp	2700 lbs	Headroom	4'3"
Ballast	900 lbs	SA/Disp	19.7
Sail Area		Disp/LWL	143
Sloop	239 sq ft	Blst/Disp	33%
Mast Ht	28'2"	Designer	
Auxiliary	opt		John Roberson
	9.9 hp	First Built	1981
	outbd	No. Built	7
Fuel Cap	5 gal	1 Design	yes
		Kit	$3,900
		Price	$10,580
			with sails

ROBERSON CABINET SHOP
2067 SW College Road
Ocala, FL 32674

Cascade 23

Adventure 23

Dutch Flyer 23

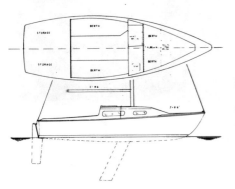

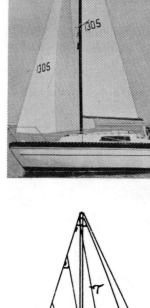

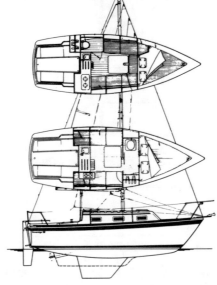

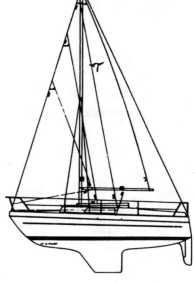

LOD .... 22'11"	Hull .... FRP/Coremat
LWL .... 20'1"	Deck ... FRP/Plywood
Beam .... 7'8"	Spar .... Alum
Draft	Pos Float .... no
db up ...... 1'8"	Cockpit .... 6'
db dn ..... 5'10"	Headroom ..... 4'7"
Disp .... 2500 lbs	Fr. Water .... 12 gal
Ballast .... 700 lbs	SA/Disp 20.6
Sail Area	Disp/LWL 138
Sloop .... 237 sq ft	Blst/Disp 28%
Mast Ht .... 33'	Designer
Auxiliary .... opt	Yacht Constructors Inc.
7.5 hp	First Built 1980
outbd	No. Built 8
	1 Design .... yes
	Kit .... available
	Price $16,000
	with sails

LOD .... 23'	Hull .... FRP
LWL .... 18'6"	Deck .... FRP
Beam .... 8'	Spar .... Alum
Draft	Cockpit .... 6'8"
Shoal ...... 2'4"	Headroom ..... 5'7"
Deep ...... 3'8"	SA/Disp 17.5
Disp .... 3250 lbs	Disp/LWL 229
Ballast ..... 1350 lbs	Blst/Disp 42%
Sail Area	Price $13,995
Sloop .... 240 sq ft	with sails
Auxiliary .... opt	

LOD .... 23'	Hull ... FRP/Corromat
LWL .... 19'2"	Deck .. FRP/Corromat
Beam .... 8'2"	Headroom .... 5'10"
Draft .... 4'5"	SA/Disp 14.9
Disp .... 3638 lbs	Disp/LWL 230
Ballast ..... 1764 lbs	Blst/Disp 48%
Sail Area	Price .... na
Sloop .... 220 sq ft	
Auxiliary .... opt	

YACHT CONSTRUCTORS INC.
7030 N.E. 42nd Ave.
Portland, OR 97218
(503) 287-5794

SOVEREIGN YACHT CO. INC.
233 Commerce Drive South
Largo, FL 33540
(813) 581-1382

HOLLAND YACHTS
Box 129
Solomons, MD 20688
(301) 326-3960

MacGregor 23

LOD . . . . 23'	Hull . . . . FRP
LWL . . . . 21'6"	Deck . . . . FRP
Beam . . . . 7'2"	Spar . . . . Alum
Draft	Pos Float . . . . yes
Swing keel up . 1'6"	Cockpit . . . . 6'6"
Swing keel dn . 5'6"	Headroom . . . . . . 6'
Disp . . . . . . 2000 lbs	Fr. Water . . . . 3 gal
Ballast . . . . . . 600 lbs	SA/Disp 19.7
Sail Area	Disp/LWL 89
Cutter . . . 195 sq ft	Blst/Disp 30%
Mast Ht . . . . . 32'	Designer
Auxiliary . . . . std	R. N. MacGregor
10 hp	First Built 1974
outbd	No. Built 3500
	1 Design . . . . yes
	Price $7,029
	with sails

MacGREGOR
1631 Placentia
Costa Mesa, CA 92627
(714) 642-6830

Pearson 23

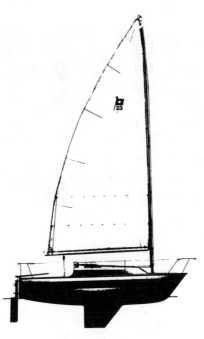

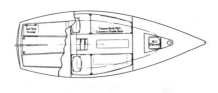

LOD . . . . 23'	Hull . . . . . FRP/Balsa
LWL . . . . 20'	Deck . . . . FRP/Balsa
Beam . . . . 8'	Spar . . . . Alum
Draft . . . . 4'	SA/Disp 16.2
Disp . . . . . . 3000 lbs	Disp/LWL 167
Ballast . . . . 1200 lbs	Blst/Disp 40%
Sail Area	Price $12,250
Cat . . . . . 210 sq ft	with sails
Mast . . . . . unstayed	
Auxiliary . . . . opt	

PEARSON YACHTS
West Shore Rd.
Portsmouth, RI 02871
(401) 683-0100

San Juan 23

LOD . . . . 23'	Hull . . . . FRP
LWL . . . . 20'4"	Deck . . . . FRP
Beam . . . . 8'	Spar . . . . Alum
Draft	Pos Float . . . . no
Swing keel up 1'11"	Cockpit . . . . 5'5"
Swing keel dn . 4'9"	Headroom . . . . . 5'1"
Disp . . . . . . 2700 lbs	Fr. Water . . . . 9 gal
Ballast . . . . . . 960 lbs	SA/Disp 19.3
Sail Area	Disp/LWL 143
Sloop . . . . 234 sq ft	Blst/Disp 36%
Auxiliary . . . . opt	Designer . . Don Clark
7.5 hp	First Built 1976
outbd	No. Built 630
	1 Design . . . . yes
	Kit . . . . available
	Price $12,795
	with sails

CLARK BOAT CO.
25-37th St. NE
Auburn, WA 98002
(206) 854-5400

Sonar

LOD . . . . 23'	Hull . . . . FRP
LWL . . . . 18'8''	Deck . . . . FRP
Beam . . . . 7'10''	Spar . . . . Alum
Draft . . . . 3'11''	Pos Float . . . . yes
Disp . . . . . . 2100 lbs	Cockpit . . . . 11''
Ballast . . . . . . 940 lbs	SA/Disp 24.4
Sail Area	Disp/LWL 144
Sloop . . . . 250 sq ft	Blst/Disp 45%
Auxiliary . . . . opt	Designer . Bruce Kirby
4 hp	Builder
	Ross Marine Inc.
	First Built 1980
	No. Built 250
	1 Design . . . . yes
	Price $10,950
	without sails

SONAR INTERNATIONAL
44 Pasture Ln.
Darien, CT 06820
(203) 655-4548

Santana 23

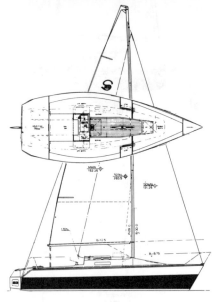

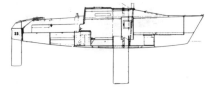

LOD . . . . 23'4''	Hull . . . . FRP
LWL . . . . 20'7''	Deck . . . . FRP
Beam . . . . 8'10''	Spar . . . . Alum
Draft	SA/Disp 24
db up . . . . 10'	Disp/LWL 133
db dn . . . . . . 5'3''	Blst/Disp 43%
Disp . . . . . . 2600 lbs	Designer . Shad Turner
Ballast . . . . . 1130 lbs	Price $16,550
Sail Area	with sails
Sloop . . . . 284 sq ft	

W. D. SCHOCK CORP.
3502 S. Greenville St.
Santa Ana, CA 92704

Stone Horse

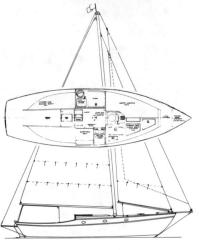

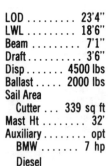

LOD . . . . 23'4''	Hull . . . . . . FRP/Foam
LWL . . . . 18'6''	Deck . . . . . FRP/Foam
Beam . . . . 7'1''	Spar . . . . Wood
Draft . . . . 3'6''	Pos Float . . . . no
Disp . . . . . . 4500 lbs	Cockpit . . . . 7'8''
Ballast . . . . 2000 lbs	Headroom . . . . . . 4'
Sail Area	Fr. Water . . . . . 11 gal
Cutter . . . 339 sq ft	SA/Disp 19.9
Mast Ht . . . . 32'	Disp/LWL 317
Auxiliary . . . . opt	Blst/Disp 44%
BMW . . . . . . 7 hp	Designer S. S. Crocker
Diesel	First Built 1970
	No. Built 130
	1 Design . . . . yes
	Price $24,800
	with sails

EDEY & DUFF INC.
15 Harbor Rd.
Mattapoisett, MA 02739
(617) 758-2743

Luna 24/SL

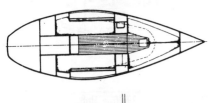

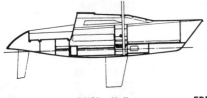

LOD	23'6"	Hull	FRP
LWL	18'6"	Deck	FRP
Beam	8'2"	Spar	Alum
Draft	4'5"	SA/Disp	29.6
Disp	2600 lbs	Disp/LWL	183
Ballast	1250 lbs	Blst/Disp	48%
Sail Area		Price	$19,800 Can
Sloop	350 sq ft		with sails
Auxiliary	opt		

LUNA YACHTS LTD.
1435 Wallace Rd.
Oakville, Ontario
Canada L6L 2Y1
(416) 825-1433

Balboa 24

LOD	23'7"	Hull	FRP
LWL	20'	Deck	FRP
Beam	8'4"	Spar	Alum
Draft	2'11"	Pos Float	no
Disp	2600 lbs	Headroom	6'
Ballast	900 lbs	SA/Disp	18.6
Sail Area		Disp/LWL	145
Sloop (FR)	220 sq ft	Blst/Disp	35%
Sloop (MH)	251 sq ft	Designer	
Mast Ht			W. Shad Turner
Sloop	26'6"	1 Design	yes
Sloop	28'	Price	$11,157
Auxiliary	opt		with sails
	10 hp		
	outbd		

LAGUNA YACHTS INC.
10960 Boatman
Stanton, CA 90680
(714) 527-7262

Moore 24

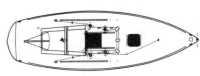

LOD	23'9"	Hull	FRP/Balsa
LWL	21'9"	Deck	FRP/Balsa
Beam	7'2"	Spar	Alum
Draft	4'1"	SA/Disp	24.5
Disp	2050 lbs	Disp/LWL	88
Ballast	1025 lbs	Blst/Disp	50%
Sail Area		1 Design	yes
Sloop	247 sq ft	Price	$17,500
Auxiliary	opt		with sails

MOORE BROS. SAILBOAT SHOP
1650 Commercial Way
Santa Cruz, CA 95065
(408) 476-3831

Wylie Wabbit

S2 7.3

Seidelmann 24

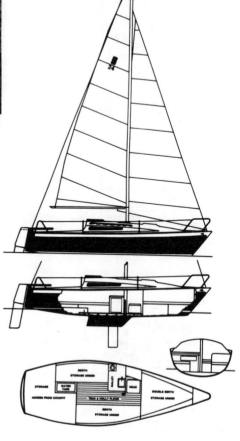

LOD	23'9"	Hull	FRP
LWL	20'	Deck	FRP
Beam	5'7"	Spar	Alum
Draft	3'6"	Cockpit	6'6"
Disp	875 lbs	SA/Disp	32.5
Ballast	440 lbs	Disp/LWL	48
Sail Area		Blst/Disp	50%
Sloop	186 sq ft	Price	$8,500
Auxiliary	opt		with sails
	4 hp		
	outbd		

LOD	23'10"	Hull	FRP
LWL	18'6"	Deck	FRP/Balsa
Beam	8'	Spar	Alum
Draft		Pos Float	no
Shoal	3'	Cockpit	6'10"
Deep	4'	Headroom	5'
Disp	3250 lbs	SA/Disp	18.3
Ballast	1300 lbs	Disp/LWL	229
Sail Area		Blst/Disp	40%
Sloop	251 sq ft	Designer	S2
Mast Ht	31'8"	1 Design	no
Auxiliary	opt	Price	$16,000
			with sails

LOD	23'10"	Hull	FRP
LWL	20'6"	Deck	FRP
Beam	8'	Spar	Alum
Draft		Pos Float	no
cb up	1'11"	Cockpit	6'10"
cb dn	4'5"	Headroom	4'
Disp	3000 lbs	Fr. Water	10 gal
Ballast	1100 lbs	SA/Disp	21.2
Sail Area		Disp/LWL	155
Sloop	276 sq ft	Blst/Disp	37%
Mast Ht	29'	Designer	
Auxiliary	opt		Bob Seidelmann
Honda	7.5 hp	First Built	1981
	outbd	No. Built	52
Fuel Cap	5 gal	1 Design	no
		Price	$19,350
			with sails

NORTH COAST YACHTS INC.
2100 Clement Ave.
Alameda, CA 94501
(415) 523-8330

S2 YACHTS INC.
725 E. 40th St.
Holland, MI 49423
(616) 392-7163

SEIDELMANN YACHTS
Cushman Ave., P. O. Box 2529
Berlin, NJ 08009
(609) 768-1707

Helms 24

Luna ¼ Ton

Luna Miniton

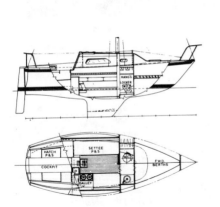

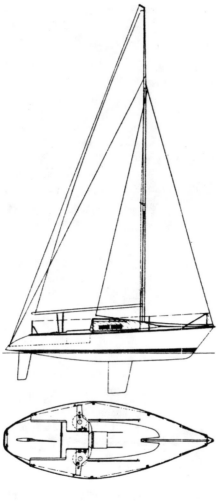

LOD .... 23'11"	Hull .... FRP
LWL .... 20'10"	Deck ..... FRP/Balsa
Beam .... 8'10"	Spar .... Alum
Draft	Headroom ..... 6'1"
Deep .... 4'	Fr. Water ..... 15 gal
Shoal ...... 2'11"	SA/Disp 17.5
Disp ...... 4000 lbs	Disp/LWL 197
Ballast ..... 1750 lbs	Blst/Disp 44%
Sail Area	Price $18,200
Sloop .... 275 sq ft	without sails
Mast Ht .... 33'9"	
Auxiliary .... opt	

LOD .... 23'11"	Hull .... FRP
LWL .... 18'6"	Deck .... FRP
Beam .... 8'2"	Spar .... Alum
Draft .... 4'5"	SA/Disp 34.7
Disp ...... 2500 lbs	Disp/LWL 176
Ballast ..... 1320 lbs	Blst/Disp 53%
Sail Area	Price ... $20,750 Can
Sloop .... 399 sq ft	with sails
Auxiliary .... opt	

LOD .... 23'11"	Hull .... FRP
LWL .... 18'6"	Deck .... FRP
Beam .... 8'2"	Spar .... Alum
Draft .... 4'4"	SA/Disp 29
Disp ...... 2090 lbs	Disp/LWL 147
Ballast ..... 970 lbs	Blst/Disp 46%
Sail Area	Price ... $19,950 Can
Sloop .... 296 sq ft	with sails
Auxiliary .... opt	

JACK A. HELMS CO.
Hwy. 60, P. O. Drawer A
Irmo, SC 29063
(803) 781-5133

LUNA YACHTS LTD.
1435 Wallace Rd.
Oakville, Ontario
Canada L6L 2Y1
(416) 825-1433

LUNA YACHTS LTD.
1435 Wallace Rd.
Oakville, Ontario
Canada L6L 2Y1
(416) 825-1433

Ranger 24

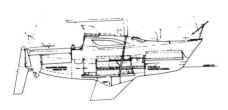

LOD	23'11"	Hull	FRP
LWL	20'	Deck	FRP
Beam	8'4"	Spar	Alum
Draft	4'1"	Pos Float	no
Disp	3150 lbs	Cockpit	6'6"
Ballast	1200 lbs	Headroom	5'7"
Sail Area		Fr. Water	20 gal
Sloop	335 sq ft	SA/Disp	24.9
Mast Ht	32'4"	Disp/LWL	176
Auxiliary	opt	Blst/Disp	38%
	10 hp	Designer	
			Raymond Richards
		First Built	1974
		No. Built	65
		1 Design	yes
		Price	$18,650
			with sails

RANGER BOAT CO.
25802 Pacific Hwy. S.
Kent, WA 98031
(206) 839-5213

Atlantic City Catboat

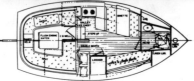

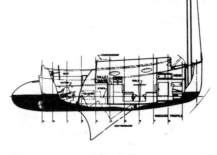

LOD	24'	Hull	FRP
LWL	22'	Deck	FRP
Beam	11'	Spar	Alum
Draft		Pos Float	no
cb up	2'	Cockpit	7'6"
cb dn	5'	Headroom	6'2"
Disp	8000 lbs	Fr. Water	25 gal
Ballast	2200 lbs	SA/Disp	18.1
Sail Area		Disp/LWL	335
Cat (Gaff)	452 sq ft	Blst/Disp	28%
Mast Ht	34'	Designer	
Auxiliary	std		David P. Martin
B.M.W.	12 hp	Builder	Mark-O Custom
Diesel		First Built	1979
Fuel Cap	20 gal	No. Built	45
		1 Design	yes
		Price	$36,875
			with sails

NAVESINK YACHT SALES INC.
1410 Ocean Ave.
Sea Bright, NJ 07760
(201) 842-3700

J — 24

LOD	24'	Hull	FRP/Balsa
LWL	20'	Deck	FRP/Balsa
Beam	8'11"	Spar	Alum
Draft	4'	Pos Float	no
Disp	2700 lbs	Cockpit	8'
Ballast	935 lbs	Headroom	4'2"
Sail Area		Fr. Water	6 gal
Sloop	261 sq ft	SA/Disp	21.5
Mast Ht	34'	Disp/LWL	150
Auxiliary	opt	Blst/Disp	35%
	4 hp	Designer	
	outbd		Rodney Johnstone
		Builder	
			Tillitson Pearson
		First Built	1978
		No. Built	3500
		1 Design	yes
		Price	$15,900
			without sails

J BOATS INC.
24 Mill St.
Newport, RI 02840
(401) 846-8410

Neptune 24

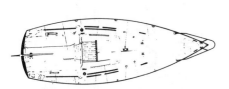

LOD	24'	Hull	FRP
LWL	21'	Deck	FRP
Beam	7'11''	Spar	Alum
Draft		SA/Disp	18.4
Shoal cb up	2'	Disp/LWL	154
Shoal cb dn	3'6''	Blst/Disp	38%
Deep	4'8''	Designer	
Disp	3200 lbs		Capital Yachts
Ballast	1200 lbs	Price	na
Sail Area			
Sloop	250 sq ft		
Sloop (tall)	267 sq ft		
Auxiliary	opt		

CAPITAL YACHTS INC.
25914 President Ave.
Harbor City, CA 90710
(213) 530-1311

Pilot Cutter

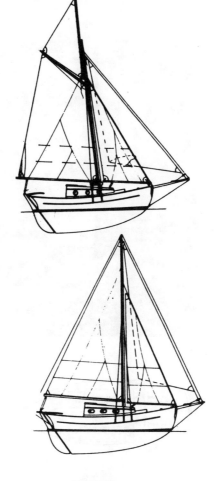

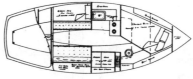

LOA	32'	Hull	FRP
LOD	24'	Deck	FRP
LWL	20'	Spar	Alum
Beam	9'	Headroom	6'3''
Draft	4'	Fr. Water	40 gal
Disp	8900 lbs	SA/Disp	15.3
Ballast	3200 lbs	Disp/LWL	497
Sail Area		Blst/Disp	36%
Cutter	410 sq ft	Designer	Frank Parish
Cutter (Gaff)	460 sq ft	Price	na
Mast Ht	37'		
Auxiliary	std		
Volvo	17 hp		
Diesel			

AQUARIUS YACHTS INC.
2014 Whitfield Park Ave.
Sarasota, FL 33580
(813) 758-7221

Rodgers 24

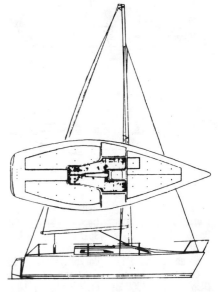

LOD	24'	Hull	FRP
LWL	20'	Deck	FRP
Beam	8'	Spar	Alum
Draft		SA/Disp	24.4
cb up	1'4''	Disp/LWL	123
cb dn	5'7''	Blst/Disp	36%
Disp	2200 lbs	Price	$14,250
Ballast	800 lbs		with sails
Sail Area			
Sloop	258 sq ft		
Auxiliary	opt		

RODGERS YACHT & DESIGN
4501 Ulmerton Rd.
Clearwater, FL 33702
(813) 577-2662

Seidelmann 245

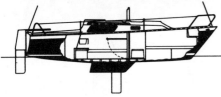

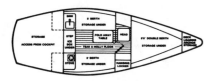

LOD	24'2"	Hull	FRP
LWL	20'6"	Deck	FRP
Beam	8'	Spar	Alum
Draft		Pos Float	no
cb up	1'11"	Cockpit	6'10"
cb dn	4'5"	Headroom	4'5"
Disp	3000 lbs	Fr. Water	10 gal
Ballast	1300 lbs	SA/Disp	21.2
Sail Area		Disp/LWL	155
Sloop	276 sq ft	Blst/Disp	43%
Mast Ht	29'7"	Designer	
Auxiliary	opt		Bob Seidelmann
Honda	7.5 hp	First Built	1982
	outbd	No. Built	58
Fuel Cap	6 gal	1 Design	no
		Price	$20,600
			with sails

SEIDELMANN YACHTS
Cushman Ave., P. O. Box 2529
Berlin, NJ 08009
(609) 768-1707

Northern 25

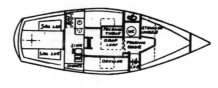

LOA	25'3"	Hull	FRP
LOD	24'5"	Deck	FRP
LWL	19'3"	Spar	Alum
Beam	8'2"	Pos Float	no
Draft	4'	Cockpit	6'6"
Disp	5100 lbs	Headroom	6'3"
Ballast	2300 lbs	Fr. Water	18 gal
Sail Area		SA/Disp	16.5
Sloop	305 sq ft	Disp/LWL	319
Mast Ht	36'6"	Blst/Disp	45%
Auxiliary	opt	Designer	
Yanmar	7.5 hp		Northern Yachts
Diesel		Builder	
Fuel Cap	10 gal		Northern Yachts
		First Built	1970
		No. Built	205
		Kit	available
		Price	$21,000
			with sails

NORTHERN YACHTS
395 Francom St.
Ajax, Ontario
Canada L1S 1R4
(416) 683-5980

Merit 25

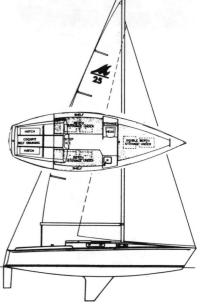

LOA	25'	Hull	FRP
LOD	24'6"	Deck	FRP
LWL	20'	Spar	Alum
Beam	8'	Pos Float	no
Draft	4'	Cockpit	8'
Disp	3000 lbs	Headroom	4'5"
Ballast	1050 lbs	Fr. Water	8 gal
Sail Area		SA/Disp	22
Sloop	286 sq ft	Disp/LWL	167
		Blst/Disp	35%
		Designer	Paul Yates
		First Built	1979
		No. Built	450
		1 Design	yes
		Price	$15,100
			with sails

MERIT MARINE
13541 Desmond St.
Pacoima, CA 91331
(213) 897-1271

Seidelmann 25

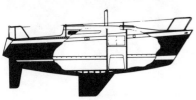

LOD	24'6"	Hull	FRP
LWL	20'	Deck	FRP
Beam	9'6"	Spar	Alum
Draft		Pos Float	no
Shoal	3'4"	Cockpit	6'8"
Deep	4'4"	Headroom	5'
Disp	4600 lbs	Fr. Water	10 gal
Ballast	2200 lbs	SA/Disp	16.3
Sail Area		Disp/LWL	257
Sloop	281 sq ft	Blst/Disp	48%
Mast Ht	33'10"	Designer	
Auxiliary	opt		Bob Seidelmann
Yanmar	12 hp	First Built	1978
Diesel		No. Built	276
Fuel Cap	6 gal	1 Design	no
		Price	$18,643
			with sails

SEIDELMANN YACHTS
Cushman Ave., P. O. Box 2529
Berlin, NJ 08009
(609) 768-1707

Yankee 26

LOA	26'	Hull	FRP
LOD	24'6"	Deck	FRP
LWL	20'8"	Spar	Alum
Beam	8'8"	Pos Float	yes
Draft	4'6"	Cockpit	6'
Disp	5335 lbs	Headroom	6'2"
Ballast	2150 lbs	Fr. Water	15 gal
Sail Area		SA/Disp	15.4
Sloop	294 sq ft	Disp/LWL	269
Mast Ht	36'	Blst/Disp	40%
Auxiliary	std	First Built	1972
BMW	7 hp	1 Design	yes
Diesel		Kit	$5,000
Fuel Cap	15 gal	Price	$36,000
			with sails

HERITAGE BOAT WORKS
1331 Country Club Rd.
Hood River, OR 97031
(503) 386-1526

Camelot 247

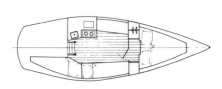

LOD	24'7"	Hull	FRP
LWL	21'	Deck	FRP
Beam	8'	Spar	Alum
Draft	3'9"	Headroom	5'8"
Disp	4000 lbs	Fr. Water	12 gal
Ballast	1600 lbs	SA/Disp	16.5
Sail Area		Disp/LWL	192
Sloop	260 sq ft	Blst/Disp	40%
Auxiliary	opt	Price	$25,000
Volvo	7.5 hp		with sails
Diesel			
Fuel Cap	12 gal		

CAMELOT YACHTS
P.O. Box 92
Ontario, NY 14519
(315) 524-4607

Capri 25

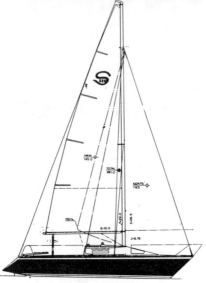

LOD	24'7''	Hull	FRP
LWL	19'2''	Deck	FRP
Beam	9'2''	Spar	Alum
Draft	4'2''	Pos Float	no
Disp	2785 lbs	SA/Disp	22.3
Ballast	900 lbs	Disp/LWL	176
Sail Area		Blst/Disp	32%
Sloop	276 sq ft	Designer	Frank Butler
Auxiliary	opt	First Built	1980
	6 hp	No. Built	358
	outbd	Price	$12,950
			without sails

CATALINA YACHTS
21200 Victory Blvd.
Woodland Hills, CA 91367
(213) 884-7700

Santana 525

LOD	24'7''	Hull	FRP
LWL	18'6''	Deck	FRP
Beam	9'4''	Spar	Alum
Draft	4'6''	Cockpit	6'6''
Disp	2400 lbs	SA/Disp	23.3
Ballast	950 lbs	Disp/LWL	169
Sail Area		Blst/Disp	40%
Sloop	261 sq ft	Designer	Shad Turner
		Price	$15,395
			with sails

W. D. SCHOCK CORP.
3502 S. Greenville St.
Santa Ana, CA 92704
(714) 549-2277

Tanzer 7.5

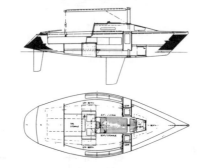

LOD	24'7''	Hull	FRP
LWL	21'10''	Deck	FRP
Beam	8'	Spar	Alum
Draft		Pos Float	no
Shoal	2'8''	Cockpit	6'
Deep	4'	Headroom	5'8''
Disp		Fr. Water	10 gal
Shoal	4150 lbs	SA/Disp	16.4
Deep	3800 lbs	Disp/LWL	178
Ballast		Blst/Disp	47%
Shoal	1950 lbs	Designer	
Deep	1600 lbs		Johann Tanzer
Sail Area		First Built	1977
Sloop	265 sq ft	No. Built	729
Mast Ht	32'	1 Design	yes
Auxiliary	opt	Price	$16,500
	7.5 hp		with sails
	outbd		

TANZER
Box 670, Cape Colony
Edenton, NC 27932
(919) 482-7404

- -

P. O. Box 67
Dorion, PQ Canada J7V 5V8
(514) 455-5681

Contest 25 OC

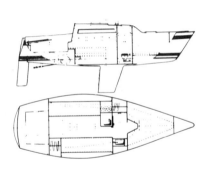

LOD	24'8"	Fr. Water	26 gal
LWL	21'5"	SA/Disp	20.1
Beam	9'	Disp/LWL	172
Draft	4'1"	Blst/Disp	40%
Disp	3788 lbs	Designer	
Ballast	1510 lbs		Jac de Ridder
Sail Area		Builder	
Sloop	306 sq ft		Conyplex, Holland
Auxiliary	std	1 Design	yes
Volvo Penta	7.5 hp	Price	na
Diesel			
Fuel Cap	20 gal		

HOLLAND YACHTS
Box 129
Solomons, MD 20688
(301) 326-3960

Lancer 25

LOD	24'8"	Hull	FRP
LWL	20'1"	Deck	FRP
Beam	8'	Spar	Alum
Draft	3'	Pos Float	no
Disp	3600 lbs	Cockpit	7'
Ballast	1300 lbs	Headroom	6'
Sail Area		Fr. Water	15 gal
Sloop	287 sq ft	SA/Disp	19.5
Mast Ht	36'	Disp/LWL	198
Auxiliary	std	Blst/Disp	36%
Honda	7.5 hp	Designer	
	outbd		W. Shad Turner
		First Built	1974
		1 Design	yes
		Price	$24,346
			with sails

LANCER YACHT CORP.
1939 Deere Ave.
Irvine, CA 92714
(714) 751-7220

O'Day 25

LOD	24'10"	Hull	FRP
LWL	21'	Deck	FRP
Beam	8'	Spar	Alum
Draft		Pos Float	no
Deep	4'6"	Cockpit	4'9"
Shoal cb up	2'3"	Headroom	5'4"
Shoal cb dn	4'6"	Fr. Water	15 gal
Disp	4007 lbs	SA/Disp	18.4
Ballast	1775 lbs	Disp/LWL	193
Sail Area		Blst/Disp	44%
Sloop (tall)	290 sq ft	Designer	
Sloop	270 sq ft		C. R. Hunt Assoc.
Mast Ht		First Built	1975
Sloop (tall)	31'	No. Built	1725
Sloop	29'	1 Design	yes
Auxiliary	opt	Price	na
Yanmar	7.5 hp		
Diesel			
Fuel Cap	12 gal		

BANGOR PUNTA MARINE
848 Airport Rd.
Box 991
Fall River, MA 02722
(617) 678-5291

Bayfield 25

LOD	25'	Hull	FRP
LWL	19'8"	Deck	FRP
Beam	8'	Spar	Alum
Draft	2'11"	Headroom	6'
Disp	3500 lbs	Fr. Water	20 gal
Ballast	1300 lbs	SA/Disp	16.7
Sail Area		Disp/LWL	205
Sloop	240 sq ft	Blst/Disp	37%
Auxiliary	std	Designer	
Diesel	7.5 hp		H. Ted Gozzard
Fuel Cap	11 gal	No. Built	500
		Price	$24,950
			with sails

Canvasback

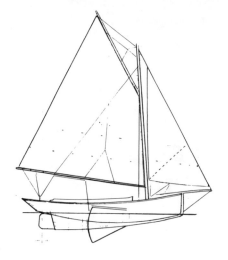

LOD	25'	Hull	Wood
LWL	21'6"	Deck	Wood
Beam	9'	Spar	Wood
Draft		SA/Disp	19.2
cb up	2'4"	Disp/LWL	224
cb dn	na	Designer	
Disp	5000 lbs		Nathaniel Benjamin
Ballast	na	Price	$25,000
Sail Area			with sails
Sloop (gaff)	350 sq ft		

Cape Dory 25 D

LOD	25'	Hull	FRP
LWL	19'	Deck	FRP/Balsa
Beam	8'	Spar	Alum
Draft	3'6"	Pos Float	no
Disp	5120 lbs	Cockpit	6'2"
Ballast	2050 lbs	Headroom	5'11"
Sail Area		Fr. Water	20 gal
Sloop	304 sq ft	SA/Disp	16.4
Mast Ht	34'11"	Disp/LWL	333
Auxiliary	std	Blst/Disp	40%
Yanmar	7.5 hp	Designer	Carl Alberg
Diesel		First Built	1981
Fuel Cap	13 gal	No. Built	95
		1 Design	yes
		Price	na

BAYFIELD BOAT YARD LTD.
Box 1076
Clinton, Ontario
Canada N0M 1L0
(519) 482-3425

GANNON & BENJAMIN
Beach Road
Vineyard Haven, MA 02568

CAPE DORY YACHTS INC.
160 Middleboro Ave.
E. Taunton, MA 02718
(617) 823-6776

Catalina 25

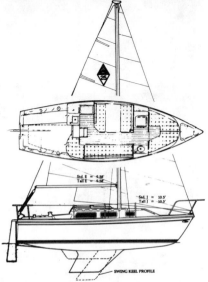

SWING KEEL PROFILE

LOD	25'	Hull	FRP
LWL	22'2''	Deck	FRP
Beam	8'	Spar	Alum
Draft		Pos Float	no
Fixed	4'	Headroom	5'4''
Swing keel up	2'8''	Fr. Water	21 gal
Swing keel dn	5'	SA/Disp	15.7
Disp		Disp/LWL	186
Fixed	4550 lbs	Blst/Disp	42%
Swing	4150 lbs	Designer	Frank Butler
Ballast		First Built	1975
Fixed	1900 lbs	No. Built	3542
Swing	1500 lbs	1 Design	no
Sail Area		Price	$10,950
Sloop	270 sq ft		without sails
Sloop (tall)	290 sq ft		
Mast Ht			
Sloop	33'		
Sloop (tall)	35'		
Auxiliary	opt		
	10 hp		
	outbd		

CATALINA YACHTS
21200 Victory Blvd.
Woodland Hills, CA 91367
(213) 884-7700

Crown 25

LOD	25'	Hull	FRP
LWL	na	Deck	FRP
Beam	7'2''	Spar	Alum
Draft		Pos Float	yes
Ver ret keel up	2'	Cockpit	7'6''
Ver ret keel dn	4'6''	SA/Disp	21.2
*Disp	2000 lbs	Blst/Disp	42%
Ballast	840 lbs	Designer	
Sail Area			Carl Schumacher
Sloop	210 sq ft	Price	na
Mast Ht	32'		
Auxiliary	opt		

SEA CROWN MARINE INC.
381D Laurelwood Rd.
Santa Clara, CA 95050
(408) 988-7605

Eastsail 25

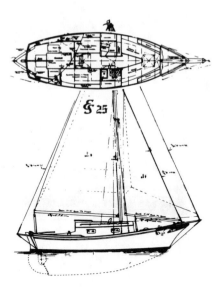

LOD	25'	Hull	FRP/Airex
LWL	20'11''	Deck	FRP
Beam	8'6''	Spar	Wood or Alum
Draft	3'8''	Pos Float	no
Disp	6600 lbs	Cockpit	6'
Ballast	2300 lbs	Headroom	6'
Sail Area		Fr. Water	20 gal
Cutter	400 sq ft	SA/Disp	18.2
Mast Ht	34'	Disp/LWL	321
Auxiliary	opt	Blst/Disp	35%
Westerbeke	14 hp	Designer	
Diesel			Eliot Spalding
Fuel Cap	20 gal	Builder	
			Rumery's Boatyard
		First Built	1982
		No. Built	1
		1 Design	no
		Kit	available
		Price	$39,900
			with sails

EASTSAIL YACHTS
3 Rochester Neck Rd.
Rochester, NH 03867

Horizon 26

LOA	26'	Hull	FRP
LOD	25'	Deck	FRP
LWL	23'	Spar	Alum
Beam	8'	Pos Float	no
Draft		Cockpit	6'1"
Shoal	2'1"	Headroom	6'1"
Deep	3'1"	Fr. Water	25 gal
Disp	4550 lbs	SA/Disp	16.3
Ballast	1600 lbs	Disp/LWL	166
Sail Area		Blst/Disp	35%
Sloop	280 sq ft	First Built	1982
Mast Ht	35'	No. Built	4
Auxiliary	opt	1 Design	no
	15 hp	Kit	available
	outbd	Price	$18,000
			with sails

HORIZON YACHT
4451 112th Terrace North
Clearwater, FL 33520
(813) 577-0624

Hunter 25

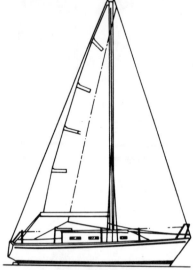

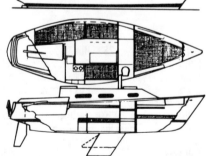

LOD	25'	Hull	FRP
LWL	20'2"	Deck	FRP
Beam	8'	Spar	Alum
Draft		Fr. Water	20 gal
Shoal	2'11"	SA/Disp	15.3
Deep	3'11"	Disp/LWL	239
Disp	4400 lbs	Blst/Disp	45%
Ballast		Price	$15,490
Shoal	2000 lbs		with sails
Deep	1800 lbs		
Sail Area			
Sloop	256 sq ft		
Mast Ht	34'1"		
Auxiliary	opt		
	outbd		

HUNTER MARINE
Box 1030, Hwy 441
Alachua, FL 32601
(904) 462-3077

MacGregor 25

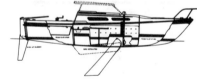

LOD	25'	Hull	FRP
LWL	23'6"	Deck	FRP
Beam	8'	Spar	Alum
Draft		Pos Float	yes
Swing keel up	1'10"	Cockpit	7'
Swing keel dn	5'8"	Headroom	6'
Disp	2100 lbs	Fr. Water	3 gal
Ballast	625 lbs	SA/Disp	23
Sail Area		Disp/LWL	72
Sloop	236 sq ft	Blst/Disp	30%
Mast Ht	32'	Designer	
Auxiliary	opt		R. N. MacGregor
	10 hp	First Built	1973
	outbd	No. Built	9000
		1 Design	yes
		Price	$7,808
			with sails

MacGREGOR
1631 Placentia
Costa Mesa, CA 92627
(714) 642-6830

Pemaquid Sloop

US 25

Dufour 25

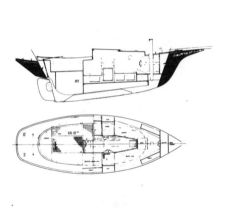

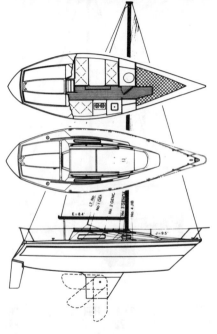

LOA . . . . 34'6"	Hull . . . . FRP
LOD . . . . 25'	Deck . . . FRP or Wood
LWL . . . . 21'	Spar . . . . Wood
Beam . . . . 8'8"	Pos Float . . . . . . no
Draft . . . . 4'3"	Cockpit . . . . 8'4"
Disp . . . . . . 7000 lbs	Headroom . . . . . . 5'
Ballast . . . . 2000 lbs	Fr. Water . . . . . 25 gal
Sail Area	SA/Disp 18.9
Sloop (Gaff) 432 sq ft	Disp/LWL 337
Mast Ht . . . . 26'	Blst/Disp 29%
Auxiliary . . . . std	Designer . . . A. Carter
Volvo . . . . . . 12 hp	First Built 1968
Diesel	No. Built 18
Fuel Cap . . . . . 15 gal	1 Design . . . . no
	Kit . . . . available
	Price $55,000
	with sails

JARVIS NEWMAN BOATS
P. O. Box 707
Southwest Harbor, ME 04679
(207) 244-3860

LOD . . . . 25'	Hull . . . . FRP
LWL . . . . 21'5"	Deck . . . . FRP
Beam . . . . 8'	Spar . . . . Alum
Draft	Pos Float . . . . . . no
Swing keel up . 2'6"	Headroom . . . . . 5'6"
Swing keel dn 5'10"	Fr. Water . . . . . 4 gal
Fixed . . . . 4'7"	SA/Disp 17
Disp . . . . . . 3750 lbs	Disp/LWL 170
Ballast . . . . 1250 lbs	Blst/Disp 33%
Sail Area	First Built 1978
Sloop . . . . 257 sq ft	1 Design . . . . no
Mast Ht . . . . . . 33'9"	Price . . . . na
Auxiliary . . . . . . opt	
15 hp	
outbd	

US YACHT
P. O. Box 24467
Seattle, WA 98134

LOD . . . . 25'1"	Hull . . . . FRP
LWL . . . . 22'	Deck . . . . FRP
Beam . . . . 8'11"	Spar . . . . Alum
Draft	Cockpit . . . . 6'2"
Shoal . . . . . . 3'4"	Headroom . . . . . 5'9"
Deep . . . . . . 4'4"	Fr. Water . . . . . 24 gal
Disp . . . . . . 3940 lbs	SA/Disp 16.5
Ballast . . . . 1650 lbs	Disp/LWL 165
Sail Area	Blst/Disp 42%
Sloop . . . . 258 sq ft	Designer
	Laurent Cordelle
	Builder
	Dufour, France
	Price . . . . na

EURO SAILBOATS LTD.
131 East Boston Post Road
Mamaroneck, NY 10543
(914) 381-4500

Page 169

C & C 25

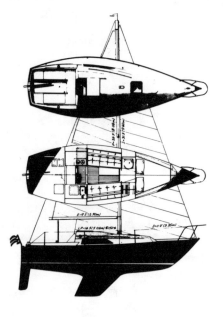

LOD	25'2"	Hull	FRP
LWL	20'8"	Deck	FRP/Balsa
Beam	8'8"	Spar	Alum
Draft	4'3"	Fr. Water	16 gal
Disp	4250 lbs	SA/Disp	18.2
Ballast	1880 lbs	Disp/LWL	214
Sail Area		Blst/Disp	44%
Sloop	299 sq ft	Price	$26,750
Mast Ht	34'10"		without sails
Auxiliary	opt		

C&C YACHTS
55 Port Street East
Mississauga, Ontario
Canada L5G 4P3
(416) 274-7131

Cal 25

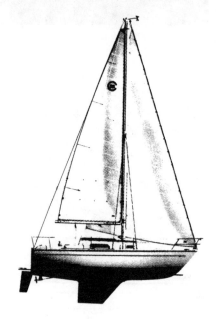

LOD	25'3"	Hull	FRP
LWL	22'	Deck	FRP
Beam	9'	Spar	Alum
Draft		Pos Float	no
Shoal	3'6"	Cockpit	6'6"
Deep	4'6"	Headroom	5'10"
Disp	4500 lbs	Fr. Water	21 gal
Ballast	2000 lbs	SA/Disp	18.5
Sail Area		Disp/LWL	188
Sloop	314 sq ft	Blst/Disp	44%
Mast Ht	36'4"	Designer	
Auxiliary	opt		Bill Lapworth
Diesel	11 hp	First Built	1977
		No. Built	390
		1 Design	yes
		Price	na

BANGOR PUNTA MARINE
848 Airport Rd.
Box 991
Fall River, MA 02722
(617) 678-5291

Montego 25

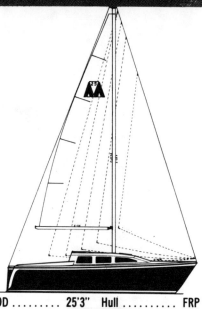

LOD	25'3"	Hull	FRP
LWL	20'6"	Deck	FRP
Beam	9'1"	Spar	Alum
Draft		Pos Float	no
Shoal	3'6"	Cockpit	7'3"
Deep	4'6"	Headroom	5'11"
Disp	4550 lbs	Fr. Water	20 gal
Ballast	1800 lbs	SA/Disp	17.1
Sail Area		Disp/LWL	236
Sloop	294 sq ft	Blst/Disp	40%
Mast Ht	37'3"	Designer	
Auxiliary	opt		J. "Jopie" Helsen
OMC	15 hp	First Built	1981
	outbd	No. Built	65
Fuel Cap	12 gal	1 Design	no
		Price	$19,950
			with sails

UNIVERSAL MARINE CORP.
1421 Bay St. S.E.
St. Petersburg, FL 33701
(813) 823-1155

Alerion

LOD	25'4"	Hull	FRP
LWL	20'	Deck	FRP
Beam	7'2"	Spar	Alum
Draft	3'7"	SA/Disp	15.1
Disp	4800 lbs	Disp/LWL	268
Ballast	2400 lbs	Blst/Disp	50%
Sail Area		Designer	
Sloop	269 sq ft		N. G. Herreshoff
Auxiliary	opt	Price	$26,000
			with sails

HALSEY C. HERRESHOFF INC.
Box 450
18 Burnside Street
Bristol, RI 02809
(401) 253-6660

Beachcomber 25

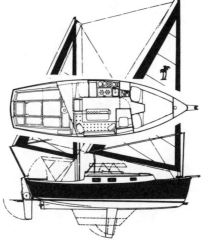

LOD	25'4"	Hull	FRP
LWL	23'3"	Deck	FRP
Beam	8'	Spar	Alum
Draft		Pos Float	no
Shoal cb up	1'3"	Cockpit	8'
Shoal cb dn	5'7"	Headroom	5'6"
Deep cb up	2'6"	Fr. Water	20 gal
Deep cb dn	5'	SA/Disp	14.5
Deep no cb	3'6"	Disp/LWL	188
Disp	5300 lbs	Blst/Disp	26%
Ballast	1400 lbs	Designer	Walt Scott
Sail Area		First Built	1979
Cat Ketch	275 sq ft	No. Built	50
Mast Ht	31'1"	1 Design	no
Mast	unstayed	Price	$22,500
Auxiliary	opt		with sails
Diesel	15 hp		
Fuel Cap	13 gal		

MARINE INNOVATORS INC.
Rt. 5 Box 190B
Homosassa, FL 32645
(904) 628-6950

Golden Gambit 7.7

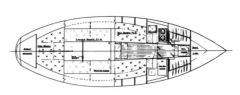

LOD	25'4"	Hull	FRP
LWL	19'7"	Deck	FRP/Balsa
Beam	8'	Spar	Alum
Draft	3'3"	Headroom	5'6"
Disp	3598 lbs	Fr. Water	11 gal
Ballast	1498 lbs	SA/Disp	21.5
Sail Area		Disp/LWL	214
Cutter	316 sq ft	Blst/Disp	42%
Auxiliary	opt	Designer	
Yanmar	7.5 hp		Deborah Berman
Diesel		Builder	
			Wikander Yacht Yard
		Price	na

SAG HARBOR MARINE INC.
Box 395 Planetarium Station
New York, NY 10024
(212) 362-1354

Ericson 25

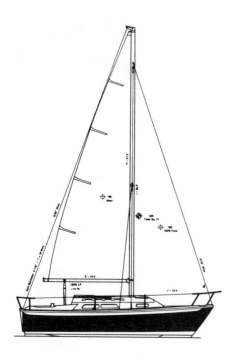

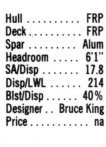

LOD	25'5"	Hull	FRP
LWL	21'10"	Deck	FRP
Beam	9'3"	Spar	Alum
Draft		Headroom	6'1"
Shoal	3'11"	SA/Disp	17.8
Deep	4'11"	Disp/LWL	214
Disp	5000 lbs	Blst/Disp	40%
Ballast	2000 lbs	Designer	Bruce King
Sail Area		Price	na
Sloop	325 sq ft		
Auxiliary	opt		
	15 hp		

ERICSON YACHTS INC.
1931 Deere Ave.
Irvine, CA 92714
(714) 540-8001

Contessa 26

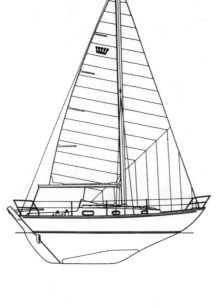

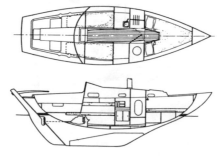

LOD	25'6"	Hull	FRP
LWL	21'	Deck	FRP
Beam	7'6"	Spar	Alum
Draft	4'	Pos Float	no
Disp	5400 lbs	Cockpit	7'
Ballast	2600 lbs	Headroom	5'8"
Sail Area		Fr. Water	20 gal
Sloop	304 sq ft	SA/Disp	15.8
Mast Ht	30'	Disp/LWL	260
Auxiliary	std	Blst/Disp	48%
Farymann	6 hp	Designer	David Sadler
Diesel		No. Built	300
Fuel Cap	15 gal	1 Design	no
		Price	$23,950 Can without sails

J. J. TAYLOR & SONS LTD.
255 Carrier Dr.
Rexdale, Ontario
Canada M9W 6A1
(416) 675-1561

Parker Dawson 26

LOD	25'7"	Hull	FRP
LWL	22'2"	Deck	FRP
Beam	8'	Spar	Alum
Draft		Pos Float	no
Swing keel up	1'8"	Cockpit	6'
Swing keel dn	5'4"	Headroom	5'10"
Disp	5000 lbs	Fr. Water	28 gal
Ballast	1250 lbs	SA/Disp	14.8
Sail Area		Disp/LWL	205
Sloop	271 sq ft	Blst/Disp	25%
Ketch	281 sq ft	Designer	Bob Finch
Mast Ht	32'6"	First Built	1973
Auxiliary	opt	No. Built	313
Diesel	15 hp	1 Design	no
		Price	$24,450 with sails

PARKER/DAWSON YACHTS
55 Park Road
South Shore Park
Hingham, MA 02043
(617) 749-6444

Freedom 25

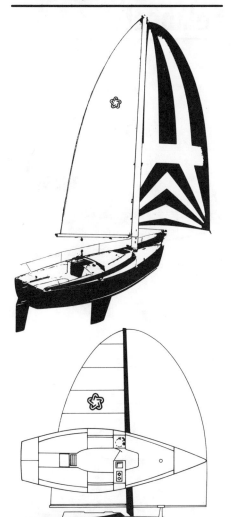

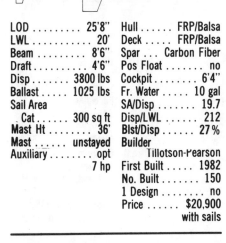

LOD	25'8"	Hull	FRP/Balsa
LWL	20'	Deck	FRP/Balsa
Beam	8'6"	Spar	Carbon Fiber
Draft	4'6"	Pos Float	no
Disp	3800 lbs	Cockpit	6'4"
Ballast	1025 lbs	Fr. Water	10 gal
Sail Area		SA/Disp	19.7
Cat	300 sq ft	Disp/LWL	212
Mast Ht	36'	Blst/Disp	27 %
Mast	unstayed	Builder	
Auxiliary	opt		Tillotson-Pearson
	7 hp	First Built	1982
		No. Built	150
		1 Design	no
		Price	$20,900
			with sails

FREEDOM YACHTS
49 America's Cup Ave.
Newport, RI 02840
(401) 847-7475

Ranger 26

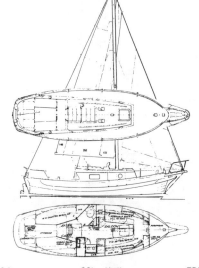

LOA	28'	Hull	FRP
LOD	25'9"	Deck	FRP
LWL	22	Spar	Alum
Beam	8'	Pos Float	no
Draft		Cockpit	6'6"
cb up	2'4"	Headroom	6'2"
cb dn	4'10"	Fr. Water	35 gal
Disp	4750 lbs	SA/Disp	18.1
Ballast	1400 lbs	Blst/Disp	29 %
Sail Area		Designer	
Sloop	320 sq ft		Raymond Richards
Mast Ht	34'5"	First Built	1974
Auxiliary	opt	No. Built	47
Yanmar	7.5 hp	1 Design	yes
Diesel		Price	$24,500
Fuel Cap	9 gal		with sails

RANGER BOAT CO.
25802 Pacific Hwy. S.
Kent, WA 98031
(206) 839-5213

San Juan 7.7

LOD	25'9"	Hull	FRP
LWL	20'	Deck	FRP
Beam	9'6"	Spar	Alum
Draft	4'	Pos Float	no
Disp	3200 lbs	Cockpit	7'3"
Ballast	1100 lbs	Headroom	5'8"
Sail Area		Fr. Water	14 gal
Sloop	304 sq ft	SA/Disp	22.4
Auxiliary	opt	Disp/LWL	178
	7.5 hp	Blst/Disp	34 %
	outbd	Designer	Don Clark
		First Built	1978
		No. Built	250
		1 Design	yes
		Price	$19,395
			with sails

CLARK BOAT CO.
25-37th St. NE
Auburn, WA 98002
(206) 854-5400

Seafarer 26

LOD	25'9"	Hull	FRP
LWL	22'3"	Deck	FRP
Beam	8'3"	Spar	Alum
Draft		Pos Float	no
Shoal	3'6"	Cockpit	7'
Deep	4'	Headroom	6'1"
Disp	5200 lbs	Fr. Water	43 gal
Ballast	1850 lbs	SA/Disp	15.2
Sail Area		Disp/LWL	211
Sloop	285 sq ft	Blst/Disp	36%
Mast Ht	33'11"	Designer	
Auxiliary	std		McCurdy/Rhodes
	15 hp	First Built	1977
	outbd	No. Built	300
		1 Design	no
		Price	$22,900
			with sails

SEAFARER YACHTS INC.
760 Park Ave.
Huntington, NY 11743
(516) 427-6670

Windrose 26

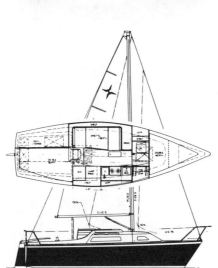

LOD	25'9"	Hull	FRP
LWL	21'6"	Deck	FRP
Beam	8'4"	Spar	Alum
Draft	3'1"	Pos Float	no
Disp	3600 lbs	Headroom	6'2"
Ballast	1200 lbs	SA/Disp	18.7
Sail Area		Disp/LWL	161
Sloop	275 sq ft	Blst/Disp	33%
Mast Ht	28'	Designer	
Auxiliary	opt		W. Shad Turner
	10 hp	1 Design	yes
	outbd	Price	$18,132
			with sails

LAGUNA YACHTS INC.
10960 Boatman
Stanton, CA 90680
(714) 527-7262

International Folkboat

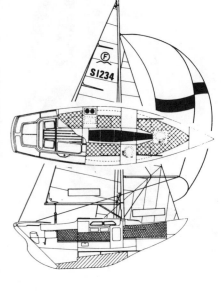

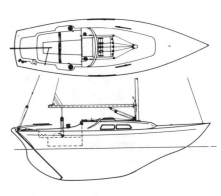

LOD	25'10"	Hull	FRP
LWL	19'10"	Deck	FRP
Beam	7'4"	Spar	Alum
Draft	3'11"	Fr. Water	28 gal
Disp	5000 lbs	SA/Disp	15.3
Ballast	2750 lbs	Disp/LWL	286
Sail Area		Blst/Disp	55%
Sloop	280 sq ft	Designer	Tord Sunden
Auxiliary	opt	Builder	
Volvo	7.5 hp		Marieholms, Sweden
Diesel		First Built	1969
Fuel Cap	6 gal	Price	$19,550
			with sails

ATKINS YACHTS
326 First St.
Annapolis, MD 21403
(301) 268-3332

Grand Slam 7.9   Alerion   Evelyn 26

LOD .... 25'11"	Hull ..... FRP/Balsa
LWL .... 21'8"	Deck ..... FRP/Balsa
Beam .... 9'	Spar .... Alum
Draft	Pos Float .... no
Ver ret keel up . 1'1"	Cockpit .... 8'
Ver ret keel dn .. 5'	Headroom ..... 5'5"
Disp ...... 4250 lbs	SA/Disp 19.8
Ballast ..... 1675 lbs	Disp/LWL 187
Sail Area	Blst/Disp 39%
Sloop .... 325 sq ft	Designer
Auxiliary .... opt	Graham/Schlageter
outbd	1 Design .... yes
	Price $20,125
	with sails

LOD .... 26'	Hull Epoxy wood fiber
LWL .... 21'9"	Deck Epoxy wood fiber
Beam .... 7'7"	Spar .... Wood
Draft	SA/Disp 17.5
cb up ...... 2'5"	Disp/LWL 263
cb dn ...... 5'6"	Blst/Disp 63%
Disp ...... 6050 lbs	Designer
Ballast .... 3800 lbs	N. Herreshoff
Sail Area	Price $44,000
Sloop .... 364 sq ft	without sails
Auxiliary .... opt	
Volvo .... inbd	
Gas	

LOD .... 26'	Hull .... FRP
LWL .... na	Deck .... FRP
Beam .... 9'6"	Spar .... Alum
Draft	SA/Disp 20.2
Deep ...... 4'6"	Blst/Disp 34%
Shoal db up .. 1'2"	Price $20,370
Shoal db dn .... 5'	with sails
Disp	
Deep .... 4100 lbs	
Shoal .... 4400 lbs	
Ballast ..... 1400 lbs	
Sail Area	
Sloop (MH) 323 sq ft	
Sloop (FR) 327 sq ft	
Auxiliary .... opt	

S2 YACHTS INC.
725 E. 40th St.
Holland, MI 49423
(616) 392-7163

SANFORD BOAT CO. INC.
Pleasant St.
Nantucket, MA 02554
(617) 228-4108

FORMULA YACHTS INC.
185 South Rd.
Croton, CT 06340
(203) 445-4413

Frances

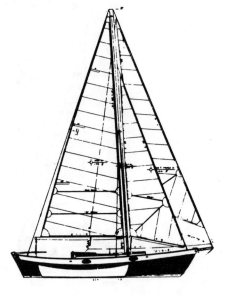

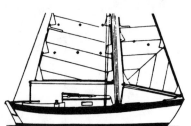

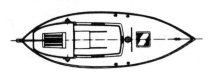

LOD	26'	Hull	FRP
LWL	21'3"	Deck	FRP
Beam	8'2"	Spar	Alum
Draft	3'10"	Fr. Water	25 gal
Disp	6800 lbs	SA/Disp	15
Ballast	3500 lbs	Disp/LWL	316
Sail Area		Blst/Disp	51%
Sloop	337 sq ft	Designer	C. W. Paine
Auxiliary	std	Price	$39,500
BMW	7 hp		with sails
Diesel			
Fuel Cap	12 gal		

MORRIS YACHTS
Box 58
Southwest Harbor, ME 04679
(207) 244-5866

Grampian 26

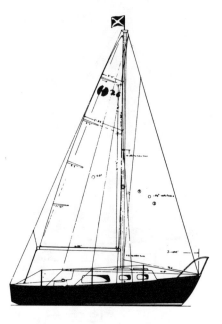

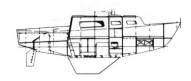

LOD	26'	Hull	FRP
LWL	21'9"	Deck	FRP
Beam	8'4"	Spar	Alum
Draft	4'3"	Headroom	6'
Disp	5600 lbs	SA/Disp	16.5
Ballast	2600 lbs	Disp/LWL	243
Sail Area		Blst/Disp	46%
Sloop	325 sq ft	Price	na
Auxiliary	opt		

SAILCAN LTD.
5230 South Service Rd.
Burlington, Ontario
Canada L7L 5K2
(416) 827-3781

Nash 26

LOD	26'	Hull	FRP
LWL	21'3"	Deck	FRP
Beam	8'6"	Spar	Alum
Draft	3'6"	Headroom	6'
Disp	5000 lbs	Fr. Water	15 gal
Ballast	2100 lbs	SA/Disp	15.7
Sail Area		Disp/LWL	232
Sloop	287 sq ft	Blst/Disp	42%
Auxiliary	opt	Price	$26,500 Can
			with sails

J & J NASH IND.
250 High St. Unit G
Strathroy, Ontario
Canada NOM 1A0
(519) 245-3380

Nonsuch 26

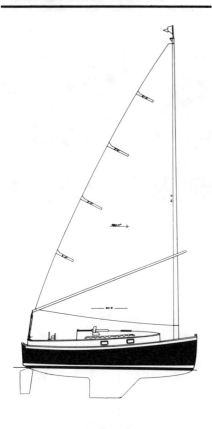

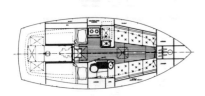

LOD	26'	Hull	FRP
LWL	24'4"	Deck	FRP/Balsa
Beam	10'6"	Spar	Alum
Draft		Cockpit	6'
Shoal	3'9"	Headroom	6'1"
Deep	4'6"	Fr. Water	60 gal
Disp	8500 lbs	SA/Disp	16.1
Ballast	2750 lbs	Disp/LWL	263
Sail Area		Blst/Disp	32%
Cat	420 sq ft	Designer	Mark Ellis
Mast Ht	49'	First Built	1981
Mast	unstayed	No. Built	90
Auxiliary	std	Price	$42,960
Westerbeke	21 hp		without sails
Diesel			
Fuel Cap	24 gal		

HINTERHOELLER YACHTS LTD.
8 Keefer Rd., St. Catharines,
Ontario L2M 7N9, Canada
(416) 937-4440

S2 8.0

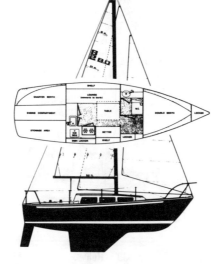

LOD	26'	Hull	FRP
LWL	21'5"	Deck	FRP/Balsa
Beam	8'	Spar	Alum
Draft		Pos Float	no
Shoal	3'6"	Cockpit	6'8"
Deep	4'	Headroom	5'10"
Disp	4600 lbs	Fr. Water	12 gal
Ballast	1800 lbs	SA/Disp	16.3
Sail Area		Disp/LWL	209
Sloop	282 sq ft	Blst/Disp	39%
Mast Ht	35'	Designer	
Auxiliary	opt		Arthur Edmunds
	inbd	1 Design	no
		Price	$22,800
			with sails

S2 YACHTS INC.
725 E. 40th St.
Holland, MI 49423
(616) 392-7163

T—26

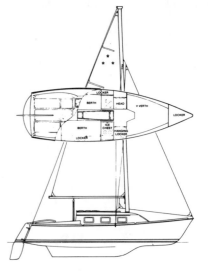

LOD	26'	Hull	FRP
LWL	22'10"	Deck	FRP
Beam	8'	Spar	Alum
Draft	2'1"	Headroom	6'1"
Disp	4400 lbs	Fr. Water	24 gal
Ballast	1500 lbs	SA/Disp	17.2
Sail Area		Disp/LWL	165
Sloop	288 sq ft	Blst/Disp	34%
Mast Ht	32'	Price	na
Auxiliary	opt		
	outbd		

COMMODORE YACHT CORP.
Rt. #1, Box 525S
Pine Island Industrial Park
St. James City, FL 33956

Thunderbird

LOD . . . . 26'	Hull . . . . FRP
LWL . . . . 20'3"	Deck . . . . FRP
Beam . . . . 7'6"	Spar . . . . Alum
Draft . . . . 4'6"	Pos Float . . . . no
Disp . . . . . . 3900 lbs	Cockpit . . . . 5'
Ballast . . . . . 1500 lbs	Headroom . . . . . 5'5"
Sail Area	Fr. Water . . . . 22 gal
Sloop . . . 360 sq ft	SA/Disp 23.2
Mast Ht . . . . 37'	Disp/LWL 209
Auxiliary . . . . opt	Blst/Disp 38%
10 hp	Designer Ben Seaborn
outbd	First Built 1971
	No. Built 50
	1 Design . . . . yes
	Kit . . . . available
	Price . . . $20,000 Can
	without sails

Voyager 26

LOA . . . . 30'	Hull . . . . FRP
LOD . . . . 26'	Deck . . . . FRP
LWL . . . . 21'3"	Spar . . . . Alum
Beam . . . . 8'3"	Pos Float . . . . no
Draft . . . . 3'4"	Cockpit . . . . 6'
Disp . . . . . . 6800 lbs	Headroom . . . . 5'10"
Ballast . . . . . 2750 lbs	Fr. Water . . . . 25 gal
Sail Area	SA/Disp 16
Cutter . . . 360 sq ft	Disp/LWL 316
Mast Ht . . . . 35'	Blst/Disp 40%
Auxiliary . . . . std	Designer Dan Avoures
BMW . . . . . 12 hp	First Built 1977
Diesel	No. Built 25
Fuel Cap . . . . . 12 gal	1 Design . . . . no
	Kit . . . . available
	Price $33,305
	with sails

Westerly Griffon II

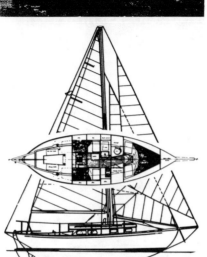

LOD . . . . 26'	Hull . . . . FRP
LWL . . . . 21'7"	Deck . . . . FRP
Beam . . . . 9'3"	Spar . . . . Alum
Draft	Pos Float . . . . no
Deep . . . . . . 4'9"	Headroom . . . . 6'
Twin . . . . . . 3'3"	Fr. Water . . . . 17 gal
Shoal cb up . . 3'3"	SA/Disp 14.4
Shoal cb dn . . 5'6"	Disp/LWL 266
Disp . . . . . . 6000 lbs	Blst/Disp 45%
Ballast . . . . . 2700 lbs	Designer . . Ed Dubois
Sail Area	Builder
Sloop . . . . 298 sq ft	Westerly-England
Mast Ht . . . . 38'	First Built 1980
Auxiliary . . . . std	No. Built 350
Bukh . . . . . . 10 hp	1 Design . . . . no
Diesel	Price $32,248
Fuel Cap . . . . . . 12 gal	with sails

Yamaha 26

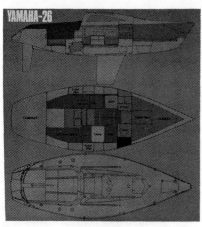

LOD	26'	Hull	FRP
LWL	21'	Deck	FRP
Beam	9'	Spar	Alum
Draft	5'	Headroom	5'1"
Disp	4349 lbs	Fr. Water	19 gal
Ballast	1435 lbs	SA/Disp	17.5
Sail Area		Disp/LWL	210
Sloop	291 sq ft	Blst/Disp	33%
Sloop (tall)	331 sq ft	Builder	Yamaha, Japan
Mast Ht		Price	na
Sloop	37'		
Sloop (tall)	39'		
Auxiliary	std		
Yanmar	7.5 hp		
Diesel			
Fuel Cap	7 gal		

YAMAHA SAILBOATS U.S.A.
6555 Katella Ave.
Cypress, CA 90630
(714) 761-7609

Pearson 26

PEARSON® 26
ONE DESIGN

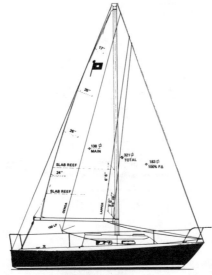

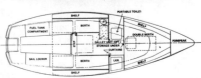

LOD	26'1"	Hull	FRP
LWL	21'8"	Deck	FRP
Beam	8'8"	Spar	Alum
Draft	4'	Cockpit	8'11"
Disp	5200 lbs	SA/Disp	17.1
Ballast	2200 lbs	Disp/LWL	228
Sail Area		Blst/Disp	42%
Sloop	321 sq ft	Designer	Bill Shaw
Mast Ht	35'2"	1 Design	yes
		Price	na

PEARSON YACHTS
West Shore Rd.
Portsmouth, RI 02871
(401) 683-0100

Island Packet 26
Mark II

LOA	30'	Hull	FRP
LOD	26'2"	Deck	FRP
LWL	24'2"	Spar	Alum
Beam	10'6"	Pos Float	no
Draft		Cockpit	7'6"
Shoal cb up	2'8"	Headroom	6'1"
Shoal cb dn	6'	Fr. Water	31 gal
Deep	3'8"	SA/Disp	16.2
Disp	8000 lbs	Disp/LWL	253
Ballast	3000 lbs	Blst/Disp	38%
Sail Area		Designer	
Cutter	405 sq ft		R. Johnson/W. Scott
Mast Ht	38'	First Built	1980
Auxiliary	std	No. Built	60
Yanmar	15 hp	1 Design	no
Diesel		Price	$36,950
Fuel Cap	18 gal		with sails

TRADITIONAL WATERCRAFT
2111 34th Way
Largo, FL 33541
(813) 535-6431

Kirby 8

LOD	26'4''	Hull	FRP
LWL	21'3''	Deck	FRP
Beam	9'6''	Spar	Alum
Draft	4'6''	Headroom	5'11''
Disp	5050 lbs	SA/Disp	17.8
Ballast	na	Disp/LWL	235
Sail Area		Designer	Bruce Kirby
Sloop	328 sq ft	Kit	$12,000 Can
Auxiliary	opt	Price	$24,950 Can
			without sails

LES VOILER EVASION SAILBOATS
7333, Place Des Roseraies,
Ste. 304
Ville D'Anjou, Quebec
Canada H1M 2X6
(514) 352-7062

Tanzer 26

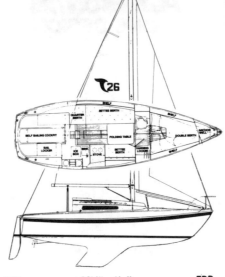

LOD	26'4''	Hull	FRP
LWL	22'6''	Deck	FRP
Beam	8'8''	Spar	Alum
Draft	3'10''	Pos Float	no
Disp	4350 lbs	Cockpit	5'9''
Ballast	1950 lbs	Headroom	5'10''
Sail Area		Fr. Water	15 gal
Sloop	260 sq ft	SA/Disp	15.6
Mast Ht	33'	Disp/LWL	170
Auxiliary	opt	Blst/Disp	45%
	inbd or outbd	Designer	
			Johann Tanzer
		First Built	1975
		No. Built	766
		1 Design	yes
		Price	$20,450
			with sails

TANZER
Box 670, Cape Colony
Edenton, NC 27932
(919) 482-7404

- -

P. O. Box 67
Dorion, PQ Canada J7V 5V8
(514) 455-5681

Tradewinds 26

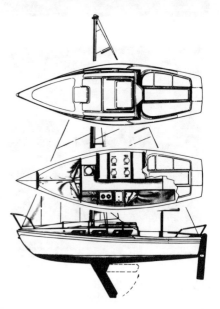

LOD	26'5''	Hull	FRP
LWL	23'3''	Deck	FRP
Beam	7'11''	Spar	Alum
Draft		Pos Float	no
Swing keel up	2'2''	Cockpit	6'9''
Swing keel dn	5'6''	Headroom	5'6''
Disp	2600 lbs	Fr. Water	5 gal
Ballast	750 lbs	SA/Disp	19.9
Sail Area		Disp/LWL	92
Sloop	235 sq ft	Blst/Disp	29%
Mast Ht	32'	Designer	Luger
Auxiliary	opt	1 Design	no
	15 hp	Kit	$4,985
	outbd		

LUGER INDUSTRIES INC.
3800 West Hwy 13
Burnsville, MN 55337
(612) 890-3000

Balboa 27

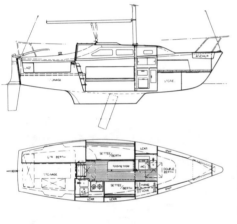

LOD . . . . 26'6"	Hull . . . . FRP
LWL . . . . 23'	Deck . . . . FRP
Beam . . . . 8'	Spar . . . . Alum
Draft	Pos Float . . . . no
cb up . . . . 2'5"	Headroom . . . . . 6'1"
cb dn . . . . 5'6"	SA/Disp 16.4
Disp . . . . 4900 lbs	Disp/LWL 179
Ballast . . . . . 2600 lbs	Blst/Disp 53%
Sail Area	Designer . . Lyle Hess
Sloop . . . . 295 sq ft	1 Design . . . . yes
Auxiliary . . . . opt	Price $21,620
10 hp	with sails

LAGUNA YACHTS INC.
10960 Boatman
Stanton, CA 90680
(714) 527-7262

Rodgers 26

LOD . . . . 26'6"	Hull . . . . FRP
LWL . . . . na	Deck . . . . FRP
Beam . . . . 9'7"	Spar . . . . Alum
Draft . . . . 4'9"	Blst/Disp 40%
Disp . . . . . . 5650 lbs	Designer O.H. Rodgers
Ballast . . . . . 2250 lbs	First Built 1979
Sail Area	Price $27,995
Sloop . . . . na	with sails
Auxiliary . . . . opt	
Yanmar . . . . . . 7 hp	
Diesel	

RODGERS YACHT & DESIGN
4501 Ulmerton Rd.
Clearwater, FL 33702
(813) 577-2662

Tanzer 27

LOD . . . . 26'7"	Hull . . . . FRP
LWL . . . . 22'6"	Deck . . . . FRP
Beam . . . . 9'6"	Spar . . . . Alum
Draft	Pos Float . . . . no
Shoal cb up . . 2'7"	Cockpit . . . . 6'9"
Shoal cb dn . . 6'7"	Headroom . . . . . 6'1"
Deep . . . . 4'6"	Fr. Water . . . . . 15 gal
Disp	SA/Disp 14.4
Shoal . . . . 6700 lbs	Disp/LWL 263
Deep . . . . 6200 lbs	Blst/Disp 41%
Ballast	Designer
Shoal . . . 2750 lbs	C. Raymond Hunt
Deep . . . 2250 lbs	First Built 1981
Sail Area	No. Built 19
Sloop . . . . 319 sq ft	1 Design . . . . no
Mast Ht . . . . 38'	Price $23,950
Auxiliary . . . . opt	with sails
DSL/Gas . . . . 15 hp	
I/O	

TANZER
Box 670, Cape Colony
Edenton, NC 27932
(919) 482-7404

- -

P. O. Box 67
Dorion, PQ Canada J7V 5V8
(514) 455-5681

Victoria 26

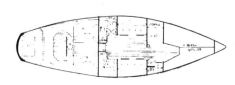

LOD	26'7''	Hull	FRP
LWL	19'6''	Deck	FRP
Beam	8'	Spar	Alum
Draft		Cockpit	7'
cb up	2'6''	Headroom	5'3''
cb dn	4'9''	Fr. Water	40 gal
Disp	4500 lbs	SA/Disp	15.8
Ballast	2000 lbs	Disp/LWL	271
Sail Area		Blst/Disp	44%
Sloop	269 sq ft	Designer	Bill McVay
Auxiliary	std	Price	na
Gas	15 hp		
	inbd		
Fuel Cap	12 gal		

VICTORIA YACHTS INC.
203 Benson Junction Rd.
Debary, FL 32713
(305) 668-8607

Cal 27 III

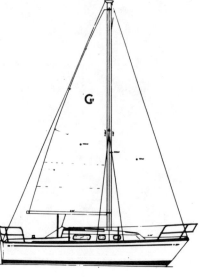

LOD	26'8''	Hull	FRP
LWL	23'3''	Deck	FRP
Beam	9'	Spar	Alum
Draft		Pos Float	no
Shoal	4'	Cockpit	8'
Deep	5'	Headroom	5'10''
Disp	5200 lbs	Fr. Water	22 gal
Ballast	2000 lbs	SA/Disp	17.9
Sail Area		Disp/LWL	184
Sloop	335 sq ft	Blst/Disp	38%
Mast Ht	36'4''	Designer	
Auxiliary	std		Bill Lapworth
Yanmar	7.5 hp	First Built	1982
Diesel		1 Design	yes
		Price	na

BANGOR PUNTA MARINE
848 Airport Rd.
Box 991
Fall River, MA 02722
(617) 678-5291

Gloucester 27

LOD	26'8''	Hull	FRP
LWL	21'6''	Deck	FRP
Beam	8'	Spar	Alum
Draft	3'8''	Pos Float	no
Disp	5500 lbs	Cockpit	6'6''
Ballast	2500 lbs	Headroom	5'10''
Sail Area		Fr. Water	15 gal
Sloop	313 sq ft	SA/Disp	16.1
Mast Ht	37'9''	Disp/lwl	247
Auxiliary	opt	Blst/Disp	45%
	9.9 hp	Designer	S. Windley
	outbd	First Built	1981
		No. Built	11
		1 Design	no
		Price	$19,995
			without sails

GLOUCESTER YACHTS
P. O. Box 307, Rte. 623
Gloucester, VA 23061
(804) 693-3818

Aloha 8.2

LOD	26'9"	Hull	FRP
LWL	22'2"	Deck	FRP
Beam	9'6"	Spar	Alum
Draft	4'4"	Fr. Water	14 gal
Disp	5200 lbs	SA/Disp	17.3
Ballast	2000 lbs	Disp/LWL	213
Sail Area		Blst/Disp	38%
Sloop	325 sq ft	Designer	Robert Perry
Auxiliary	std	Price	$38,316 Can
BMW	7 hp		with sails
Diesel			
Fuel Cap	10 gal		

ALOHA YACHTS INT'L
1638 Charles St.
Whitby, Ontario
Canada Lin 1B9
(416) 686-2127

Horizon 27

LOA	27'4"	Hull	FRP
LOD	26'9"	Deck	FRP
LWL	23'	Spar	Alum
Beam	9'6"	Pos Float	no
Draft	4'	Cockpit	7'
Disp	6200 lbs	Headroom	6'
Ballast	2200 lbs	Fr. Water	30 gal
Sail Area		SA/Disp	15.2
Sloop	320 sq ft	Disp/LWL	227
Cutter	366 sq ft	Blst/Disp	35%
Mast Ht	36'	Designer	
Auxiliary	std		Michael Vollmer
Volvo	9 hp	First Built	1981
Diesel		No. Built	30
Fuel Cap	10 gal	1 Design	yes
		Price	$29,900
			with sails

HALMAN MFG.
Durham Rd., P. O. Box 659
Beamsville, Ontario
Canada L0R 1B0
(416) 945-6666

Catalina 27

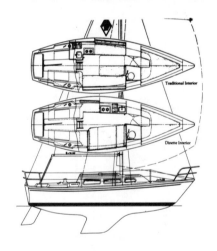

LOD	26'10"	Hull	FRP
LWL	21'9"	Deck	FRP
Beam	8'10"	Spar	Alum
Draft	4'	Pos Float	no
Disp	6850 lbs	Headroom	6'
Ballast	2700 lbs	Fr. Water	20 gal
Sail Area		SA/Disp	15.1
Sloop	340 sq ft	Disp/LWL	297
Sloop (tall)	364 sq ft	Blst/Disp	39%
Mast Ht		Designer	Frank Butler
Sloop	38'3"	First Built	1970
Sloop (tall)	39'8"	No. Built	5275
Auxiliary	opt	1 Design	yes
	25 hp	Price	$16,250
			without sails

CATALINA YACHTS
21200 Victory Blvd.
Woodland Hills, CA 91367
(213) 884-7700

Helms 27

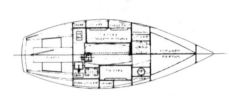

LOD	26'10"	Hull	FRP
LWL	21'7"	Deck	FRP
Beam	9'8"	Spar	Alum
Draft	4'3"	Cockpit	6'9"
Disp	6200 lbs	Headroom	6'2"
Ballast	2400 lbs	Fr. Water	30 gal
Sail Area		SA/Disp	16.5
Sloop	347 sq ft	Disp/LWL	275
Mast Ht	38'6"	Blst/Disp	39%
Auxiliary	std	Designer	
Yanmar	15 hp		Stuart Windley
Diesel		Price	$27,560
			without sails

JACK A. HELMS CO.
Hwy. 60, P. O. Drawer A
Irmo, SC 29063
(803) 781-5133

Soling

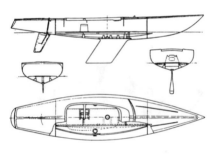

LOD	26'11"	Hull	FRP
LWL	20'	Deck	FRP
Beam	6'3"	Spar	Alum
Draft	4'4"	Pos Float	yes
Disp	2277 lbs	SA/Disp	21.6
Ballast	1276 lbs	Disp/LWL	127
Sail Area		Blst/Disp	56%
Sloop	234 sq ft	Designer	Jan Linge
		Builder	Denmark
		First Built	1980
		No. Built	17
		1 Design	yes
		Price	$14,000
			with sails

A/S BORRESENS BAADEBYGGERI
Dragevej
Box 187
7100 Vejle, Denmark

CS 27

LOD	27'	Hull	FRP
LWL	23'11"	Deck	FRP
Beam	9'4"	Spar	Alum
Draft		Pos Float	no
Shoal	3'11"	headroom	6'
Deep	5'2"	Fr. Water	16 gal
Disp	6100 lbs	SA/Disp	14.3
Ballast	2400 lbs	Disp/LWL	199
Sail Area		Blst/Disp	39%
Sloop	299 sq ft	Designer	
Auxiliary	std		Camper & Nicholsons
Auxiliary	8 hp	First Built	1975
Diesel		No. Built	480
Fuel Cap	12 gal	1 Design	no
		Price	$33,900
			without sails

CS YACHTS LTD
79 Bramsteele Rd.
Brampton, Ont. Canada
(416) 457-6713

CY 27

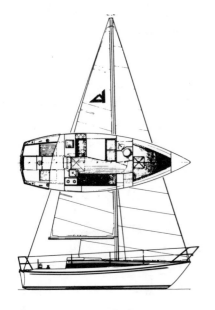

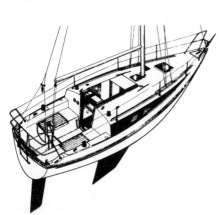

LOD	27'	Hull	FRP
LWL	21'6"	Deck	FRP
Beam	9'1"	Spar	Alum
Draft	4'3"	SA/Disp	19.3
Disp	5500 lbs	Disp/LWL	247
Ballast	2408 lbs	Blst/Disp	44%
Sail Area		Designer	
Sloop	376 sq ft		C&C Design Group
Auxiliary	opt	Kit	$9,000 Can

J & C FIBERCRAFT
P. O. Box 263
Barrie, Ontario
Canada L4M 4T2
(705) 326-8880

Dockrell 27

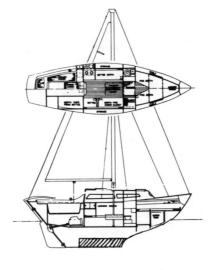

LOD	27'	Hull	FRP
LWL	21'	Deck	FRP
Beam	8'	Spar	Alum
Draft	3'	Headroom	6'2"
Disp	7000 lbs	Fr. Water	40 gal
Ballast	3200 lbs	SA/Disp	17.5
Sail Area		Disp/LWL	337
Cutter	400 sq ft	Blst/Disp	46%
Auxiliary	opt	Builder	
	15 hp	Dockrell Yachts, England	
		Price	$14,000
			with sails

DOCKRELL YACHTS
1839 Route 46
Parsippany, NJ 07054
(201) 226-3200

EB 27

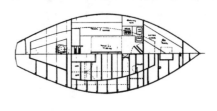

LOA	30'9"	Hull	Wood
LOD	27'	Deck	Wood
LWL	23'9"	Spar	Wood
Beam	11'3"	Pos Float	no
Draft	3'6"	Headroom	5'8"
Disp	10,000 lbs	Fr. Water	40 gal
Ballast	4900 lbs	SA/Disp	18.2
Sail Area		Disp/LWL	333
Cutter (gaff)	528 sq ft	Blst/Disp	49%
Mast Ht	30'	Designer	D. Condino
Auxiliary	std	First Built	1981
Diesel	30 hp	No. Built	1
Fuel Cap	20 gal	1 Design	no
		Price	$35,000
			with sails

ESSEX BAY BOAT CO.
P. O. Box 520
Gloucester, MA 01930
(617) 281-2189

Hotfoot 27

LOD	27'	Hull	FRP/Foam
LWL	22'	Deck	FRP/Foam
Beam	9'4"	Spar	Alum
Draft	5'5"	Pos Float	no
Disp	3600 lbs	Headroom	5'7"
Ballast	1500 lbs	Fr. Water	12 gal
Sail Area		SA/Disp	23.6
Sloop	347 sq ft	Disp/LWL	150
Auxiliary	opt	Blst/Disp	42%
	10 hp	Designer	
	outbd		Doug Hemphill
		First Built	1981
		No. Built	10
		1 Design	yes
		Price	$22,000
			with sails

HOT FOOT BOATS
6795 Veyaness Rd.
Saanichton, B.C.
Canada VOS 1M0
(604) 652-2453

Newport 27 — SII

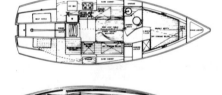

LOD	27'	Hull	FRP
LWL	22'	Deck	FRP
Beam	9'3"	Spar	Alum
Draft		Headroom	6'3"
Shoal	4'3"	Fr. Water	20 gal
Deep	5'2"	SA/Disp	17.9
Disp	6000 lbs	Disp/LWL	251
Ballast	na	Price	na
Sail Area			
Sloop	369 sq ft		
Auxiliary	opt		
Diesel	15 hp		
Fuel Cap	20 gal		

CAPITAL YACHTS INC.
25914 President Ave.
Harbor City, CA 90710
(213) 530-1311

Santa Cruz 27

LOD	27'	Hull	FRP/Balsa
LWL	24'	Deck	FRP/Balsa
Beam	8'	Spar	Alum
Draft	4'6"	Pos Float	yes
Disp	3000 lbs	Cockpit	6'
Ballast	1500 lbs	Headroom	5'
Sail Area		SA/Disp	30.5
Sloop	396 sq ft	Disp/LWL	96
Auxiliary	opt	Blst/Disp	50%
	7.5 hp	Designer	Bill Lee
		First Built	1975
		No. Built	147
		1 Design	yes
		Price	$22,900
			without sails

BILL LEE OF SAUSALITO
2573 Mission St.
Santa Cruz, CA 95060
(408) 425-8198

Ticon 27

LOD	27'	Hull	FRP
LWL	22'1"	Deck	FRP
Beam	10'	Spar	Alum
Draft	3'6"	Fr. Water	25 gal
Disp	6000 lbs	Disp/LWL	249
Ballast	2800 lbs	Blst/Disp	47%
Sail Area		Designer	
Sloop	na		Mark Swanson
Auxiliary	std	Price	$28,975
Renault			with sails
Diesel			

TICON YACHTS LIMITED
2508 Lakeshore Rd. W.
Oakville, Ontario
Canada L6L 1H8
(416) 827-4322

US 27

LOD	27'	Hull	FRP
LWL	23'3"	Deck	FRP
Beam	9'6"	Spar	Alum
Draft		Pos Float	no
Shoal	3'6"	Headroom	6'
Deep	5'2"	Fr. Water	28 gal
Disp	6250 lbs	SA/Disp	14.8
Ballast	2024 lbs	Disp/LWL	222
Sail Area		Blst/Disp	32%
Sloop	313 sq.ft	First Built	1980
Mast Ht	38'10"	1 Design	no
Auxiliary	opt	Price	na
Volvo	7.5 hp		
Diesel			
Fuel Cap	18 gal		

US YACHT
P. O. Box 24467
Seattle, WA 98134

Watkins 27

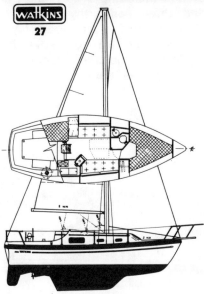

LOD	27'	Hull	FRP
LWL	23'8"	Deck	FRP
Beam	10'	Spar	Alum
Draft	3'8"	Headroom	6'2"
Disp	7500 lbs	Fr. Water	40 gal
Ballast	3500 lbs	SA/Disp	14.5
Sail Area		Disp/LWL	253
Sloop	347 sq ft	Blst/Disp	47%
Mast Ht	38'7"	Price	$44,995
Auxiliary	std		with sails
Yanmar	8 hp		
Diesel			
Fuel Cap	20 gal		

WATKINS YACHTS INC.
12645 49th St. N.
Clearwater, FL 33520
(813) 577-3684

Over the years, Robert Harris' VANCOUVER 27 has become a classic. Built to Lloyds' requirements and to Pheon Yachts' superior quality standards, she is an outstanding offshore cruiser and a safe investment. With a 23' waterline, high freeboard and spacious accommodation, she has proved in many ocean passages to be a dry, comfortable, safe boat. Her efficient sail plan and superior tracking ability are a delight for the single handler. Below deck, the luxurious all teak interior offers to the serious sailor a complete navigation station including a 2'x3' chart table and three seaworthy berths. Four standard and customized lay-outs are available. An exhaustive list of equipment including fenders and mooring lines is standard.

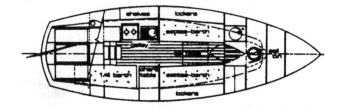

LOD	27'	Hull	FRP
LWL	22'11"	Deck	FRP/Balsa
Beam	8'8"	Spar	Alum
Draft	4'6"	Pos Float	no
Disp	8960 lbs	Cockpit	6'
Ballast	3465 lbs	Headroom	6'2"
Sail Area		Fr. Water	45 gal
Cutter	356 sq ft	SA/Disp	13.2
Mast Ht	32'	Disp/LWL	332
Auxiliary	std	Blst/Disp	39%
Westerbeke	20 hp	Designer	
Diesel			Robert Harris
Fuel Cap	45 gal	Builder	
			Pheon Yachts Ltd.
		First Built	1970
		No. Built	200
		1 Design	yes
		Kit	available
		Price	$46,500
			with sails

VANCOUVER 27

WINNER

RAY G. VANHEUSDEN TREMAYNE CORPORATION
1611 N. Kent Street, Suite 801
Arlington, VA 22209
(703) 522-3355

Cascade 27

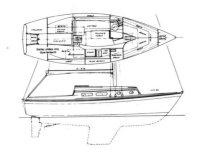

Dufour 28

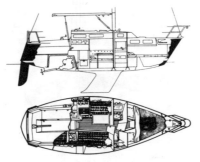

Fairwinds 27

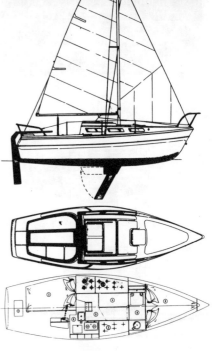

LOD	27'1"	Hull	FRP
LWL	21'6"	Deck	FRP/Plywood
Beam	8'10"	Spar	Alum
Draft	4'6"	Pos Float	no
Disp	6000 lbs	Cockpit	7'
Ballast	2275 lbs	Headroom	6'
Sail Area		Fr. Water	42 gal
Sloop	351 sq ft	SA/Disp	17
Mast Ht	37'6"	Disp/LWL	270
Auxiliary	std	Blst/Disp	38%
Farymann	7 hp	Designer	
Diesel			Robert A. Smith
Fuel Cap	18 gal	First Built	1978
		No. Built	44
		Kit	$20,000

LOD	27'2"	Hull	FRP
LWL	22'5"	Deck	FRP
Beam	9'6"	Spar	Alum
Draft		Headroom	6'
Shoal	3'11"	Fr. Water	35 gal
Deep	4'11"	Disp/LWL	244
Disp	6160 lbs	Blst/Disp	32%
Ballast	1980 lbs	Builder	
Sail Area			Dufour, France
Sloop	na	Price	na
Auxiliary	std		
Volvo	17 hp		
Diesel			

LOD	27'2"	Hull	FRP
LWL	23'2"	Deck	FRP
Beam	8'	Spar	Alum
Draft		Pos Float	no
Swing keel up	2'3"	Cockpit	6'
Swing keel dn	6'9"	Headroom	6'3"
Disp	2800 lbs	Fr. Water	18 gal
Ballast	800 lbs	SA/Disp	18.9
Sail Area		Disp/LWL	99
Sloop	235 sq ft	Blst/Disp	29%
Mast Ht	33'3"	Designer	Luger
Auxiliary	opt	1 Design	no
	15 hp	Kit	$6,463
	outbd		

YACHT CONSTRUCTORS INC.
7030 N.E. 42nd Ave.
Portland, OR 97218
(503) 287-5794

EURO SAILBOATS LTD.
131 East Boston Post Road
Mamaroneck, NY 10543
(914) 381-4500

LUGER INDUSTRIES INC.
3800 West Hwy 13
Burnsville, MN 55337
(612) 890-3000

Gulf 27

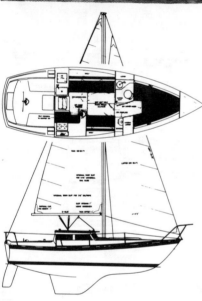

LOD	27'2"	Hull	FRP
LWL	22'6"	Deck	FRP
Beam	9'4"	Spar	Alum
Draft	4'2"	Headroom	6'1"
Disp	6900 lbs	Fr. Water	20 gal
Ballast	2750 lbs	SA/Disp	15.5
Sail Area		Disp/LWL	270
Sloop	350 sq ft	Blst/Disp	40%
Auxiliary	std	Price	na
Diesel	12 hp		
Fuel Cap	20 gal		

CAPITAL YACHTS INC.
25914 President Ave.
Harbor City, CA 90710
(213) 530-1311

Hunter 27

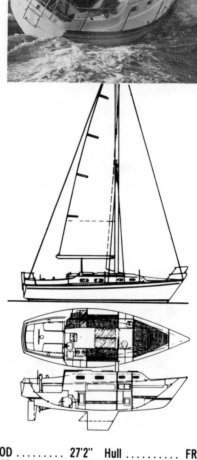

LOD	27'2"	Hull	FRP
LWL	22'	Deck	FRP
Beam	9'3"	Spar	Alum
Draft		Fr. Water	36 gal
Shoal	3'3"	SA/Disp	15.8
Deep	4'3"	Disp/LWL	293
Disp	7000 lbs	Blst/Disp	46%
Ballast		Price	$27,960
Shoal	3200 lbs		with sails
Deep	3000 lbs		
Sail Area			
Sloop	362 sq ft		
Mast Ht	40'11"		
Auxiliary	std		
Yanmar	7.5 hp		
Diesel			
Fuel Cap	12.5 gal		

HUNTER MARINE
Box 1030, Hwy 441
Alachua, FL 32601
(904) 462-3077

Express

LOD	27'3"	Hull	FRP/Klegecell
LWL	23'9"	Deck	FRP/Balsa
Beam	8'1"	Spar	Alum
Draft	4'6"	SA/Disp	24.3
Disp	2450 lbs	Disp/LWL	81
Ballast	1100 lbs	Blst/Disp	45%
Sail Area		Designer	
Sloop	276 sq ft		Carl Schumacher
Auxiliary	opt	1 Design	yes
		Price	$24,900
			without sails

ALSBERG BROS. BOATWORKS
953-A Tower Place
Santa Cruz, CA 95062
(408) 476-0529

H – Boat

LOA	27'3"	Hull	FRP
LWL	20'8"	Deck	FRP
Beam	7'2"	Spar	Alum
Draft	4'3"	Pos Float	no
Disp	3190 lbs	Cockpit	5'5"
Ballast	1595 lbs	Headroom	4'5"
Sail Area		SA/Disp	19.5
Sloop	264 sq ft	Disp/LWL	161
Mast Ht	34'5"	Blst/Disp	50%
Auxiliary	opt	Designer . Hans Groop	
	6 hp	Builder	
	outbd	Artekno O.Y., Finland	
		First Built	1970
		No. Built	3000
		1 Design	yes
		Price	$19,300
			without sails

ATKINS YACHTS
326 First St.
Annapolis, MD 21403
(301) 268-3332

WINDOVER SAILS, INC.
Longfleet House
Barnstable, MA 02630
(617) 362-9586

Kelt 7.6

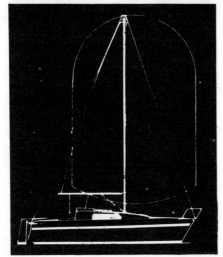

LOD	27'3"	Hull	FRP
LWL	21'	Deck .. FRP/Klegecell	
Beam	9'5"	Spar	Alum
Draft		Headroom	6'
Deep	4'3"	SA/Disp	16.6
Shoal cb up	2'5"	Disp/LWL	216
Shoal cb dn	5'3"	Blst/Disp	39%
Disp	4500 lbs	Builder ... Kelt Marine	
Ballast			Canada & France
Deep	1765 lbs	No. Built	300+
Shoal	1950 lbs	Price	$23,500
Sail Area			without sails
Sloop	282 sq ft		
Auxiliary	opt		
Dsl/Gas	10 hp		
	I/O		

ATKINS YACHTS
326 First St.
Annapolis, MD 21403
(301) 268-3332

Orion 27 MK II

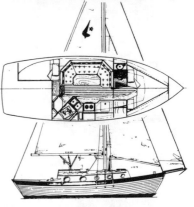

LOA	30'11"	Hull	FRP
LOD	27'4"	Deck ... FRP/Plywood	
LWL	22'2"	Spar	Alum
Beam	9'3"	Pos Float	no
Draft	4'	Cockpit	6'8"
Disp	10,000 lbs	Headroom	6'2"
Ballast	3500 lbs	Fr. Water	40 gal
Sail Area		SA/Disp	14.7
Sloop	425 sq ft	Disp/LWL	410
Cutter	508 sq ft	Blst/Disp	35%
Mast Ht	40'11"	Designer	
Auxiliary	std	Henry Morschladt	
Yanmar	15 hp	No. Built	60
Diesel		1 Design	no
		Kit	$12,831
		Price	$43,900
			with sails

PACIFIC SEACRAFT CORP.
3301 S. Susan St.
Santa Ana, CA 92704
(714) 751-1343

Caliber 28

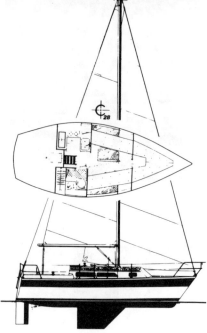

LOD	27'6"	Hull	FRP
LWL	24'2"	Deck	FRP
Beam	10'10"	Spar	Alum
Draft	3'11"	Pos Float	no
Disp	6000 lbs	Cockpit	7'
Ballast	3000 lbs	Headroom	6'1"
Sail Area		Fr. Water	24 gal
Sloop MH	428 sq ft	SA/Disp	20.7
Sloop FR	424 sq ft	Disp/LWL	189
Auxiliary	std	Blst/Disp	50%
Yanmar	15 hp	Designer	
Diesel			Mike McCreary
Fuel Cap	22 gal	First Built	1981
		No. Built	6
		1 Design	no
		Kit	available
		Price	$36,950
			with sails

CALIBER YACHT CORP.
6554 123rd Ave. North
Largo, FL 33543
(813) 531-4371

Show 27

LOD	27'6"	Hull	FRP
LWL	22'	Deck	FRP
Beam	9'8"	Spar	Alum
Draft	5'6"	SA/Disp	16.7
Disp	4840 lbs	Disp/LWL	203
Ballast	1430 lbs	Blst/Disp	30%
Sail Area		Designer	
Sloop	298 sq ft		Barbaris/Soma
Auxiliary	std	Builder	Barberis-
Renault	8 hp		Cantieri, Italy
Diesel		Price	$32,750
			with sails

SATELLITE MANAGEMENT INC.
P. O. Box 357
Larchmont, NY 10538
(914) 833-0043

Southerly 28

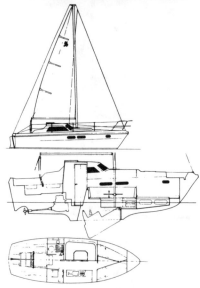

LOD	27'6"	Hull	FRP
LWL	24'	Deck	FRP/Balsa
Beam	9'	Spar	Alum
Draft		Pos Float	no
cb up	2'6"	Cockpit	6'
cb dn	4'9"	Headroom	6'
Disp	8500 lbs	Fr. Water	35 gal
Ballast	2600 lbs	SA/Disp	9.5
Sail Area		Disp/LWL	274
Sloop	247 sq ft	Blst/Disp	31%
Mast Ht	33'6"	Designer	
Auxiliary	std		Northshore, England
Yanmar	20 hp	Builder	
Diesel			Northshore, England
Fuel Cap	30 gal	First Built	1972
		No. Built	100
		1 Design	yes
		Price	$31,800
			with sails

PARKER YACHTS
South Freeport, ME 04078
(207) 865-6692

Lancer 28

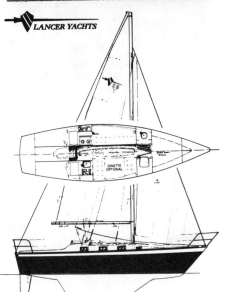

LOD	27'8"	Hull	FRP
LWL	23'11"	Deck	FRP
Beam	8'	Spar	Alum
Draft	3'	Pos Float	no
Disp	5200 lbs	Cockpit	7'
Ballast	2600 lbs	Headroom	6'
Sail Area		Fr. Water	15 gal
Sloop	328 sq ft	SA/Disp	17.5
Mast Ht	38'	Disp/LWL	169
Auxiliary	std	Blst/Disp	50%
Honda	10 hp outbd	Designer	
		W. Shad Turner	
		First Built	1976
		1 Design	yes
		Price	$30,946 with sails

LANCER YACHT CORP.
1939 Deere Ave.
Irvine, CA 92714
(714) 751-7220

Moody 27

LOD	27'8"	Hull	FRP
LWL	21'10"	Deck	FRP
Beam	9'8"	Spar	Alum
Draft	4'8"	Fr. Water	18 gal
Disp	5750 lbs	SA/Disp	20.5
Ballast	2530 lbs	Disp/LWL	246
Sail Area		Blst/Disp	44%
Sloop	412 sq ft	Designer	
Auxiliary	std		Angus Primrose
Bukh	10 hp	Builder	
Diesel		Marine Projects, England	
Fuel Cap	12 gal	Price	$33,500 with sails

IMPEX MARINE
Box 445
Reading, PA 19603
(215) 375-8048

Pied Piper 28

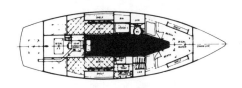

LOD	27'9"	Hull	FRP
LWL	21'3"	Deck	FRP
Beam	8'8"	Spar	Alum
Draft		Pos Float	no
cb up	3'3"	Cockpit	8'6"
cb dn	6'3"	Headroom	6'3"
Disp	8300 lbs	Fr. Water	30 gal
Ballast	2740 lbs	SA/Disp	13.5
Sail Area		Disp/LWL	386
Sloop	345 sq ft	Blst/Disp	33%
Mast Ht	36'	Designer	Cyrus Hamlin
Auxiliary	std	First Built	1977
Yanmar	15 hp	No. Built	6
Diesel		1 Design	no
Fuel Cap	25 gal	Kit	$4,775+
		Price	$38,735 with sails

LIBERTY YACHT CORP. (of NC)
Rt. 2 Box 548
Leland, NC 28451
(919) 371-3999

Southern Cross 28

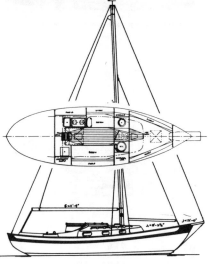

LOA	30'5"	Hull	FRP/Airex
LOD	27'9"	Deck	FRP/Balsa
LWL	20'2"	Spar	Alum
Beam	8'6"	Pos Float	no
Draft	4'8"	Cockpit	6'
Disp	8500 lbs	Headroom	6'2"
Ballast	3400 lbs	Fr. Water	47 gal
Sail Area		SA/Disp	14.5
Cutter	378 sq ft	Disp/LWL	463
Mast Ht	36'	Blst/Disp	40%
Auxiliary	std	Designer	Tom Gillmer
Universal	11 hp	First Built	1978
Diesel		No. Built	67
Fuel Cap	20 gal	1 Design	no
		Kit	available
		Price	na

C.E. RYDER CORP.
47 Gooding Ave.
Bristol, RI 02809
(401) 253-8554

Dutch Flyer 28

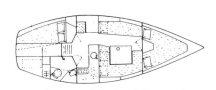

LOA	27'10"	Hull	FRP
LOD	27'10"	Deck	FRP
LWL	22'	SA/Disp	16.9
Beam	9'6"	Disp/LWL	230
Draft	4'7"	Blst/Disp	47%
Disp	5500 lbs	Price	na
Ballast	2600 lbs		
Sail Area			
Sloop	330 sq ft		
Auxiliary	opt		

HOLLAND YACHTS
Box 129
Solomons, MD 20688
(301) 326-3960

Bahama 28

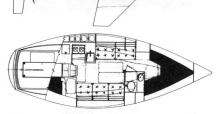

LOD	27'11"	Hull	FRP
LWL	23'1"	Deck	FRP
Beam	9'10"	Spar	Alum
Draft	5'	Fr. Water	20 gal
Disp	7000 lbs	SA/Disp	15.8
Ballast	3000 lbs	Disp/LWL	254
Sail Area		Blst/Disp	43%
Sloop	361 sq ft	Designer	Robert Perry
Mast Ht	41'	Price	na
Auxiliary	std		
Yanmar	15 hp		
Diesel			
Fuel Cap	20 gal		

ISLANDER YACHTS
1922 Barranca Rd.
Irvine, CA 92714
(714) 549-8526

Contest 28

LOD	27'11"	Headroom	6'1"
LWL	22'5"	Fr. Water	32 gal
Beam	9'4"	SA/Disp	22.8
Draft		Disp/lwl	260
Shoal	4'7"	Blst/Disp	50%
Deep	5'4"	Designer	Dick Zaal
Disp		Builder	
Shoal	6570 lbs		Conyplex, Holland
Deep	6173 lbs	Price	na
Ballast			
Shoal	3307 lbs		
Deep	2910 lbs		
Sail Area			
Sloop	499 sq ft		
Mast Ht	38'9"		

HOLLAND YACHTS
Box 129
Solomons, MD 20688
(301) 326-3960

Sea Sprite 27

LOD	27'11"	Hull	FRP
LWL	20'	Deck	FRP/Balsa
Beam	8'10"	Spar	Alum
Draft	4'3"	Pos Float	no
Disp	7600 lbs	Cockpit	6'3"
Ballast	3000 lbs	Headroom	6'
Sail Area		Fr. Water	45 gal
Sloop	340 sq ft	SA/Disp	14.1
Mast Ht	38'	Disp/LWL	424
Auxiliary	std	Blst/Disp	39%
Universal	11hp	Designer	Bill Luders
Diesel		First Built	1980
Fuel Cap	12 gal	No. Built	41
		1 Design	no
		Kit	available
		Price	na

C.E. RYDER CORP.
47 Gooding Ave.
Bristol, RI 02809
(401) 253-8554

Tanzer 8.5

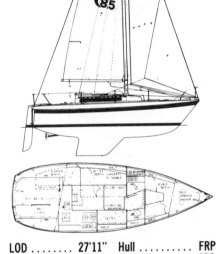

LOD	27'11"	Hull	FRP
LWL	23'9"	Deck	FRP
Beam	9'6"	Spar	Alum
Draft	4'4"	Pos Float	no
Disp	7400 lbs	Cockpit	6'9"
Ballast	3000 lbs	Headroom	6'1"
Sail Area		Fr. Water	15 gal
Sloop	394 sq ft	SA/Disp	16.6
Mast Ht	41'	Disp/LWL	247
Auxiliary	opt	Blst/Disp	41%
Diesel	15 hp	Designer	
			Johann Tanzer
		First Built	1978
		No. Built	73
		1 Design	no
		Price	$26,950
			with sails

TANZER INDUSTRIES
P. O. Box 67
Dorion, PQ Canada J7V 5V8
(514) 455-5681

Aloha 8.5

LOD . . . . 28'	Hull . . . . FRP
LWL . . . . 24'6"	Deck . . . . FRP
Beam . . . . 9'5"	Spar . . . . Alum
Draft . . . . 4'4"	Fr. Water . . . . 30 gal
Disp . . . . . . 6750 lbs	SA/Disp 15.1
Ballast . . . . . 2750 lbs	Disp/LWL 204
Sail Area	Blst/Disp 41%
Sloop . . . . 337 sq ft	Designer
Auxiliary . . . . std	Brewer & Wallstrom
Universal . . . 16 hp	Price . . . $44,805 Can
Diesel	with sails
Fuel Cap . . . . . . 10 gal	

ALOHA YACHTS INT'L
1638 Charles St.
Whitby, Ontario
Canada L1N 1B9
(416) 686-2127

E Scow

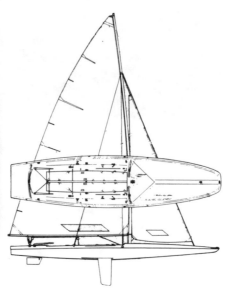

LOD . . . . 28'	Hull . . . . FRP
LWL . . . . na	Deck . . . . FRP
Beam . . . . 6'9"	Spar . . . . Alum
Draft	Pos Float . . . . . . yes
lb up . . . . 9"	SA/Disp 52.9
lb dn . . . . 3'9"	First Built 1923
Disp . . . . . . 965 lbs	1 Design . . . . . . yes
Ballast . . . . 0 lbs	Price $8,995
Sail Area	without sails
Sloop . . . . 323 sq ft	
Mast Ht . . . . 29'	

MELGES BOAT WORKS
Zenda, WI 53195

JOHNSON BOAT WORKS
323 S. Lake Ave.
White Bear Lake, MN 55110

Great Dane 28

LOD . . . . 28'	Hull . . . . FRP
LWL . . . . 21'4"	Deck . . . . FRP
Beam . . . . 8'2"	Spar . . . . Alum
Draft . . . . 4'6"	Pos Float . . . . . . no
Disp . . . . . . 8500 lbs	Headroom . . . . . 6'2"
Ballast . . . . , . 4000 lbs	Fr. Water . . . . 20 gal
Sail Area	SA/Disp 15.4
Sloop . . . . 400 sq ft	Disp/LWL 391
Mast Ht . . . . 35'	Blst/Disp 47%
Auxiliary . . . . std	Designer . Aage Vtson
Volvo Penta . 25 hp	Builder . . Klaus Baess
Diesel	First Built 1965
Fuel Cap . . . . . . 20 gal	No. Built 450
	1 Design . . . . . . yes
	Kit . . . . available
	Price $40,000
	with sails

SCANDINAVIAN YACHTS
2658 Musgrave St.
Victoria, B.C. Canada V8R 5Y5

Hawkfarm

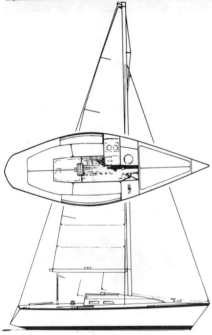

LOD	28'	Hull	FRP/Balsa
LWL	23'6"	Deck	FRP/Balsa
Beam	9'11"	Spar	Alum
Draft	5'2"	Disp/LWL	196
Disp	5700 lbs	Blst/Disp	47%
Ballast	2700 lbs	Price	$37,950
Sail Area			without sails
Sloop	na		
Auxiliary	std		
BMW			
Diesel			

NORTH COAST YACHTS INC.
2100 Clement Ave.
Alameda, CA 94501
(415) 523-8330

Liberty 28

LOA	31'6"	Hull	FRP
LOD	28'	Deck	FRP
LWL	24'4"	Spar	Alum
Beam	9'7"	Pos Float	no
Draft	4'	Cockpit	5'
Disp	12,000 lbs	Headroom	6'1"
Ballast	5000 lbs	Fr. Water	55 gal
Sail Area		SA/Disp	15.7
Cutter	515 sq ft	Disp/LWL	371
Mast Ht	40'	Blst/Disp	42%
Auxiliary	std	Designer	
Westerbeke	13 hp		J. W. Fennell
Diesel		First Built	1976
Fuel Cap	30 gal	No. Built	24
		1 Design	no
		Kit	available
		Price	$51,300
			with sails

LIBERTY YACHTS
2060 Ave. L.
Riviera Beach, FL 33404
(305) 842-2261

Lindenberg 28

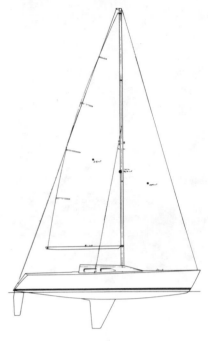

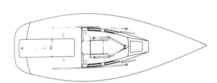

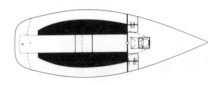

LOD	28'	Hull	FRP
LWL	24'5"	Deck	FRP
Beam	9'6"	Spar	Alum
Draft	5'4"	SA/Disp	26.9
Disp	4000 lbs	Disp/LWL	122
Ballast	2000 lbs	Blst/Disp	50%
Sail Area		Designer	
Sloop	424 sq ft		Paul A. Lindenberg
Auxiliary	opt	Price	$27,950
			without sails

LINDENBERG YACHTS INC.
798 Clearlake Rd.
Cocoa, FL 32922
(305) 631-1451

Newport 28 II

LOD	28'	Hull	FRP
LWL	23'6"	Deck	FRP
Beam	9'9"	Spar	Alum
Draft		Headroom	6'2"
Shoal	4'	Fr. Water	25 gal
Deep	5'2"	SA/Disp	15.6
Disp	7000 lbs	Disp/LWL	240
Ballast	na	Price	na
Sail Area			
Sloop	356 sq ft		
Auxiliary	std		
Diesel			
Fuel Cap	20 gal		

CAPITAL YACHTS INC.
25914 President Ave.
Harbor City, CA 90710
(213) 530-1311

Ranger 8.5

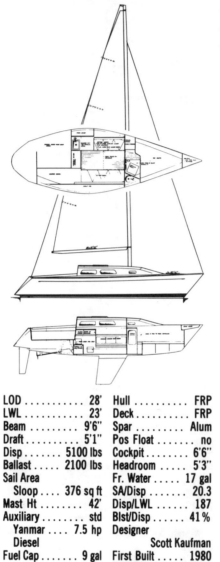

LOD	28'	Hull	FRP
LWL	23'	Deck	FRP
Beam	9'6"	Spar	Alum
Draft	5'1"	Pos Float	no
Disp	5100 lbs	Cockpit	6'6"
Ballast	2100 lbs	Headroom	5'3"
Sail Area		Fr. Water	17 gal
Sloop	376 sq ft	SA/Disp	20.3
Mast Ht	42'	Disp/LWL	187
Auxiliary	std	Blst/Disp	41%
Yanmar	7.5 hp	Designer	
Diesel			Scott Kaufman
Fuel Cap	9 gal	First Built	1980
		No. Built	10
		1 Design	yes
		Price	$29,150
			with sails

RANGER BOAT CO.
25802 Pacific Hwy. S.
Kent, WA 98031
(206) 839-5213

S2 8.5

LOD	28'	Hull	FRP
LWL	22'6"	Deck	FRP/Balsa
Beam	9'6"	Spar	Alum
Draft		Pos Float	no
Shoal	3'11"	Cockpit	7'6"
Deep	4'6"	Headroom	6'
Disp	7600 lbs	Fr. Water	37 gal
Ballast	3000 lbs	SA/Disp	16.6
Sail Area		Disp/LWL	298
Sloop	400 sq ft	Blst/Disp	39%
Mast Ht	41'	Designer	
Auxiliary	std		Arthur Edmunds
bmw	12 hp	1 Design	no
Diesel		Price	$38,300
Fuel Cap	18 gal		with sails

S2 YACHTS INC.
725 E. 40th St.
Holland, MI 49423
(616) 392-7163

Shannon 28

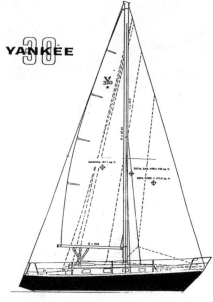

LOA . . . . 32'	Hull . . . . FRP
LOD . . . . 28'	Deck . . . . . FRP/Balsa
LWL . . . . 22'11"	Spar . . . . Alum
Beam . . . . 9'6"	Pos Float . . . . . . no
Draft . . . . 4'3"	Cockpit . . . . 8'
Disp . . . . . . 9300 lbs	Headroom . . . . . 6'3"
Ballast . . . . . 3600 lbs	Fr. Water . . . . 65 gal
Sail Area	SA/Disp 17
Cutter . . . 470 sq ft	Disp/LWL 345
Mast Ht . . . . 42'	Blst/Disp 39%
Auxiliary . . . . std	Designer
Yanmar . . . . 15 hp	Schultz & Assoc.
Diesel	First Built 1978
Fuel Cap . . . . . 20 gal	No. Built 47
	1 Design . . . . no
	Price $78,430
	with sails

Yankee 30

LOA . . . . 30'	Hull . . . . FRP
LOD . . . . 28'	Deck . . . . FRP
LWL . . . . 25'	Spar . . . . Alum
Beam . . . . 9'	Pos Float . . . . . . no
Draft . . . . na	Cockpit . . . . 6'
Disp . . . . 10,000 lbs	Headroom . . . . . 6'2"
Ballast . . . . 4850 lbs	Fr. Water . . . . 30 gal
Sail Area	SA/Disp 15.6
Sloop . . . . 453 sq ft	Disp/LWL 285
Mast Ht . . . . 45'	Blst/Disp 49%
Auxiliary . . . . std	First Built 1970
BMW . . . . . 12 hp	1 Design . . . . yes
Diesel	Kit $26,600
Fuel Cap . . . . . 20 gal	Price $60,000
	with sails

Bristol Channel Cutter

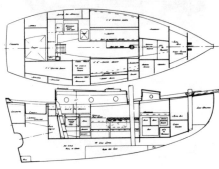

LOA . . . . 37'9"	Hull . . . . FRP
LOD . . . . 28'1"	Deck . . . . FRP
LWL . . . . 26'3"	Spar . . . . Alum
Beam . . . . 10'1"	Pos Float . . . . . . no
Draft . . . . 4'10"	Cockpit . . . . . . 2'9"
Disp . . . . 14,000 lbs	Headroom . . . . . 6'1"
Ballast . . . . 4600 lbs	Fr. Water . . . . 49 gal
Sail Area	SA/Disp 16.2
Cutter . . . 587 sq ft	Disp/LWL 345
Mast Ht . . . . . . 42'4"	Blst/Disp 33%
Auxiliary . . . . std	Designer . . L. C. Hess
Volvo . . . . . 13 hp	First Built 1976
Diesel	No. Built 63
Fuel Cap . . . . . 32 gal	1 Design . . . . no
	Kit . . . . available
	Price $66,458
	without sails

SHANNON BOAT CO. INC.
19 Broad Common Rd.
Bristol, RI 02809
(401) 253-2441

HERITAGE BOAT WORKS
1331 Country Club Rd.
Hood River, OR 97031
(503) 386-1526

SAM L. MORSE CO.
1626 Placentia Ave.
Costa Mesa, CA 92627
(714) 645-1843

Viking 28

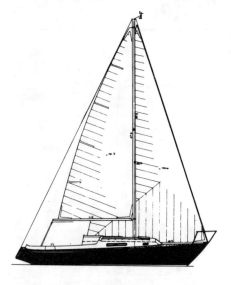

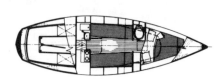

LOD	28'2"	Hull	FRP
LWL	22'	Deck	FRP
Beam	8'4"	Spar	Alum
Draft	4'6"	Disp/LWL	199
Disp	4755 lbs	Blst/Disp	47%
Ballast	2250 lbs	Price	$28,900 Can
			with sails
Sail Area			
Sloop	na		
Auxiliary	opt		

O'Day 28

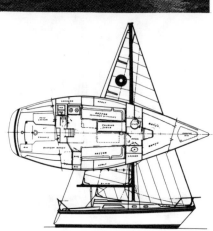

LOD	28'3"	Hull	FRP
LWL	22'11"	Deck	FRP
Beam	10'3"	Spar	Alum
Draft		Pos Float	no
Deep	4'8"	Headroom	5'9"
Shoal cb up	3'3"	Fr. Water	25 gal
Shoal cb dn	6'10"	SA/Disp	15.7
Disp	7300 lbs	Disp/LWL	270
Ballast		Blst/Disp	34%
Deep	2500 lbs	Designer	
Shoal	2725 lbs		C. R. Hunt Assoc.
Sail Area		First Built	1978
Sloop	370 sq ft	No. Built	369
Mast Ht	40'1"	1 Design	yes
Auxiliary	std	Price	na
Universal	11 hp		
Diesel			
Fuel Cap	18 gal		

Freedom 28

LOD	28'4"	Hull	FRP/Balsa
LWL	25'9"	Deck	FRP/Balsa
Beam	9'4"	Spar	Carbon Fiber
Draft	4'5"	Pos Float	no
Disp	7000 lbs	Cockpit	5'6"
Ballast	3800 lbs	Headroom	6'1"
Sail Area		Fr. Water	50 gal
Cat Ketch	454 sq ft	SA/Disp	19.9
Mast Ht	36'	Disp/LWL	183
Mast	unstayed	Blst/Disp	54%
Auxiliary	std	Builder	
Yanmar	13 hp		Tillotson-Pearson
Diesel		First Built	1979
Fuel Cap	22 gal	No. Built	31
		1 Design	no
		Price	$39,900
			without sails

Northern 29

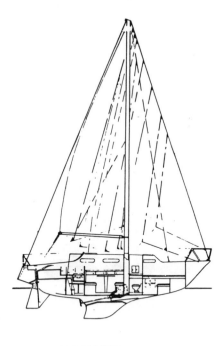

LOA	29'	Hull	FRP
LOD	28'4"	Deck	FRP
LWL	22'3"	Spar	Alum
Beam	3750	Pos Float	no
Draft	4'6"	Cockpit	6'3"
Disp	8250 lbs	Headroom	6'2"
Ballast	3750 lbs	Fr. Water	20 gal
Sail Area		SA/Disp	15
Sloop	384 sq ft	Disp/LWL	334
Mast Ht	42'	Blst/Disp	45%
Auxiliary	std	Designer	
Universal	15 hp		Sparkman & Stephens
Diesel		Builder	
Fuel Cap	10 gal		Northern Yachts
		First Built	1971
		No. Built	115
		Kit	available
		Price	$34,650
			with sails

NORTHERN YACHTS
395 Francom St.
Ajax, Ontario
Canada L1S 1R4
(416) 683-5980

Sabre 28

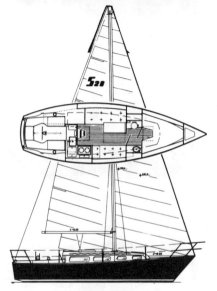

LOD	28'5"	Hull	FRP
LWL	22'10"	Deck	FRP
Beam	9'2"	Spar	Alum
Draft		Pos Float	no
Shoal	3'10"	Cockpit	7'2"
Deep	4'8"	Headroom	6'
Disp	7800 lbs	Fr. Water	30 gal
Ballast	3100 lbs	SA/Disp	16.4
Sail Area		Disp/LWL	293
Sloop	403 sq ft	Blst/Disp	40%
Mast Ht	43'	Designer	
Auxiliary	std		Sabre Design Team
Westerbeke	13 hp	First Built	1972
Diesel		No. Built	550
Fuel Cap	20 gal	1 Design	no
		Price	$41,800
			without sails

SABRE YACHTS
Hawthorne Rd.
S. Casco, ME 04077
(207) 655-3831

Ericson 28

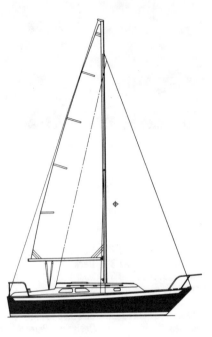

LOD	28'6"	Hull	FRP
LWL	24'2"	Deck	FRP
Beam	10'6"	Spar	Alum
Draft		Headroom	6'1"
Shoal	4'	SA/Disp	17.7
Deep	5'	Disp/LWL	237
Disp	7500 lbs	Blst/Disp	40%
Ballast	3000 lbs	Designer	Bruce King
Sail Area		Price	na
Sloop	424 sq ft		
Auxiliary	std		
Universal	11 hp		
Diesel			

ERICSON YACHTS INC.
1931 Deere Ave.
Irvine, CA 92714
(714) 540-8001

Albin Cumulus

LOD . . . . 28'7"	Hull . . . . FRP
LWL . . . . 22'3"	Deck . . . . FRP
Beam . . . . 9'6"	Spar . . . . Alum
Draft . . . . 5'3"	SA/Disp 18.9
Disp . . . . . . 7056 lbs	Disp/LWL 285
Ballast . . . . . 2810 lbs	Blst/Disp 40%
Sail Area	Designer . Peter Norlin
Sloop . . . 435 sq ft	Builder Albin, Sweden
Auxiliary . . . . std	Price $36,900
Yanmar . . . . 12 hp	with sails
Diesel	

ALBIN MARINE
Box 228
143 River Road
Cos Cob, CT 06807
(203) 661-4341

C & C 29

LOD . . . . 28'7"	Hull . . . . FRP
LWL . . . . 22'4"	Deck . . . . . FRP/Balsa
Beam . . . . 9'6"	Spar . . . . Alum
Draft . . . . 4'3"	Headroom . . . . . 6'1"
Disp . . . . . . 7500 lbs	Fr. Water . . . . 32 gal
Ballast . . . . . 2800 lbs	SA/Disp 16.5
Sail Area	Disp/LWL 300
Sloop . . . . 395 sq ft	Blst/Disp 37%
Auxiliary . . . . std	Price $43,250
Yanmar . . . . 15 hp	without sails
Diesel	
Fuel Cap . . . . . . 20 gal	

C&C YACHTS
55 Port Street East
Mississauga, Ontario
Canada L5G 4P3
(416) 274-7131

Lancer 29

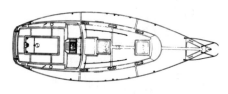

LOD . . . . 28'8"	Hull . . . . FRP
LWL . . . . 23'6"	Deck . . . . FRP
Beam . . . . 10'	Spar . . . . Alum
Draft	Pos Float . . . . no
Shoal . . . . . . 4'2"	Cockpit . . . . 7'1"
Deep . . . . . . 5'2"	Headroom . . . . 6'
Disp . . . . . . 7800 lbs	Fr. Water . . . . 24 gal
Ballast . . . . . 3000 lbs	SA/Disp 15.4
Sail Area	Disp/LWL 268
Sloop . . . 379 sq ft	Blst/Disp 38%
Mast Ht . . . . 40'	Designer . . . . . C & C
Auxiliary . . . . std	First Built 1978
Yanmar . . . . 15 hp	1 Design . . . . yes
Diesel	Price $47,126
	with sails

LANCER YACHT CORP.
1939 Deere Ave.
Irvine, CA 92714
(714) 751-7220

San Juan 28

Spirit

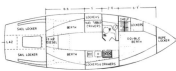

Westerly Konsort

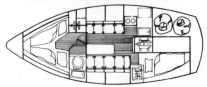

LOA	32'9"	Hull	FRP
LOD	28'9"	Deck	FRP
LWL	23'4"	Spar	Alum
Beam	8'11"	Fr. Water	40 gal
Draft	3'6"	SA/Disp	15
Disp	9600 lbs	Disp/LWL	337
Ballast	2600 lbs	Blst/Disp	27%
Sail Area		Designer	
Cutter	423 sq ft		L. F. Herreshoff
Auxiliary	std	First Built	1977
Volvo	13 hp	Price	$42,370
Diesel			without sails
Fuel Cap	18 gal		

LOD	28'8"	Hull	FRP
LWL	22'4"	Deck	FRP
Beam	10'	Spar	Alum
Draft	4'6"	Pos Float	no
Disp	6200 lbs	Cockpit	6'3'
Ballast	3200 lbs	Headroom	6'2"
Sail Area		Fr. Water	39 gal
Sloop	385 sq ft	SA/Disp	18.3
Mast Ht	41	Disp/LWL	248
Auxiliary	std	Blst/Disp	52%
Yanmar		Designer	Don Clark
Diesel		First Built	1977
Fuel Cap	22 gal	No. Built	250
		1 Design	no
		Price	$33,995
			with sails

LOD	28'10"	Hull	FRP
LWL	25'6"	Deck	FRP/Balsa
Beam	10'9"	Spar	Alum
Draft		Pos Float	no
Deep	5'4"	Headroom	6'
Twin	3'2"	Fr. Water	36 gal
Shoal cb up	3'6"	SA/Disp	14
Shoal cb dn	6'9"	Disp/LWL	212
Disp	7900 lbs	Blst/Disp	41%
Ballast		Designer	
Deep	3200 lbs		Laurent Giles
Twin	3200 lbs	Builder	
Shoal	4695 lbs		Westerly-England
Sail Area		First Built	1979
Sloop	348 sq ft	No. Built	500
Mast Ht	42'	1 Design	no
Auxiliary	std	Price	$42,147
Bukh	20 hp		with sails
Diesel			
Fuel Cap	18 gal		

CLARK BOAT CO.
25-37th St. NE
Auburn, WA 98002
(206) 854-5400

PARKINS MARINE INC.
809 SW Coconut Dr.
Ft. Lauderdale, FL 33315
(305) 525-7421

ANDREW GEMENY & SONS
5809 Annapolis Rd.
Hyattsville, MD 20784
(301) 779-6190

Bayfield 29

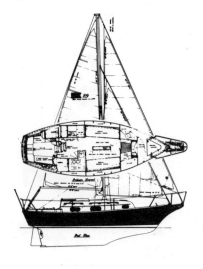

LOD . . . . 29'	Hull . . . . FRP
LWL . . . . 21'9''	Deck . . . . . FRP/Balsa
Beam . . . . 10'2''	Spar . . . . Alum
Draft . . . . 3'6''	Fr. Water . . . . . 25 gal
Disp . . . . 7100 lbs	SA/Disp 20.3
Ballast . . . . . 3000 lbs	Disp/LWL 308
Sail Area	Blst/Disp 42%
Cutter . . . 468 sq ft	Designer
Auxiliary . . . . std	H. Ted Gozzard
Diesel . . . . . . 15 hp	Price $42,950
Fuel Cap . . . . . 19 gal	with sails

BAYFIELD BOAT YARD LTD.
Box 1076
Clinton, Ontario
Canada N0M 1L0
(519) 482-3425

Cascade 29

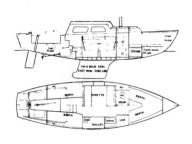

LOD . . . . 29'	Hull . . . . FRP
LWL . . . . 24'	Deck . . . . FRP
Beam . . . . 8'2''	Spar . . . . Alum
Draft . . . . 4'9''	Pos Float . . . . no
Disp . . . . . . 8000 lbs	Cockpit . . . . 7'
Ballast . . . . . 2450 lbs	Headroom . . . . . . 6'2''
Sail Area	Fr. Water . . . . . 42 gal
Sloop . . . . 405 sq ft	SA/Disp 16.2
Mast Ht . . . . 39'	Disp/LWL 258
Auxiliary . . . . std	Blst/Disp 31%
Farymann . . . 12 hp	Designer
Diesel	Robert G. Buttke
Fuel Cap . . . . . 32 gal	First Built 1961
	No. Built 360
	Kit $28,000

YACHT CONSTRUCTORS INC.
7030 N.E. 42nd Ave.
Portland, OR 97218
(503) 287-5794

Dragon

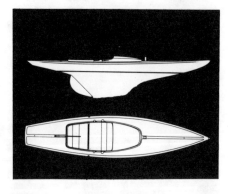

LOD . . . . 29'2''	Hull . . . . FRP
LWL . . . . na	Deck . . . . FRP
Beam . . . . 6'5''	Spar . . . . Alum
Draft . . . . 3'2''	Pos Float . . . . no
Disp . . . . . . 3740 lbs	SA/Disp 19.3
Ballast . . . . . 2200 lbs	Blst/Disp 59%
Sail Area	Designer Johan Anker
Sloop . . . . 290 sq ft	Builder . . . . Denmark
Auxiliary . . . . opt	First Built 1936
Gas . . . . 4 hp	No. Built 540
outbd	1 Design . . . . yes
	Price $18,000
	with sails

**A/S BORRESENS
BAADEBYGGERI**
Dragevej
Box 187
7100 Vejle, Denmark

Alberg 29

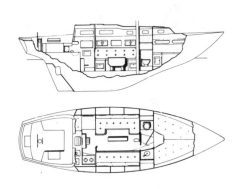

LOD	29'3"	Hull	FRP
LWL	22'3"	Deck	FRP
Beam	9'2"	Spar	Alum
Draft	4'7"	Pos Float	no
Disp	9000 lbs	Cockpit	8'2"
Ballast	4000 lbs	Headroom	6'2"
Sail Area		Fr. Water	30 gal
Sloop	416 sq ft	SA/Disp	15.4
Auxiliary	std	Disp/LWL	365
Yanmar	15 hp	Blst/Disp	44%
Diesel		Designer	
Fuel Cap	15 gal		Carl L. Alberg
		First Built	1979
		No. Built	50
		1 Design	yes
		Kit	available
		Price	$48,500
			without sails

NYE YACHTS
25 Dundas St. W.
Belleville, Ontario
Canada K8P 3M7

Seidelmann 295

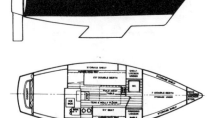

LOD	29'5"	Hull	FRP
LWL	24'5"	Deck	FRP
Beam	10'2"	Spar	Alum
Draft		Pos Float	no
cb up	3'3"	Cockpit	7'10"
cb dn	6'2"	Headroom	6'3"
Disp	7200 lbs	Fr. Water	30 gal
Ballast	3200 lbs	SA/Disp	17.5
Sail Area		Disp/LWL	221
Sloop	408 sq ft	Blst/Disp	44%
Mast Ht	39'	Designer	
Auxiliary	opt		Bob Seidelmann
Yanmar	12 hp	First Built	1982
Diesel		No. Built	15
Fuel Cap	12 gal	1 Design	no
		Price	$36,600
			with sails

SEIDELMANN YACHTS
Cushman Ave., P. O. Box 2529
Berlin, NJ 08009
(609) 768-1707

Annie

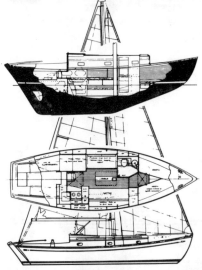

LOD	29'6"	Hull	FRP
LWL	24'6"	Deck	FRP
Beam	9'6"	Spar	Alum
Draft	4'6"	Headroom	6'
Disp	11,027 lbs	Fr. Water	40 gal
Ballast	4400 lbs	SA/Disp	14.7
Sail Area		Disp/LWL	334
Sloop	456 sq ft	Blst/Disp	40%
Cutter	465 sq ft	Designer	C. W. Paine
Auxiliary	std	Price	$67,900
Westerbeke			without sails
Diesel			
Fuel Cap	20 gal		

MORRIS YACHTS
Box 58
Southwest Harbor, ME 04679
(207) 244-5866

Capri 30

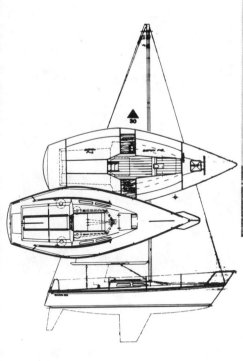

LOD	29'6''	Hull	FRP
LWL	24'2''	Deck	FRP
Beam	11'2''	Spar	Alum
Draft	5'4''	Pos Float	no
Disp	4985 lbs	Headroom	5'2''
Ballast	2300 lbs	Fr. Water	5 gal
Sail Area		SA/Disp	25.1
Sloop	458 sq ft	Disp/LWL	157
Auxiliary	opt	Blst/Disp	46%
Diesel	10 hp	Designer	Frank Butler
		First Built	1982
		No. Built	25
		1 Design	no
		Price	$21,985
			without sails

CATALINA YACHTS
21200 Victory Blvd.
Woodland Hills, CA 91367
(213) 884-7700

J — 29

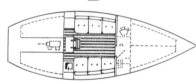

LOD	29'6''	Hull	FRP/Balsa
LWL	25'	Deck	FRP/Balsa
Beam	11'	Spar	Alum
Draft	5'7''	Pos Float	no
Disp	6000 lbs	Cockpit	10'
Ballast	2100 lbs	Headroom	5'2''
Sail Area		Fr. Water	6 gal
Sloop (FR)	450 sq ft	SA/Disp	21.8
Sloop (MH)	453 sq ft	Disp/LWL	171
Mast Ht		Blst/Disp	35%
Sloop (FR)	46'	Designer	
Sloop (MH)	43'		Rodney Johnstone
Auxiliary	opt	Builder	
Yanmar	7.5 hp		Tillitson Pearson Inc.
Diesel		First Built	1982
Fuel Cap	10 gal	No. Built	50
		1 Design	yes
		Price	$27,500
			without sails

J BOATS INC.
24 Mill St.
Newport, RI 02840
(401) 846-8410

Lancer 30

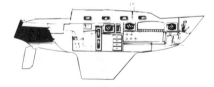

LOD	29'6''	Hull	FRP
LWL	24'	Deck	FRP
Beam	10'	Spar	Alum
Draft		Pos Float	no
Shoal	4'2''	Cockpit	7'1''
Deep	5'2''	Headroom	6'
Dis	8200 lbs	Fr. Water	24 gal
Ballast	3000 lbs	SA/Disp	17.6
Sail Area		Disp/LWL	264
Sloop	448 sq ft	Blst/Disp	37%
Mast Ht	45'	Designer	C & C
Auxiliary	std	First Built	1976
Yanmar	15 hp	1 Design	yes
Diesel		Price	$50,609
			with sails

LANCER YACHT CORP.
1939 Deere Ave.
Irvine, CA 92714
(714) 751-7220

Show 29

Formosa 30

Formosa Boat

Vixen Overnighter

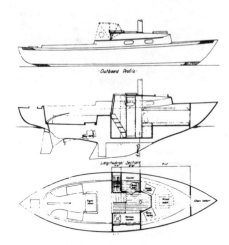

Outboard Profile

Longitudinal Section

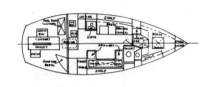

LOD	29'6"	Hull	FRP
LWL	22'3"	Deck	FRP
Beam	10'2"	Spar	Alum
Draft	5'7"	Fr. Water	26 gal
Disp	6380 lbs	SA/Disp	16.3
Ballast	2420 lbs	Disp/LWL	259
Sail Area		Blst/Disp	38%
Sloop	350 sq ft	Designer	A. Jezequel
Auxiliary	std	Builder	Barberis-
Bukh	12 hp		Cantieri, Italy
Diesel		Price	$39,975
			with sails

LOD	29'7"	Hull	FRP
LWL	25'	Deck	FRP
Beam	10'6"	Spar	Alum
Draft	3'6"	Disp/LWL	309
Disp	10,800 lbs	Blst/Disp	37%
Ballast	4000 lbs	Price	$36,850
Sail Area			with sails
Ketch	na		
Auxiliary	std		
Volvo	25 hp		
Diesel			

LOD	29'7"	Hull	FRP
LWL	23'	Deck	FRP
Beam	8'6"	Spar	Alum
Draft	4'6"	Pos Float	no
Disp	8000 lbs	Cockpit	10'
Ballast	3000 lbs	Headroom	5'8"
Sail Area		Fr. Water	20 gal
Sloop	309 sq ft	SA/Disp	12.4
Mast Ht	36'	Disp/LWL	293
Auxiliary	opt	Blst/Disp	38%
Volvo	13 hp	Designer	Thomas Hale
Diesel		First Built	1973
		No. Built	30
		1 Design	yes
		Price	$32,000
			with sails

Kelt 9M

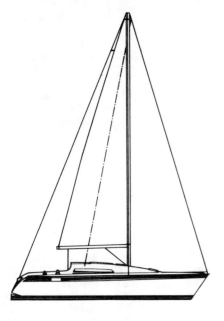

LOA	31'	Hull	FRP
LOD	29'8"	Deck	FRP
LWL	24'7"	Spar	Alum
Beam	10'2"	Headroom	6'
Draft		SA/Disp	7.8
Deep	5'11"	Disp/LWL	218
Shoal cb up	3'5"	Blst/Disp	41%
Shoal cb dn	6'6"	Designer	
Disp	7275 lbs		Philippe Briand
Ballast	2998 lbs	Builder	
Sail Area			Kelt, Canada & France
Sloop	183 sq ft	Price	$46,500
			with sails

ATKINS YACHTS
326 First St.
Annapolis, MD 21403
(301) 268-3332

Leigh 30

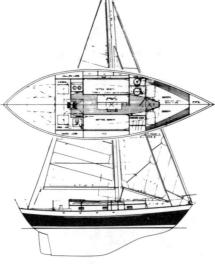

LOD	29'8"	Hull	FRP
LWL	23'4"	Deck	FRP
Beam	9'7"	Spar	Alum
Draft	4'7"	Headroom	6'1"
Disp	9100 lbs	Fr. Water	40 gal
Ballast	4400 lbs	SA/Disp	15.4
Sail Area		Disp/LWL	319
Cutter	420 sq ft	Blst/Disp	48%
Auxiliary	std	Designer	C. W. Paine
Volvo	13 hp	Price	$65,900
Diesel			without sails
Fuel Cap	15 gal		

MORRIS YACHTS
Box 58
Southwest Harbor, ME 04679
(207) 244-5866

Moody 29

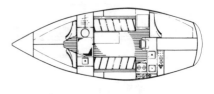

LOD	29'8"	Hull	FRP
LWL	25'	Deck	FRP
Beam	10'6"	Spar	Alum
Draft		Fr. Water	50 gal
Shoal	3'6"	SA/Disp	15.6
Deep	4'6"	Disp/LWL	208
Disp	7300 lbs	Blst/Disp	38%
Ballast	2750 lbs	Designer	
Sail Area			Angus S. Primrose
Sloop	367 sq ft	Builder	
Auxiliary	std	Marine Projects, England
Bukh	20 hp	Price	$38,500
Diesel			with sails
Fuel Cap	25 gal		

IMPEX MARINE
Box 445
Reading, PA 19603
(215) 375-8048

Naja 30

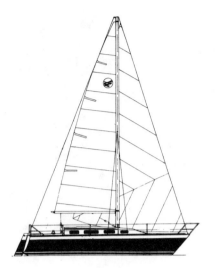

LOD	29'8"	Hull	Wood Epoxy
LWL	27'2"	Deck	Wood Epoxy
Beam	10'6"	Spar	Alum
Draft		Disp/LWL	138
Shoal	4'3"	Kit	$10,495
Deep	5'9"	Price	$45,907
Disp	6240 lbs		with sails
Ballast	na		
Sail Area			
Sloop	na		
Auxiliary	std		
Renault			
Diesel			

A & T MARINE SERVICES
P. O. Box 1423
Tacoma, WA 98401
(206) 584-8563

Botnia 30NF

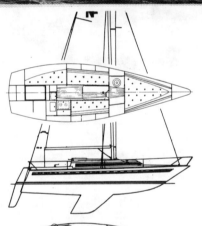

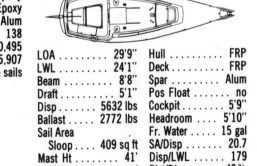

LOA	29'9"	Hull	FRP
LWL	24'1"	Deck	FRP
Beam	8'8"	Spar	Alum
Draft	5'1"	Pos Float	no
Disp	5632 lbs	Cockpit	5'9"
Ballast	2772 lbs	Headroom	5'10"
Sail Area		Fr. Water	15 gal
Sloop	409 sq ft	SA/Disp	20.7
Mast Ht	41'	Disp/LWL	179
Auxiliary	std	Blst/Disp	49%
Diesel	9.5 hp	Builder	Finland
		First Built	1976
		No. Built	280
		Price	na

BOTNIA—MARIN OY
Box 9 SF—66100 Malax, Finland

Friendship 30

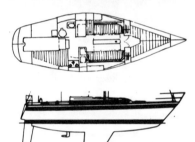

LOD	29'9"	Hull	FRP
LWL	23'4"	Deck	FRP
Beam	9'2"	Spar	Alum
Draft		Pos Float	yes
Shoal cb up	3'6"	Cockpit	8'
Shoal cb dn	6'9"	Headroom	6'3"
Deep	5'4"	Fr. Water	20 gal
Disp	8377 lbs	SA/Disp	17.8
Ballast	3362 lbs	Disp/LWL	294
Sail Area		Blst/Disp	40%
Sloop (Fr)	459 sq ft	Designer	
Auxiliary	std		E. G. Van De Staat
Volvo Penta	17 hp	Builder	
Diesel			Meijer, Holland
Fuel Cap	11 gal	First Built	1974
		No. Built	527
		1 Design	yes
		Price	$39,900
			with sails

SAILSPIRIT
P. O. Box 340007
Miami, FL 33114
(305) 441-9193

Grampian 30

LOD .... 29'9"	Hull .... FRP
LWL .... 25'6"	Deck .... FRP
Beam .... 9'6"	Spar .... Alum
Draft .... 4'8"	SA/Disp 16.2
Disp ...... 8600 lbs	Disp/LWL 232
Ballast ..... 3870 lbs	Blst/Disp 45%
Sail Area	Price .... na
Sloop .... 425 sq ft	

SAILCAN LTD.
5230 South Service Rd.
Burlington, Ontario
Canada L7L 5K2
(416) 827-3781

J — 30

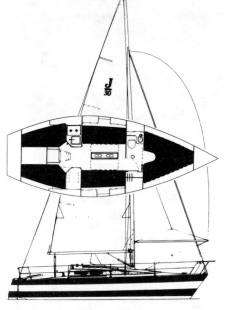

LOD .... 29'10"	Hull ...... FRP/Balsa
LWL .... 25'	Deck ..... FRP/Balsa
Beam .... 11'2"	Spar .... Alum
Draft .... 5'3"	Pos Float .... no
Disp ...... 7000 lbs	Cockpit .... 8'
Ballast ..... 2100 lbs	Headroom .... 6'
Sail Area	Fr. Water ... 18 gal
Sloop .... 450 sq ft	SA/Disp 19.7
Mast Ht ...... 46'	Disp/LWL 200
Auxiliary .... std	Blst/Disp 30%
Yanmar ..... 15 hp	Designer
Diesel	Rodney Johnstone
Fuel Cap ..... 14 gal	Builder
	Tillitson Pearson Inc.
	First Built 1979
	No. Built 500
	1 Design .... yes
	Price $44,000
	without sails

J BOATS INC.
24 Mill St.
Newport, RI 02840
(401) 846-8410

Metalmast 30

LOD .... 29'10"	SA/Disp 21.3
LWL .... 23'9"	Disp/LWL 216
Beam .... 10'2"	Blst/Disp 48%
Draft .... 5'6"	Designer
Disp ...... 6500 lbs	Peter Canning
Ballast ..... 3100 lbs	Price $38,000
Sail Area	with sails
Sloop .... 464 sq ft	
Sloop .... 418 sq ft	
Auxiliary .... std	
Diesel	

METALMAST MARINE
55 Providence St.
Putnam, CT 06260
(203) 928-2776

S2 9.1

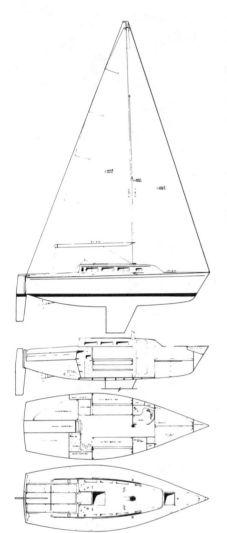

LOD	29'10"	Hull	FRP/Balsa
LWL	25'	Deck	FRP/Balsa
Beam	10'6"	Spar	Alum
Draft	5'6"	Pos Float	no
Disp	7500 lbs	Headroom	6'2"
Ballast	3500 lbs	SA/Disp	18.5
Sail Area		Disp/LWL	214
Sloop	444 sq ft	Blst/Disp	47%
Auxiliary	std	Designer	G & S
Diesel		First Built	1983
		1 Design	no
		Price	na

S2 YACHTS INC.
725 E. 40th St.
Holland, MI 49423
(616) 392-7163

Bahama 30

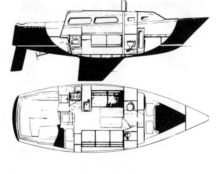

LOD	29'11"	Hull	FRP
LWL	24'7"	Deck	FRP
Beam	10'	Spar	Alum
Draft		Fr. Water	25 gal
Shoal	4'	SA/Disp	17.5
Deep	5'	Disp/LWL	250
Disp		Blst/Disp	39%
Shoal	8322 lbs	Designer	Bob Finch
Deep	8230 lbs	Price	na
Ballast			
Shoal	3222 lbs		
Deep	3130 lbs		
Sail Area			
Sloop	449 sq ft		
Mast Ht	43'6"		
Auxiliary	std		
Volvo	13 hp		
Diesel			
Fuel Cap	20 gal		

ISLANDER YACHTS
1922 Barranca Rd.
Irvine, CA 92714
(714) 549-8526

Bristol 29.9

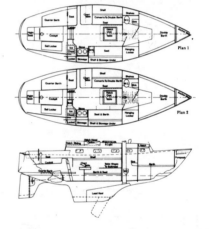

LOD	29'11"	Hull	FRP
LWL	24'	Deck	FRP
Beam	10'2"	Spar	Alum
Draft		Pos Float	yes
cb up	3'6"	Headroom	6'4"
cb dn	7'6"	Fr. Water	50 gal
Disp	8650 lbs	SA/Disp	14.8
Ballast	3600 lbs	Disp/LWL	279
Sail Area		Blst/Disp	42%
Sloop	391 sq ft	Designer	
Auxiliary	std		Halsey Herreshoff
Universal	16 hp	First Built	1977
Diesel		No. Built	203
Fuel Cap	18 gal	1 Design	no
		Price	$47,170
			without sails

BRISTOL YACHT CO.
Franklin St.
Bristol, RI 02809
(401) 253-5200

Cal 9.2

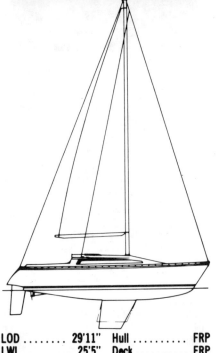

LOD	29'11"	Hull	FRP
LWL	25'5"	Deck	FRP
Beam	10'4"	Spar	Alum
Draft		Pos Float	no
Shoal	4'7"	Headroom	5'9"
Deep	5'7"	Fr. Water	21 gal
Disp	7000 lbs	SA/Disp	17
Ballast	2730 lbs	Disp/LWL	190
Sail Area		Blst/Disp	39%
Sloop	388 sq ft	Designer	Ron Holland
Mast Ht	42'3"	First Built	1981
Auxiliary	std	No. Built	74
Universal	11 hp	1 Design	yes
Diesel		Price	na

BANGOR PUNTA MARINE
848 Airport Rd.
Box 991
Fall River, MA 02722
(617) 678-5291

Cal 9.2R

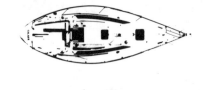

LOD	29'11"	Hull	FRP
LWL	25'5"	Deck	FRP
Beam	10'4"	Spar	Alum
Draft	5'10"	Pos Float	no
Disp	7000 lbs	Headroom	5'9"
Ballast	2730 lbs	Fr. Water	21 gal
Sail Area		SA/Disp	18.2
Sloop	417 sq ft	Disp/LWL	190
Mast Ht	43'9"	Blst/Disp	39%
Auxiliary	std	Designer	Ron Holland
Universal	11 hp	First Built	1982
Diesel		No. Built	2
		1 Design	yes
		Price	na

BANGOR PUNTA MARINE
848 Airport Rd.
Box 991
Fall River, MA 02722
(617) 678-5291

Catalina 30

LOD	29'11"	Hull	FRP
LWL	25'	Deck	FRP
Beam	10'10"	Spar	Alum
Draft	5'3"	Pos Float	no
Disp	10,200	Headroom	6'2"
Ballast	4200 lbs	Fr. Water	49 gal
Sail Area		SA/Disp	15.2
Sloop	446 sq ft	Disp/LWL	291
Sloop (tall)	505 sq ft	Blst/Disp	41%
Mast Ht		Designer	Frank Butler
Sloop	45'6"	First Built	1974
Sloop (tall)	47'5"	No. Built	3000
Auxiliary	opt	1 Design	yes
	25 hp	Price	$26,975 without sails

CATALINA YACHTS
21200 Victory Blvd.
Woodland Hills, CA 91367
(213) 884-7700

Ericson 30

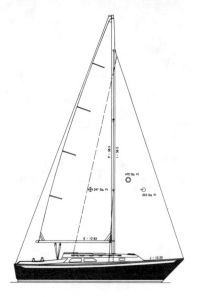

LOD . . . . 29'11"	Hull . . . . FRP
LWL . . . . 25'4"	Deck . . . . FRP
Beam . . . . 10'5"	Spar . . . . Alum
Draft	Headroom . . . . . 6'2"
Shoal . . . . 4'	SA/Disp 17.4
Deep . . . . . . 5'10"	Disp/LWL 247
Disp . . . . . . 9000 lbs	Blst/Disp 44%
Ballast . . . . . 4000 lbs	Designer . . Bruce King
Sail Area	Price . . . . na
Sloop . . . . 470 sq ft	
Auxiliary . . . . std	
Universal . . . 16 hp	
Diesel	

ERICSON YACHTS INC.
1931 Deere Ave.
Irvine, CA 92714
(714) 540-8001

Hunter 30

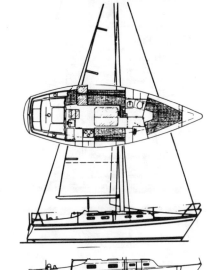

LOD . . . . 29'11"	Hull . . . . FRP
LWL . . . . 25'9"	Deck . . . . FRP
Beam . . . . 10'1"	Spar . . . . Alum
Draft	Fr. Water . . . . 40 gal
Shoal . . . . 4'	SA/Disp 16.6
Deep . . . . 5'3"	Disp/LWL 253
Disp . . . . . . 9700 lbs	Blst/Disp 41%
Ballast . . . . 4000 lbs	Price $36,390
Sail Area	with sails
Sloop . . . . 473 sq ft	
Mast Ht . . . . 47'	
Auxiliary . . . . std	
Yanmar . . . . . 15 hp	
Diesel	
Fuel Cap . . . . 12.5 gal	

HUNTER MARINE
Box 1030, Hwy 441
Alachua, FL 32601
(904) 462-3077

Islander 30/A

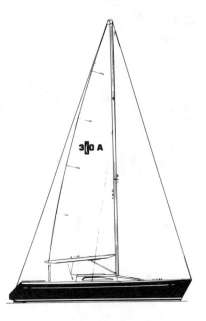

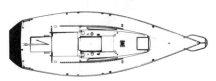

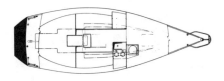

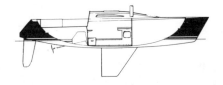

LOD . . . . 29'11"	Hull . . . . . . FRP/Balsa
lwl . . . . 25'3"	Deck . . . . . FRP/Balsa
Beam . . . . 10'	Spar . . . . Alum
Draft . . . . 5'6"	Fr. Water . . . . 10 gal
Disp . . . . . . 7125 lbs	SA/Disp 19.8
Ballast . . . . . 3400 lbs	Disp/LWL 197
Sail Area	Blst/Disp 48%
Sloop . . . . 458 sq ft	Designer
Auxiliary . . . . opt	Alan Andrews
I/O	Price $40,000
	with sails

ISLANDER YACHTS
1922 Barranca Rd.
Irvine, CA 92714
(714) 549-8526

Nordica 30

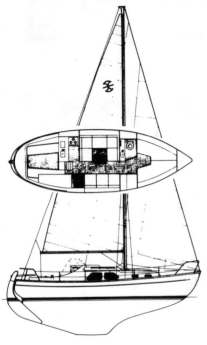

LOD	29'11"	Hull	FRP
LWL	25'1"	Deck	FRP
Beam	9'6"	Spar	Alum
Draft	5'1"	Headroom	6'
Disp	10,350 lbs	SA/Disp	14.5
Ballast	4360 lbs	Disp/LWL	292
Sail Area		Blst/Disp	42%
Sloop	430 sq ft	Price	$44,800
Mast Ht	44'		with sails
Auxiliary	std		
Volvo	17 hp		
Diesel			
Fuel Cap	25 gal		

EXE FIBRECRAFT LTD.
London Rd. S
Exeter, Ontario
Canada N0M 1S0
(519) 235-0610

O'Day 30

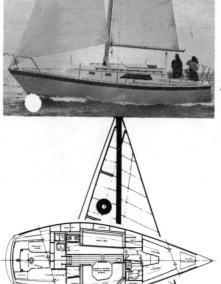

LOD	29'11"	Hull	FRP
LWL	25'5"	Deck	FRP
Beam	10'9"	Spar	Alum
Draft		Pos Float	no
Deep	4'11"	Cockpit	6'8"
Shoal cb up	3'6"	Headroom	6'
Shoal cb dn	7'2"	Fr. Water	25 gal
Disp		SA/Disp	15.1
Deep	10,150 lbs	Disp/LWL	275
Shoal	10,600 lbs	Blst/Disp	39%
Ballast		Designer	
Deep	4000 lbs		C. R. Hunt Assoc.
Shoal	4300 lbs	First Built	1977
Sail Area		No. Built	293
Sloop	441 sq ft	1 Design	yes
Mast Ht	44'	Price	na
Auxiliary	std		
Universal	16 hp		
Diesel			
Fuel Cap	26 gal		

BANGOR PUNTA MARINE
848 Airport Rd.
Box 991
Fall River, MA 02722
(617) 678-5291

Pearson Flyer 30

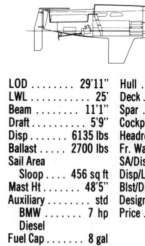

LOD	29'11"	Hull	FRP
LWL	25'	Deck	FRP
Beam	11'1"	Spar	Alum
Draft	5'9"	Cockpit	8'
Disp	6135 lbs	Headroom	5'6"
Ballast	2700 lbs	Fr. Water	4 gal
Sail Area		SA/Disp	21.8
Sloop	456 sq ft	Disp/LWL	175
Mast Ht	48'5"	Blst/Disp	44%
Auxiliary	std	Designer	Bill Shaw
BMW	7 hp	Price	na
Diesel			
Fuel Cap	8 gal		

PEARSON YACHTS
West Shore Rd.
Portsmouth, RI 02871
(401) 683-0100

S2 9.2A

LOD	29'11"	Hull	FRP
LWL	25'	Deck	FRP/Balsa
Beam	10'3"	Spar	Alum
Draft		Pos Float	no
Shoal	3'11"	Cockpit	8'
Deep	4'11"	Headroom	6'3"
Disp	9800 lbs	Fr. Water	37 gal
Ballast	4000 lbs	SA/Disp	16.4
Sail Area		Disp/LWL	280
Sloop	468 sq ft	Blst/Disp	41%
Mast Ht	43'6"	Designer	
Auxiliary	std		Arthur Edmunds
Yanmar	15 hp	1 Design	no
Diesel		Price	$48,800
Fuel Cap	30 gal		with sails

S2 YACHTS INC.
725 E. 40th St.
Holland, MI 49423
(616) 392-7163

S2 9.2C

LOD	29'11"	Hull	FRP
LWL	25'	Deck	FRP/Balsa
Beam	10'3"	Spar	Alum
Draft		Pos Float	no
Shoal	3'1"	Cockpit	6'
Deep	4'11"	Headroom	6'2"
Disp	9800 lbs	Fr. Water	37 gal
Ballast	4000 lbs	SA/Disp	16.4
Sail Area		Disp/LWL	280
Sloop	468 sq ft	Blst/Disp	41%
Mast Ht	43'6"	Designer	
Auxiliary	std		Arthur Edmunds
Yanmar	15 hp	1 Design	no
Diesel		Price	$53,250
Fuel Cap	31 gal		with sails

S2 YACHTS INC.
725 E. 40th St.
Holland, MI 49423
(616) 392-7163

Sabre 30

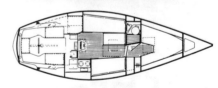

LOD	29'11"	Hull	FRP
LWL	24'0"	Deck	FRP
Beam	10'10"	Spar	Alum
Draft		Pos Float	no
Shoal	4'	Cockpit	7'2"
Deep	5'2"	Headroom	6'1"
Disp		Fr. Water	22 gal
Shoal	8800 lbs	SA/Disp	17
Deep	8600 lbs	Disp/LWL	284
Ballast		Blst/Disp	43%
Shoal	3800 lbs	Designer	
Deep	3600 lbs		Sabre Design Team
Sail Area		First Built	1979
Sloop	454 sq ft	No. Built	110
Mast Ht	46'6"	1 Design	no
Auxiliary	std	Price	$49,800
Westerbeke	20 hp		without sails
Diesel			
Fuel Cap	20 gal		

SABRE YACHTS
Hawthorne Rd.
S. Casco, ME 04077
(207) 655-3831

Santana 30/30

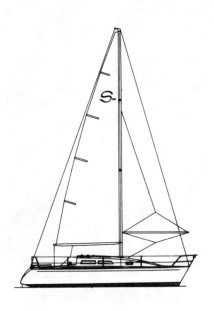

LOD	29'11"	Hull	FRP
LWL	25'5"	Deck	FRP
Beam	10'3"	Spar	Alum
Draft	5'6"	Fr. Water	20 gal
Disp	6800 lbs	SA/Disp	28.4
Ballast	2435 lbs	Disp/LWL	185
Sail Area		Blst/Disp	36%
Sloop	637 sq ft	Designer	
Auxiliary	std		Nelson/Marek
Volvo Penta	13 hp	Price	$46,150
Diesel			with sails
Fuel Cap	20 gal		

W. D. SCHOCK CORP.
3502 S. Greenville St.
Santa Ana, CA 92704
(714) 549-2277

Seafarer 30

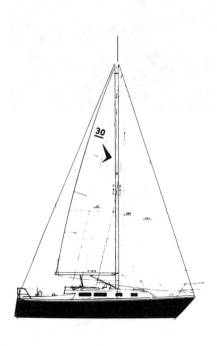

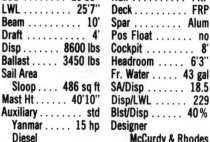

LOD	29'11"	Hull	FRP
LWL	25'7"	Deck	FRP
Beam	10'	Spar	Alum
Draft	4'	Pos Float	no
Disp	8600 lbs	Cockpit	8'
Ballast	3450 lbs	Headroom	6'3"
Sail Area		Fr. Water	43 gal
Sloop	486 sq ft	SA/Disp	18.5
Mast Ht	40'10"	Disp/LWL	229
Auxiliary	std	Blst/Disp	40%
Yanmar	15 hp	Designer	
Diesel			McCurdy & Rhodes
Fuel Cap	12 gal	First Built	1978
		No. Built	100
		1 Design	no
		Price	$45,500
			with sails

SEAFARER YACHTS INC.
760 Park Ave.
Huntington, NY 11743
(516) 427-6670

Seidelmann 30T

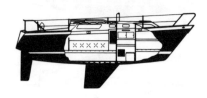

LOD	29'11"	Hull	FRP
LWL	24'	Deck	FRP
Beam	11'	Spar	Alum
Draft		Pos Float	no
Shoal	4'2"	Cockpit	6'10"
Deep	5'5"	Headroom	6'5"
Disp	8800 lbs	Fr. Water	30 gal
Ballast	3600 lbs	SA/Disp	15.8
Sail Area		Disp/LWL	284
Sloop	420 sq ft	Blst/Disp	41%
Mast Ht	42'6"	Designer	
Auxiliary	std		Bob Seidelmann
Yanmar	12 hp	First Built	1980
Diesel		No. Built	64
		1 Design	no
		Price	$51,600
			with sails

SEIDELMANN YACHTS
Cushman Ave., P. O. Box 2529
Berlin, NJ 08009
(609) 768-1707

T – 30

Tartan 3000

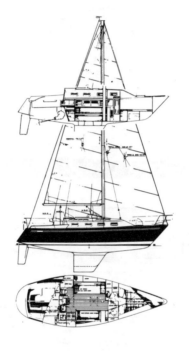

US 30

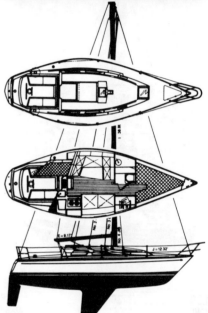

T – 30		Tartan 3000		US 30	
LOD .... 29'11"	Hull .... FRP	LOD .... 29'11"	Hull .... FRP	LOD .... 29'11"	Hull .... FRP
LWL .... 26'	Deck .... FRP	LWL .... 25'3"	Deck .... FRP	LWL .... 25'	Deck .... FRP
Beam .... 11'	Spar .... Alum	Beam .... 10'1"	Spar .... Alum	Beam .... 10'3"	Spar .... Alum
Draft	Fr. Water .... 30 gal	Draft	Fr. Water .... 40 gal	Draft	Pos Float ...... no
Shoal ...... 3'11"	SA/Disp 15.4	Shoal ...... 4'1"	SA/Disp 17.7	Shoal ...... 3'11"	Headroom ...... 6'2"
Deep ...... 4'11"	Disp/LWL 244	Deep ...... 5'2"	Disp/LWL 220	Deep .... 5'7"	Fr. Water ..... 19 gal
Disp ...... 9600 lbs	Blst/Disp 44%	Disp ...... 7950 lbs	Blst/Disp 48%	Disp ...... 7000 lbs	SA/Disp 16.7
Ballast ..... 4250 lbs	Designer	Ballast ..... 3830 lbs	Designer	Ballast ..... 2850 lbs	Disp/LWL 200
Sail Area		Sail Area	Sparkman & Stephens	Sail Area	Blst/Disp 41%
Sloop .... 434 sq ft	H. Herreshoff	Sloop .... 441 sq ft	Price .... na	Sloop .... 381 sq ft	First Built 1980
Auxiliary .... std	Price $47,975	Auxiliary .... std		Mast Ht ...... 41'10"	1 Design .... no
Diesel	with sails	Universal		Auxiliary .... std	Price .... na
Fuel Cap ...... 18 gal		Diesel		Volvo ...... 13 hp	
		Fuel Cap ...... 19 gal		Diesel	
				Fuel Cap ...... 16 gal	

TICON YACHTS LIMITED
2508 Lakeshore Rd. W.
Oakville, Ontario
Canada L6L 1H8
(416) 827-4322

TARTAN MARINE CO.
320 River St.
Grand River, OH 44045
(216) 354-5671

US YACHT
P. O. Box 24467
Seattle, WA 98134

Benford 30

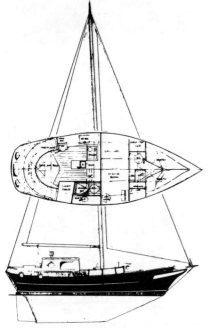

LOD	30'	Hull	FRP
LWL	23'6"	Deck	Wood
Beam	10'6"	Spar	Alum/Wood
Draft	4'6"	Pos Float	no
Disp	10,965 lbs	Cockpit	7'6"
Ballast	3300 lbs	Headroom	6'3"
Sail Area		SA/Disp	19.5
Sloop	600 sq ft	Disp/LWL	377
Schooner (Gaff)		Blst/Disp	30%
	600 sq ft	Designer	
Auxiliary	std		Jay R. Benford
BMW	12 hp	First Built	1976
Diesel		No. Built	8
		Kit	$8,000
		Price	$82,000
			with sails

HERITAGE BOAT WORKS
1331 Country Club Rd.
Hood River, OR 97031
(503) 386-1526

C & C 30

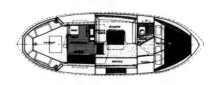

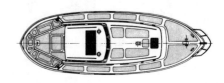

LOD	30'	Hull	FRP
LWL	24'9"	Deck	FRP/Balsa
Beam	10'	Spar	Alum
Draft	5'	Headroom	6'1"
Disp	8000 lbs	Fr. Water	42 gal
Ballast	3450 lbs	SA/Disp	18.4
Sail Area		Disp/LWL	235
Sloop	459 sq ft	Blst/Disp	43%
Mast Ht	42'6"	Price	na
Auxiliary	std		
Yanmar	15 hp		
Diesel			
Fuel Cap	20 gal		

C&C YACHTS
55 Port Street East
Mississauga, Ontario
Canada L5G 4P3
(416) 274-7131

Dartsailer 30

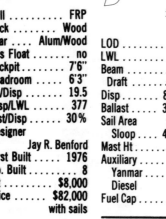

LOD	30'	Hull	FRP
LWL	25'9"	Deck	FRP
Beam	10'2"	Spar	Alum
Draft	4'1"	Pos Float	no
Disp	15,400 lbs	Cockpit	6'5"
Ballast	5060 lbs	Headroom	6'3"
Sail Area		Fr. Water	79 gal
Sloop	399 sq ft	SA/Disp	10.3
Cutter	478 sq ft	Disp/LWL	402
Ketch	429 sq ft	Blst/Disp	33%
Mast Ht		Designer	
Sloop	38'8"		W. De Vries Lentsch
Cutter	40'8"	Builder	
Ketch	38'8"		Neptunus, Holland
Auxiliary	std	Price	$48,000
Perkins	47 hp		with sails
Diesel			

HOLLAND BOAT CO.
P. O. Box 32 4250 DA
Werkendam, Holland
04187-2821

Fair Wind 30

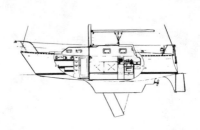

LOD	30'	Spar	Alum
LWL	26'	Fr. Water	50 gal
Beam	9'6"	SA/Disp	16.6
Draft		Disp/LWL	241
cb up	3'6"	Blst/Disp	37%
cb dn	7'	Designer	Bill Soverel
Disp	9500 lbs	Price	$46,500
Ballast	3500 lbs		with sails
Sail Area			
Sloop	466 sq ft		
Auxiliary	std		
Diesel	15 hp		
Fuel Cap	22 gal		

FAIRWIND MARINE CORP.
3685 N.W. 41st St.
Miami, FL 33142
(305) 635-9900

Mystic 30

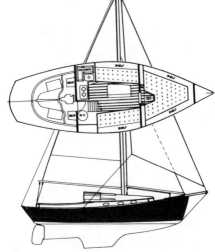

LOA	33'8"	Hull	FRP
LOD	30'	Deck	FRP
LWL	25'4"	Spar	Alum
Beam	10'3"	Fr. Water	37 gal
Draft	4'4"	SA/Disp	18.8
Disp	9500 lbs	Disp/LWL	260
Ballast	3000 lbs	Blst/Disp	32%
Sail Area		Price	$54,900
Cutter	526 sq ft		with sails
Auxiliary	std		
Yanmar	15 hp		
Diesel			
Fuel Cap	22 gal		

LEGNOS BOAT BUILDING CO.
973 North Rd.
Groton, CT 06340
(203) 446-8058

Olson 30

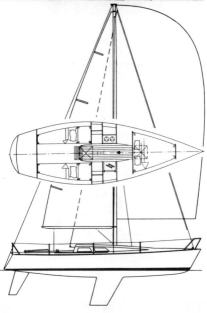

LOD	30'	Hull	FRP/Balsa
LWL	27'6"	Deck	FRP/Balsa
Beam	9'	Spar	Alum
Draft	5'1"	Cockpit	8'
Disp	3600 lbs	Headroom	4'5"
Ballast	1800 lbs	Fr. Water	2.5 gal
Sail Area		SA/Disp	25.9
Sloop	380 sq ft	Disp/LWL	77
Auxiliary	opt	Blst/Disp	50%
	7 hp	Designer	George Olson
		First Built	1978
		No. Built	210
		1 Design	yes
		Price	$25,495
			without sails

PACIFIC BOATS INC.
1041 17th Ave.
Santa Cruz, CA 95062
(408) 475-8586

Pyramid 30

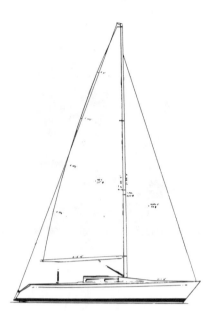

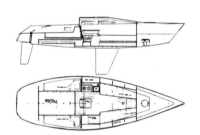

LOD	30'	Hull	FRP
LWL	25'	Deck	FRP
Beam	9'6''	Spar	Alum
Draft	5'6''	SA/Disp	27.6
Disp	3800 lbs	Disp/LWL	109
Ballast	1800 lbs	Blst/Disp	47%
Sail Area		Designer	
Sloop	420 sq ft		Carl Schumacher
Auxiliary	opt	1 Design	yes
		Price	$25,900
			without sails

PYRAMID BOATWORKS
2429 Pratt Ave.
Hayward, CA 94544
(415) 489-8025

Wolf Trap 30

LOA	40'	Hull	Alum
LOD	30'	Deck	Alum
LWL	27'	Spar	Alum
Beam	10'	SA/Disp	20.9
Draft		Disp/LWL	170
cb up	2'	Blst/Disp	28%
cb dn	5'6''	Designer	
Disp	7500 lbs		Philip C. Bolger
Ballast	2100 lbs	Kit	available
Sail Area		Price	$36,000
Cat Yawl	500 sq ft		with sails
Ketch	500 sq ft		
Mast			
Cat Yawl	unstayed		
Ketch	stayed		
Auxiliary	std		
Diesel	12 hp		

MARS MACHINE WORKS INC.
P. O. Box 190
Gloucester Pt., VA 23062
(804) 642-4760

Cape Dory 30

LOD	30'2''	Hull	FRP
LWL	22'10''	Deck	FRP/Balsa
Beam	9'	Spar	Alum
Draft	4'10''	Cockpit	6'8''
Disp	10,000 lbs	Headroom	6'1''
Ballast	4000 lbs	Fr. Water	60 gal
Sail Area		SA/Disp	15.1
Cutter	437 sq ft	Disp/LWL	375
Ketch	437 sq ft	Blst/Disp	40%
Mast Ht		Designer	Carl Alberg
Cutter	40'6''	First Built	1976
Ketch	38'6''	No. Built	280
Auxiliary	std	1 Design	yes
Volvo Penta	13 hp	Price	na
Diesel			

CAPE DORY YACHTS INC.
160 Middleboro Ave.
E. Taunton, MA 02718
(617) 823-6776

Clark 31   Rajo — Sailer 30   Shields

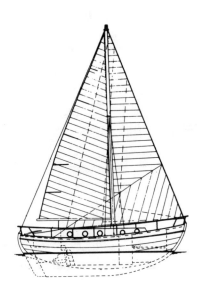

LOD	30'2"	Hull	FRP
LWL	20'	Deck	FRP
Beam	6'5"	Spar	Alum
Draft	4'9"	SA/Disp	20.8
Disp	4600 lbs	Disp/LWL	256
Ballast	2800 lbs	Blst/Disp	61%
Sail Area		Designer	
Sloop	360 sq ft	Sparkman & Stephens	
		1 Design	yes
		Price	$20,028
			with sails

LOA	38'7"	Hull	FRP
LOD	30'2"	Deck	FRP/Kledgecell
LWL	26'3"	Spar	Alum or Wood
Beam	9'3"	Fr. Water	70 gal
Draft	5'	SA/Disp	17.9
Disp	11,800 lbs	Disp/LWL	291
Ballast	4300 lbs	Blst/Disp	36%
Sail Area		Designer	
Cutter	579 sq ft	L. F. Herreshoff	
Auxiliary	std	Kit	$7,147
Volvo		Price	$47,357
Diesel			with sails
Fuel Cap	40 gal		

LOA	32'10"	Hull	Steel
LOD	30'2"	Deck	Steel
LWL	26'11"	Spar	Alum
Beam	10'7"	Pos Float	yes
Draft	3'1"	Cockpit	6'
Disp	17,000 lbs	Headroom	6'6"
Ballast	4500 lbs	Fr. Water	66 gal
Sail Area		SA/Disp	12.4
Cutter	514 sq ft	Disp/LWL	389
Mast Ht	43'	Blst/Disp	26%
Auxiliary	std	Designer	M. Bekebrede
Volvo	40 hp	First Built	1978
Diesel		No. Built	8
Fuel Cap	66 gal	Price	$61,500
			with sails

Alberg 30

LOD	30'3"	Hull	FRP
LWL	21'8"	Deck	FRP
Beam	8'9"	Spar	Alum
Draft	4'3"	Headroom	6'
Disp	9000 lbs	SA/Disp	15.2
Ballast	3300 lbs	Disp/LWL	395
Sail Area		Blst/Disp	37%
Sloop	410 sq ft	Price	$38,300 Can
Auxiliary	std		without sails
Volvo			
Diesel			
Fuel Cap	15 gal		

WHITBY BOAT WORKS LTD.
1710 Charles St.
Whitby, Ontario
Canada L1N 1C2
(416) 668-7755

Pearson 303

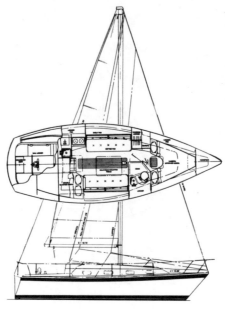

LOD	30'3"	Hull	FRP
LWL	25'4"	Deck	FRP
Beam	10'11"	Spar	Alum
Draft	4'4"	Fr. Water	38 gal
Disp	10,400 lbs	SA/Disp	15.2
Ballast	3550 lbs	Disp/LWL	286
Sail Area		Blst/Disp	34%
Sloop	453 sq ft	Price	$45,000
Mast Ht	44'3"		with sails
Auxiliary	std		
Yanmar	13 hp		
Diesel			
Fuel Cap	22 gal		

PEARSON YACHTS
West Shore Rd.
Portsmouth, RI 02871
(401) 683-0100

Lippincott 30

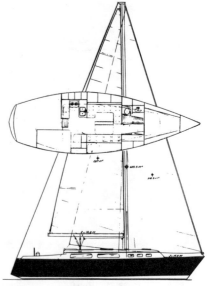

LOD	30'4"	Hull	FRP
LWL	25'	Deck	FRP/Balsa
Beam	10'	Spar	Alum
Draft		Headroom	6'3"
Shoal	4'2"	Fr. Water	30 gal
Deep	4'11"	SA/Disp	17.3
Disp	8600 lbs	Disp/LWL	245
Ballast	4000 lbs	Blst/Disp	47%
Sail Area		Designer	
Sloop	454 sq ft		Skip Lippincott
Mast Ht	43'	Price	$42,900
Auxiliary	std		with sails
Yanmar	15 hp		
Diesel			
Fuel Cap	12 gal		

LIPPINCOTT BOAT WORKS INC.
470 N. Canal Ave., Box 139
Riverton, NJ 08077
(609) 829-2024

Nonsuch 30

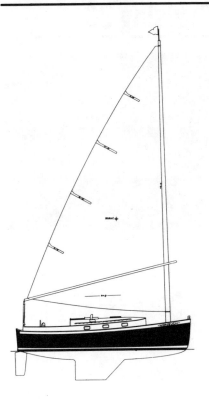

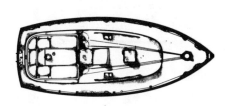

LOD .... 30'4"	Hull ...... FRP/Balsa
Lwl .... 28'9"	Deck ..... FRP/Balsa
Beam .... 11'10"	Spar .... Alum
Draft	Cockpit .... 7'
Shoal ...... 3'11"	Headroom ..... 6'3"
Deep .... 4'11"	Fr. Water .... 80 gal
Disp ..... 11,500 lbs	SA/Disp 17
Ballast ..... 4500 lbs	Disp/LWL 216
Sail Area	Blst/Disp 39%
Cat ..... 540 sq ft	Designer .. Mark Ellis
Mast Ht .... 53'	First Built 1978
Mast ..... unstayed	No. Built 175
Auxiliary .... std	Price $62,500
Westerbeke .. 29 hp	without sails
Diesel	
Fuel Cap ..... 28 gal	

HINTERHOELLER YACHTS LTD.
8 Keefer Rd., St. Catharines,
Ontario L2M 7N9, Canada
(416) 937-4440

Knarr

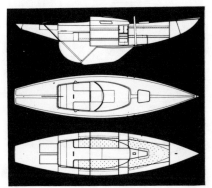

LOD .... 30'5"	Hull .... FRP
LWL .... 20'4"	Deck .... FRP
Beam .... 6'11"	Spar .... Alum
Draft .... 4'3"	SA/Disp 15.8
Disp ..... 4950 lbs	Disp/LWL 263
Ballast .... 2860 lbs	Blst/Disp 58%
Sail Area	Designer
Sloop .... 286 sq ft	Erling Kristoffersen
Auxiliary .... opt	Builder .... Denmark
4 hp	First Built 1955
outbd	No. Built 137
	1 Design .... yes
	Price $19,300
	with sails

A/S BORRESENS
BAADEBYGGERI
Dragevej
Box 187
7100 Vejle, Denmark

Dufour 31 Frers

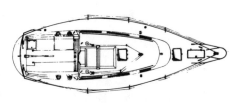

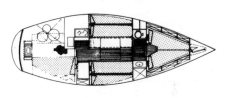

LOD .... 30'6"	Hull .... FRP
LWL .... 25'3"	Deck .... FRP
Beam .... 10'8"	Spar .... Alum
Draft	Headroom ..... 6'1"
Shoal .... 4'5"	Disp/LWL 231
Deep .... 5'6"	Blst/Disp 43%
Disp ...... 8360 lbs	Designer German Frers
Ballast .... 3630 lbs	Builder
Sail Area	Dufour, France
Sloop .... na	Price .... na
Auxiliary .... std	
Volvo ...... 17 hp	
Diesel	

EURO SAILBOATS LTD.
131 East Boston Post Road
Mamaroneck, NY 10543
(914) 381-4500

E 22

LOD .... 30'6"	Hull .... FRP
LWL .... 22'	Deck .... FRP
Beam .... 6'11"	Spar .... Alum
Draft .... 4'6"	Pos Float ...... yes
Disp ...... 3400 lbs	SA/Disp 20.6
Ballast .... na	Disp/LWL 143
Sail Area	Designer
Sloop .... 291 sq ft	E. W. Etchells
	1 Design .... yes
	Price .... $16,500 US
	with sails

ONTARIO YACHTS CO. LTD.
243 Speers Rd.
Oakville, Ontario
Canada L6K 2EB
(416) 845-1153

Newport 30 III

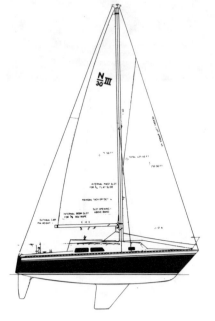

LOD .... 30'6"	Hull .... FRP
LWL .... 26'6"	Deck .... FRP
Beam .... 10'8"	Spar .... Alum
Draft	Headroom ..... 6'4"
Deep .... 5'1"	Fr. Water .... 70 gal
Shoal .... 4'	SA/Disp 16.3
Disp ...... 8500 lbs	Disp/LWL 203
Ballast .... na	Price .... na
Sail Area	
Sloop .... 425 sq ft	
Auxiliary .... std	
Diesel	
Fuel Cap ...... 30 gal	

CAPITAL YACHTS INC.
25914 President Ave.
Harbor City, CA 90710
(213) 530-1311

Rawson Cruising 30

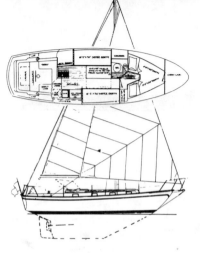

LOD .... 30'6"	Hull .... FRP
LWL .... 22'	Deck .... FRP
Beam .... 9'	Spar .... Alum
Draft .... 5'	Cockpit .... 4'
Disp ... 12,000 lbs	Headroom ..... 6'3"
Ballast .... 5000 lbs	Fr. Water .... 45 gal
Sail Area	SA/Disp 12.5
Sloop .... 410 sq ft	Disp/LWL 503
Mast Ht .... 42'	Blst/Disp 42%
Auxiliary .... opt	Designer
Volvo ...... 27 hp	William Garden
Diesel	First Built 1959
Fuel Cap ...... 37 gal	No. Built 252
	1 Design .... yes
	Kit $7,995
	Price $54,355
	with sails

RAWSON INC.
Box 83
9001 151st Avenue NE
Redmond, WA 98052
(206) 885-4455

Rawson Pilothouse 30

LOD	30'6"	Hull	FRP
LWL	22'	Deck	FRP
Beam	9'	Spar	Alum
Draft	5'	Cockpit	4'
Disp	12,500 lbs	Headroom	6'3"
Ballast	5000 lbs	Fr. Water	80 gal
Sail Area		SA/Disp	12.2
Sloop	410 sq ft	Disp/LWL	524
Mast Ht	42'	Blst/Disp	40%
Auxiliary	opt	Designer	Rawson/Monk
Volvo	35 hp	First Built	1977
Diesel		No. Built	35
Fuel Cap	60 gal	1 Design	yes
		Kit	$7,995
		Price	$58,205
			with sails

RON RAWSON INC.
Box 83
9001 151st Avenue NE
Redmond, WA 98052
(206) 885-4455

Voyager 30

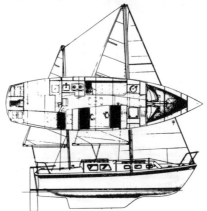

LOD	30'6"	Hull	FRP
LWL	26'2"	Deck	FRP
Beam	8'	Spar	Alum
Draft		Cockpit	7'
Swing keel up	3'	Headroom	6'4"
Swing keel dn	6'	Fr. Water	18 gal
Disp	7000 lbs	SA/Disp	15.6
Ballast	3300 lbs	Disp/LWL	174
Sail Area		Blst/Disp	47%
Sloop	356 sq ft	Designer	Edwin Monk
Ketch	406 sq ft	Kit	$12,773
Mast Ht			
Sloop	37'9"		
Ketch	33'9"		
Auxiliary	opt		
	15 hp		
	inbd or outbd		

LUGER INDUSTRIES INC.
3800 West Hwy 13
Burnsville, MN 55337
(612) 890-3000

Island Packet 31

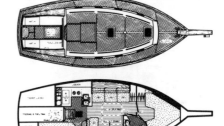

LOA	34'3"	Hull	FRP
LOD	30'7"	Deck	FRP
LWL	27'9"	Spar	Alum
Beam	11'3"	Cockpit	7'
Draft		Headroom	6'3"
Shoal cb up	3'	Fr. Water	40 gal
Shoal cb dn	6'6"	SA/Disp	17.2
Deep	4'	Disp/LWL	230
Disp	11,000 lbs	Blst/Disp	41%
Ballast	4500 lbs	Designer	
Sail Area			Robert Johnson
Cutter	531 sq ft	First Built	1983
Mast Ht	43'6"	Price	$54,950
Auxiliary	std		with sails
Yanmar	22 hp		
Diesel			
Fuel Cap	22 gal		

TRADITIONAL WATERCRAFT
2111 34th Way
Largo, FL 33541
(813) 535-6431

Nicholson 31

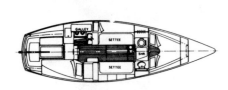

LOD . . . . 30'7"	Hull . . . . FRP
LWL . . . . 24'2"	Deck . . . . FRP
Beam . . . . 10'3"	Spar . . . . Alum
Draft . . . . 5'	SA/Disp 17.6
Disp . . . . . 13,200 lbs	Disp/LWL 417
Ballast . . . . 4800 lbs	Blst/Disp 36%
Sail Area	Builder . . . . . England
Sloop . . . . 614 sq ft	Price $51,200
Auxiliary . . . . std	with sails
Yanmar . . . . . 20 hp	
Diesel	

CAMPER & NICHOLSONS
Box 3296
Annapolis, MD 21403
(301) 267-0933

Allmand 31

LOD . . . . 30'9"	Hull . . . . FRP
LWL . . . . 27'11"	Deck . . . . FRP
Beam . . . . 11'4"	Spar . . . . Alum
Draft . . . . , 4'	headroom . . . . . 6'5"
Disp . . . . 12,850 lbs	Fr. Water . . . . 50 gal
Ballast . . . . 4300 lbs	SA/Disp 13.4
Sail Area	Disp/LWL 263
Sloop . . . . 461 sq ft	Blst/Disp 33%
Mast Ht . . . . . . 44'6"	Designer . Walter Scott
Auxiliary . . . . std	& T. R. Allmand
Universal . . . 20 hp	Price $57,500
Diesel	with sails
Fuel Cap . . . . . 40 gal	

ALLMAND BOATS INC.
P. O. Drawer 4910
Hialeah, FL 33014
(305) 821-4070

Allmand 312

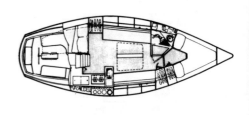

LOD . . . . 30'9"	Hull . . . . FRP
LWL . . . . 27'8"	Deck . . . . FRP
Beam . . . . 11'4"	Spar . . . . Alum
Draft . . . . 3'10"	Headroom . . . . . 6'5"
Disp . . . . 11,100 lbs	Fr. Water . . . . 50 gal
Ballast . . . . 4300 lbs	SA/Disp 14.8
Sail Area	Disp/LWL 233
Sloop . . . . 461 sq ft	Blst/Disp 39%
Sloop (tall) 485 sq ft	Designer . Walter Scott
Mast Ht	Price $51,900
Sloop . . . . . 44'6"	with sails
Sloop (tall) . . 46'6"	
Auxiliary . . . . std	
Yanmar	
Diesel	
Fuel Cap . . . . . 40 gal	

ALLMAND BOATS INC.
P. O. Drawer 4910
Hialeah, FL 33014
(305) 821-4070

Dictator

Bombay Clipper 31

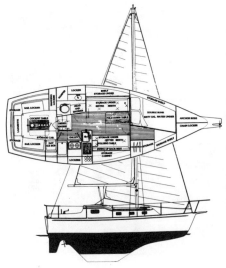

Herreshoff 31

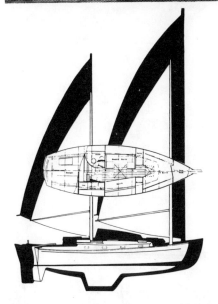

LOA	42'	Hull	FRP
LOD	30'10"	Deck	FRP or Wood
LWL	26"	Spar	Wood
Beam	10'8"	Cockpit	9'
Draft	5'	Headroom	6'
Disp	17,500 lbs	Fr. Water	70 gal
Ballast	5300 lbs	SA/Disp	18.1
Sail Area		Disp/LWL	444
Cutter (gaff)	761 sq ft	Blst/Disp	30%
Schooner	795 sq ft	Designer	
Mast Ht			Robert McLain
Cutter (gaff)	32'	First Built	1973
Schooner	38'	No. Built	19
Auxiliary	std	Kit	available
Perkins	30 hp	Price	$75,000
Diesel			with sails
Fuel Cap	40 gal		

LOD	31'	Hull	FRP
LWL	25'7"	Deck	FRP
Beam	11'6"	Spar	Alum
Draft	3'5"	Headroom	6'6"
Disp	12,000 lbs	Fr. Water	60 gal
Ballast	3900 lbs	SA/Disp	12.8
Sail Area		Disp/LWL	319
Sloop	419 sq ft	Blst/Disp	33%
Mast Ht	42'	Price	$47,200
Auxiliary	std		with sails
Yanmar	22 hp		
Diesel			
Fuel Cap	30 gal		

LOD	31'	Hull	Wood
LWL	27'6"	Deck	Wood
Beam	10'4"	Spar	Wood
Draft	4'	SA/Disp	14.9
Disp	8640 lbs	Disp/LWL	185
Ballast	3350 lbs	Blst/Disp	39%
Sail Area		Designer	
Ketch Cat	393 sq ft		H. Herreshoff
Mast	unstayed	Price	$50,000
Auxiliary	std		with sails
Universal	15 hp		
Diesel			

JARVIS NEWMAN BOATS
P. O. Box 707
Southwest Harbor, ME 04679
(207) 244-3860

CHAPARRAL BOATS INC.
P. O. Drawer 928
Nashville, GA 31639
(912) 686-7484

CAT KETCH INC.
4483 S.W. 75 Avenue
Miami, FL 33155
(305) 266-8275

Hobie 33

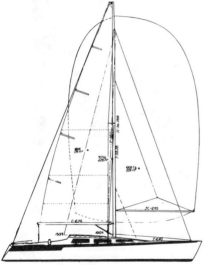

LOA	33'	Hull	FRP
LOD	31'	Deck	FRP
LWL	30'6"	Spar	Alum
Beam	8'	Cockpit	8'2"
Draft		Headroom	4'6"
Ver ret keel up	1'10"	Fr. Water	5 gal
Ver ret keel dn	5'5"	SA/Disp	26.9
Disp	4000 lbs	Disp/LWL	62
Ballast	1800 lbs	Blst/Disp	45%
Sail Area		Designer	Hobie Alter
Sloop	423 sq ft	First Built	1982
Mast Ht	41'	1 Design	yes
Auxiliary	opt	Price	$31,950
	10 hp		without sails

HOBIE CAT
Box 1008, 4925 E. Oceanside Blvd.
Oceanside, CA 92054
(714) 758-9100

Southern Cross 31

LOA	34'6"	Hull	FRP/Airex
LOD	31'	Deck	FRP/Balsa
LWL	25'	Spar	Alum
Beam	9'6"	Cockpit	6'
Draft	4'7"	Headroom	6'2"
Disp	13,600 lbs	Fr. Water	47 gal
Ballast	4453 lbs	SA/Disp	12.6
Sail Area		Disp/LWL	389
Cutter	447 sq ft	Blst/Disp	33%
Mast Ht	40'	Designer	Tom Gillmer
Auxiliary	std	First Built	1975
Yanmar	22 hp	No. Built	150
Diesel		Kit	available
Fuel Cap	34 gal	Price	$62,500
			with sails

C.E. RYDER CORP.
47 Gooding Ave.
Bristol, RI 02809
(401) 253-8554

Contest 31 HT

LOD	31'2"	Hull	FRP
LWL	25'4"	Deck	FRP
Beam	10'4"	Headroom	6'4"
Draft		Fr. Water	61 gal
Shoal	4'9"	SA/Disp	14.7
Deep	5'9"	Disp/LWL	306
Disp		Blst/Disp	50%
Shoal	11,157 lbs	Designer	Dick Zaal
Deep	10,509 lbs	Builder	
Ballast			Conyplex, Holland
Shoal	5613 lbs	Price	na
Deep	4966 lbs		
Sail Area			
Sloop	460 sq ft		
Mast Ht	44'4"		
Auxiliary	std		
Volvo Penta	25 hp		
Diesel			
Fuel Cap	26 gal		

HOLLAND YACHTS
Box 129
Solomons, MD 20688
(301) 326-3960

Dutch Flyer 31

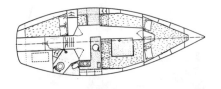

LOD . . . . 31'2"	Hull . . . . FRP
LWL . . . . 25'3"	Deck . . . . FRP
Beam . . . . 5'5"	Fr. Water . . . . 80 gal
Draft . . . . 5'5"	SA/Disp 16.2
Disp . . . . . . 9900 lbs	Disp/LWL 274
Ballast . . . . . 4400 lbs	Blst/Disp 44%
Sail Area	Price . . . . na
Sloop . . . . 468 sq ft	
Auxiliary . . . . std	
Yanmar . . . . . 24 hp	
Diesel	
Fuel Cap . . . . . . 28 gal	

HOLLAND YACHTS
Box 129
Solomons, MD 20688
(301) 326-3960

Irwin 31

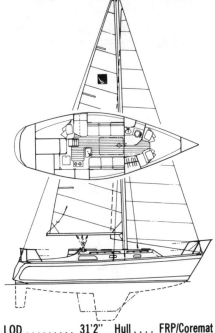

LOD . . . . 31'2"	Hull . . . . FRP/Coremat
LWL . . . . 28'3"	Deck . . . . FRP
Beam . . . . 11'	Spar . . . . Alum
Draft	Fr. Water . . . . 40 gal
Deep . . . . 6'	SA/Disp 19.2
Shoal cb up . . . . 4'	Disp/LWL 184
Shoal cb dn . . 8'1"	Blst/Disp 37%
Disp . . . . . . 9300 lbs	Price $39,950
Ballast	with sails
Deep . . . . 3400 lbs	
Shoal . . . . 3800 lbs	
Sail Area	
Sloop . . . . 530 sq ft	
Mast Ht . . . . 46'1"	
Auxiliary . . . . std	
Yanmar . . . . . 15 hp	
Diesel	
Fuel Cap . . . . . . 30 gal	

IRWIN YACHTS
13055 49th St. N.
Clearwater, FL 33520
(813) 577-4581

Douglas 31

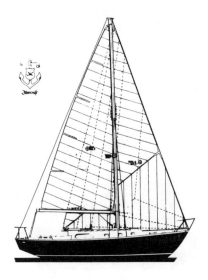

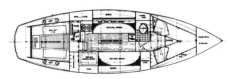

LOD . . . . 31'3"	Hull . . . . FRP
LWL . . . . 22'8"	Deck . . . . FRP
Beam . . . . 9'3"	Spar . . . . Alum
Draft . . . . 4'8"	SA/Disp 13.9
Disp . . . . 10,350 lbs	Disp/LWL 397
Ballast . . . . . 4350 lbs	Blst/Disp 42%
Sail Area	Kit . . . . . $11,500 Can
Sloop . . . . 412 sq ft	Price . . . $52,500 Can
Auxiliary . . . . std	without sails
Yanmar . . . . . 15 hp	
Diesel	

J & C FIBERCRAFT
P. O. Box 263
Barrie, Ontario
Canada L4M 4T2
(705) 326-8880

Niagara 31

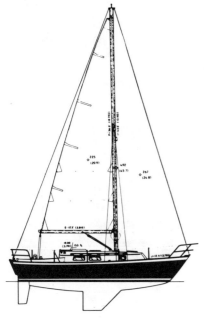

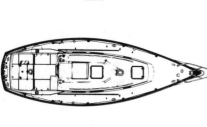

LOD	31'3"	Hull	FRP
LWL	24'3"	Deck	FRP
Beam	10'3"	Spar	Alum
Draft	5'	Fr. Water	40 gal
Disp	8500 lbs	SA/Disp	18.9
Ballast	3550 lbs	Disp/LWL	266
Sail Area		Blst/Disp	42%
Sloop	492 sq ft	Designer	German Frers
Mast Ht	47'	First Built	1981
Auxiliary	std	Price	na
Westerbeke			
Diesel			
Fuel Cap	22 gal		

HINTERHOELLER YACHTS LTD.
8 Keefer Rd., St. Catharines,
Ontario L2M 7N9, Canada
(416) 937-4440

Sarah 32

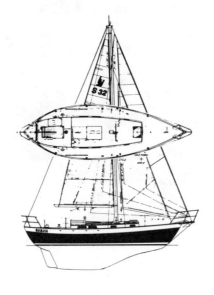

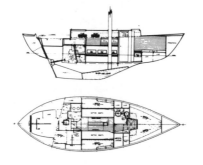

LOA	34'3"	Hull	FRP
LOD	31'5"	Deck	FRP
LWL	25'10"	Spar	Alum
Beam	10'4"	Cockpit	6'7"
Draft	4'9"	Headroom	6'2"
Disp	11,100 lbs	Fr. Water	38 gal
Ballast	5100 lbs	SA/Disp	15.2
Sail Area		Disp/LWL	287
Cutter	473 sq ft	Blst/Disp	46%
Mast Ht	43'	Designer	C. W. Paine
Auxiliary	std	First Built	1980
Yanmar	21 hp	No. Built	6
Diesel		Kit	$19,500
Fuel Cap	26 gal	Price	$69,500
			without sails

LOOMIS YACHTS
Box 575
South Dartmouth, MA 02748
(617) 999-3200

Cal 31

LOA	31'6"	Hull	FRP
LOD	31'6"	Deck	FRP
LWL	25'8"	Spar	Alum
Beam	10'	Cockpit	7'
Draft		Headroom	6'3"
Shoal	4'3"	Fr. Water	56 gal
Deep	5'	SA/Disp	17.9
Disp	9170 lbs	Disp/LWL	242
Ballast	3600 lbs	Blst/Disp	39%
Sail Area		Designer	
Sloop	490 sq ft		Bill Lapworth
Mast Ht	45'5"	First Built	1979
Auxiliary	std	No. Built	77
Universal	16 hp	1 Design	yes
Diesel		Price	na

BANGOR PUNTA MARINE
848 Airport Rd.
Box 991
Fall River, MA 02722
(617) 678-5291

C & C 32

Cooper 316

Hotfoot 31

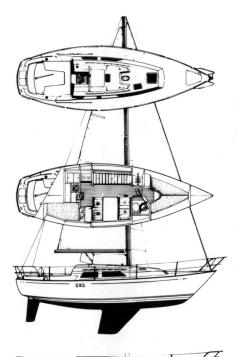

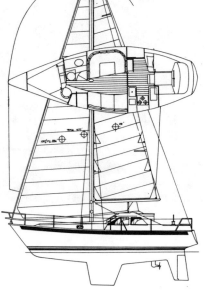

LOA	32'6"	Hull	FRP
LOD	31'6"	Deck	FRP/Balsa
LWL	24'8"	Spar	Alum
Beam	10'3"	Fr. Water	30 gal
Draft		SA/Disp	16.3
Deep	5'8"	Disp/LWL	287
Shoal cb up	4'	Blst/Disp	40%
Shoal cb dn	6'11"	Price	$62,950
Disp			without sails
Deep	9680 lbs		
Shoal	10,485 lbs		
Ballast			
Deep	3900 lbs		
Shoal	4705 lbs		
Sail Area			
Sloop	462 sq ft		
Mast Ht	44'8"		
Auxiliary	std		
Yanmar	15 hp		
Diesel			
Fuel Cap	20 gal		

C&C YACHTS
55 Port Street East
Mississauga, Ontario
Canada L5G 4P3
(416) 274-7131

LOD	31'6"	Hull	FRP
LWL	25'6"	Deck	FRP
Beam	10'11"	Spar	Alum
Draft	5'5"	Cockpit	5'
Disp	10,500 lbs	Headroom	6'4"
Ballast	3600 lbs	Fr. Water	45 gal
Sail Area		SA/Disp	15.9
Sloop	477 sq ft	Disp/LWL	282
Auxiliary	std	Blst/Disp	34%
Volvo	17 hp	Designer	
Diesel			S. Huntingford
Fuel Cap	45 gal	First Built	1982
		No. Built	5
		Price	$52,900
			with sails

COOPER ENTERPRISES LTD.
1642 Langan Ave.
Port Coquituam, B.C.
Canada V3C 1K5
(604) 942-5945

LOD	31'6"	Hull	FRP/Foam
LWL	26'	Deck	FRP/Foam
Beam	10'6"	Spar	Alum
Draft	5'9"	Headroom	6'
Disp	5000 lbs	Fr. Water	15 gal
Ballast	2000 lbs	SA/Disp	23.5
Sail Area		Disp/LWL	127
Sloop	430 sq ft	Blst/Disp	40%
Auxiliary	std	Designer	
Yanmar	15 hp		Doug Hemphill
Diesel		First Built	1983
Fuel Cap	10 gal	No. Built	0
		1 Design	yes
		Price	na

HOT FOOT BOATS
6795 Veyaness Rd.
Saanichton, B.C.
Canada V0S 1M0
(604) 652-2453

Southerly 95

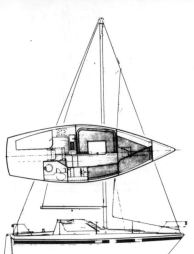

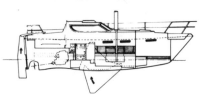

LOD	31'8"	Hull	FRP
LWL	25'	Deck	FRP/Balsa
Beam	9'11"	Spar	Alum
Draft		Cockpit	6'
Swing keel up	1'10"	Headroom	6'
Swing keel dn	5'10"	Fr. Water	33 gal
Disp	9500 lbs	SA/Disp	13.7
Ballast	na	Disp/LWL	271
Sail Area		Designer	Dick Carter
Sloop	385 sq ft	Builder	
Mast Ht	36'9"		Northshore, England
Auxiliary	std	First Built	1976
Bukh	20 hp	No. Built	60
Diesel		1 Design	yes
Fuel Cap	24 gal	Price	$44,200
			with sails

PARKER YACHTS
South Freeport, ME 04078
(207) 865-6692

Contest 32 CS

LOD	31'10"	Hull	FRP
LWL	25'8"	Deck	FRP
Beam	10'11"	Headroom	6'5"
Draft		Fr. Water	92 gal
Shoal	4'3"	SA/Disp	12.9
Deep	5'3"	Disp/LWL	377
Disp		Blst/Disp	45%
Shoal	14,300 lbs	Designer	Dick Zaal
Deep	13,860 lbs	Builder	
Ballast			Conyplex, Holland
Shoal	6380 lbs	Price	na
Deep	5940 lbs		
Sail Area			
Sloop	475 sq ft		
Ketch	561 sq ft		
Mast Ht	46'3"		
Auxiliary	std		
Volvo Penta			
Diesel			
Fuel Cap	58 gal		

HOLLAND YACHTS
Box 129
Solomons, MD 20688
(301) 326-3960

Morgan 32

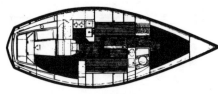

LOD	31'11"	Hull	FRP
LWL	25'	Deck	FRP
Beam	11'6"	Spar	alum
Draft	4'	Fr. Water	35 gal
Disp	11,000 lbs	SA/Disp	15.7
Ballast	4000 lbs	Disp/LWL	314
Sail Area		Blst/Disp	36%
Sloop	484 sq ft	Price	na
Mast Ht	45'8"		
Auxiliary	std		
Yanmar	22.5 hp		
Diesel			
Fuel Cap	27 gal		

MORGAN YACHT INC.
7200 Bryan Dairy Rd.
Largo, FL 33543
(813) 544-6681

Westerly Fulmar

World famous designer Ed Dubois scores again with his new Westerly Fulmar, combining the traditional rugged cruising characteristics for which Westerly is famous with a generous sprinkle of the performance which has made Dubois famous on the Grand Prix Circuit. Fulmar is the ultimate for the cruising sailor desiring a sparkle of performance in his 32.

The Westerly Fulmar is a fast yet highly manageable 32' sloop whose blend of elegant looks and superb sailing qualities is rarely approached by others in the same class. She provides enjoyable cruising in comfort for all the family as well as a level of performance that's right at home in racing company.

Her well-proportioned hull and balanced sail plan, with ¾ rig, keep headsails and spinnakers to a manageable size, and insure stability in any weather. This in turn opens up the intriguing possibility of long-distance, deep-water cruising which every yachtsman sooner or later wants to undertake.

Despite her size, Fulmar can be handled "solo" with ease. All halyards, spinnaker pole controls and reefing lines are led aft to tough 2-speed winches and stoppers located abeam the main hatch, to be worked from the cockpit.

With the interior lavishly finished in teak, Fulmar offers 6/7 berths, spacious aft galley to starboard, and an extremely large navigators station forward of the double sized port quarterberth.

The 2 cylinder Bukh 20 hp diesel is standard. Ratsey sails, pulpits, lifelines, Barlow winches, 35 lb. plow anchor, and much, much, more are all included in her "landed, East Coast, duty paid" base price.

As with all Westerly sailboats, from the 26' Griffon to the new 38'6" Westerly Sealord, Fulmar is molded under the supervision of Lloyd's Register of Shipping, and each boat comes with its own Lloyd's Hull Construction Certificate. Similarly, all Westerlies (except Sealord which is presently available only in single keel) are available either single or twin keel, and a keel/centerboard option is available for Fulmar, Griffon, and the 29' Konsort.

Purchasers desiring to take delivery on any Westerly in England and cruise through the French Canals to the Med prior to sailing or shipping their boat home may do so on an attractive "factory delivery" basis, and may write or phone Hyattsville for details.

WESTERLY
Fulmar
SAIL AREAS

Mainsail	253 sq. ft.	23.5 sq. m.
No. 1 Genoa	313 sq. ft.	29.1 sq. m.
No. 2 Genoa	254 sq. ft.	23.6 sq. m.
No. 1 Jib	194 sq. ft.	18.0 sq. m.
No. 2 Jib	93 sq. ft.	8.6 sq. m.
Spinnaker	760 sq. ft.	70.61 sq. m.

Lloyds Hull Construction Certificate

Westerly Yachts Limited,
47 Aston Road, Waterlooville, Portsmouth, Hampshire PO7 7XJ
Telephone: Waterlooville (07014) 54511 Telex: 86328

The boat as described, to specification and standard inventory are liable to change according to availability of bought in and manufactured supplies. Some items shown in the photographs are not included in the standard price.

LOD	31'10"	Hull	FRP
LWL	26'	Deck	FRP
Beam	10'11"	Spar	Alum
Draft		Headroom	6'1"
Deep	5'3"	Fr. Water	35 gal
Twin	4'	SA/Disp	15.5
Shoal cb up . .	3'6"	Disp/LWL	251
Shoal cb dn . .	5'9"	Blst/Disp	42%
Disp	9900 lbs	Designer . . Ed Dubois
Ballast		Builder	
Deep	4200 lbs		Westerly-England
Twin	4200 lbs	First Built	1980
Shoal	4350 lbs	No. Built	200
Sail Area		Price	$53,697
Sloop	447 sq ft		with sails
Mast Ht	48'6"		
Auxiliary	std		
Bukh	20 hp		
Diesel			

Bayfield 32

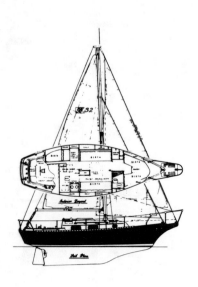

LOD	32'	Hull	FRP
LWL	23'3"	Deck	FRP/Balsa
Beam	10'6"	Spar	Alum
Draft	3'9"	Fr. Water	20 gal
Disp	9600 lbs	SA/Disp	18.6
Ballast	4000 lbs	Disp/LWL	341
Sail Area		Blst/Disp	42%
Cutter	525 sq ft	Designer	
Ketch	na		H. Ted Gozzard
Auxiliary	std	No. Built	125
Yanmar	21 hp	Price	$54,950
Diesel			with sails
Fuel Cap	20 gal		

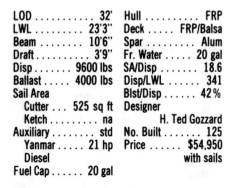

BAYFIELD BOAT YARD LTD.
Box 1076
Clinton, Ontario
Canada N0M 1L0
(519) 482-3425

Contessa 32

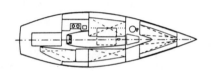

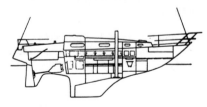

LOD	32'	Hull	FRP
LWL	24'	Deck	FRP
Beam	9'6"	Spar	Alum
Draft	5'6"	Cockpit	7'
Disp	9600 lbs	Headroom	6'
Ballast	4600 lbs	Fr. Water	20 gal
Sail Area		SA/Disp	14.8
Sloop	417 sq ft	Disp/LWL	310
Mast Ht	39'	Blst/Disp	48%
Auxiliary	std	Designer	David Sadler
Bukh	20 hp	First Built	1972
Diesel		No. Built	50
Fuel Cap	20 gal	Price	$46,950 Can
			without sails

J. J. TAYLOR & SONS LTD.
255 Carrier Dr.
Rexdale, Ontario
Canada M9W 6A1
(416) 675-1561

Gulf 32

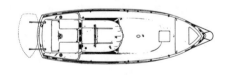

LOD	32'	Hull	FRP
LWL	25'	Deck	FRP
Beam	10'	Spar	Alum
Draft	5'2"	Fr. Water	70 gal
Disp	15,000 lbs	SA/Disp	14.6
Ballast	na	Disp/LWL	428
Sail Area		Price	na
Sloop	555 sq ft		
Auxiliary	std		
Diesel			
Fuel Cap	70 gal		

CAPITAL YACHTS INC.
25914 President Ave.
Harbor City, CA 90710
(213) 530-1311

Vancouver 32

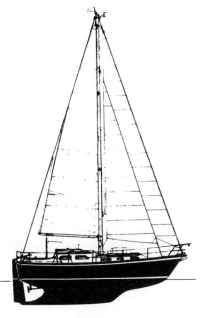

The VANCOUVER 32 comes from the board of Robert Harris as a natural development of the highly successful VANCOUVER 27. This concept combines the thinking behind the racing yacht and the traditional offshore cruiser. The 27'6" waterline is unusually long for a 32 ft yacht resulting in higher than expected hull speed. Tremendous stability, perfect balance and maneuverability are qualities the short handed crew will appreciate to its fullest.

The VANCOUVER 32 offers three basic and customized lay-outs, including three seaworthy berths. The quality of the all teak joinery is reflected in every detail. Abundant storage space makes the VANCOUVER 32 particularly suitable as a live aboard.

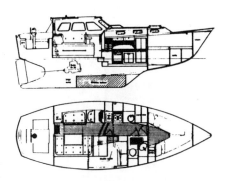

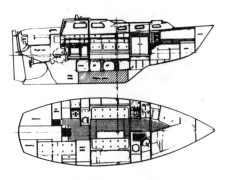

LOD	32'	Hull	FRP
LWL	27'6"	Deck	FRP/Balsa
Beam	10'7"	Spar	Alum
Draft	4'9"	Cockpit	6'6"
Disp	14,000 lbs	Headroom	6'6"
Ballast	6600 lbs	Fr. Water	72 gal
Sail Area		SA/Disp	20.2
Cutter	734 sq ft	Disp/lwl	301
Mast Ht	40'	Blst/Disp	47%
Auxiliary	std	Designer	
Westerbeke	20 hp		Robert Harris
Diesel		Builder	Pheon Yachts
Fuel Cap	45 gal	First Built	1978
		No. Built	25
		1 Design	yes
		Kit	available
		Price	$76,000 with sails

RAY G. VANHEUSDEN TREMAYNE CORPORATION
1611 N. Kent Street, Suite 801
Arlington, VA 22209
(703) 522-3355

Helms 32

LOD	32'	Hull	FRP
LWL	24'6"	Deck	FRP
Beam	10'6"	Spar	Alum
Draft	4'10"	Cockpit	8'6"
Disp	9500 lbs	Headroom	6'4"
Ballast	4000 lbs	Fr. Water	60 gal
Sail Area		SA/Disp	16.3
Sloop	458 sq ft	Disp/LWL	288
Mast Ht	43'6"	Blst/Disp	42%
Auxiliary	std	Designer	
Yanmar	15 hp		Stuart Windley
Diesel		Price	$48,000
Fuel Cap	20 gal		without sails

JACK A. HELMS CO.
Hwy. 60, P. O. Drawer A
Irmo, SC 29063
(803) 781-5133

Whistler 32

LOD	32'	Hull	FRP
LWL	25'10"	Deck	FRP/Core
Beam	10'6"	Spar	Alum
Draft		Cockpit	8'
cb up	3'7"	Headroom	6'2"
cb dn	7'6"	Fr. Water	100 gal
Disp	11,986 lbs	SA/Disp	15.9
Ballast	5000 lbs	Disp/LWL	310
Sail Area		Blst/Disp	42%
Cat Ketch	520 sq ft	Designer . C. W. Paine	
Cutter	520 sq ft	First Built	1980
Mast Ht	45'	No. Built	10
Mast		Price	$90,000
Cat Ketch . unstayed			with sails
Cutter	stayed		
Auxiliary	std		
Diesel	16-20 hp		
Fuel Cap	30 gal		

ABLE MARINE COMPANY
Clark Point Road
SW Harbor, ME 04679
(207) 244-5135

Evelyn 32

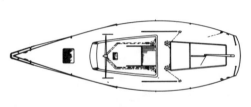

LOD	32'1"	Hull	FRP
LWL	28'2"	Deck	FRP
Beam	9'10"	Spar	Alum
Draft	6'	SA/Disp	25.9
Disp	4500 lbs	Disp/LWL	89
Ballast	2000 lbs	Blst/Disp	44%
Sail Area		Designer . Bob Evelyn	
Sloop	441 sq ft	Price	$28,900
Auxiliary	opt		with sails

FORMULA YACHTS INC.
185 South Rd.
Croton, CT 06340
(203) 445-4413

Roughwater 33

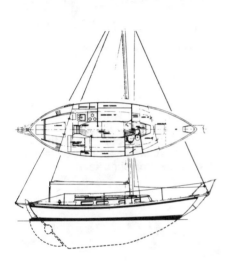

LOA . . . . 37'	Hull . . . . FRP
LOD . . . . 32'1''	Deck . . . . FRP
LWL . . . . 26'	Spar . . . . Alum
Beam . . . . 9'9''	Cockpit . . . . 5'
Draft . . . . 4'9''	Headroom . . . . . 6'2''
Disp . . . . . 15,000 lbs	Fr. Water . . . . . 45 gal
Ballast . . . . 5000 lbs	SA/Disp 11
Sail Area	Disp/LWL 381
Sloop . . . . 417 sq ft	Blst/Disp . . . . . 33 %
Mast Ht . . . . . . 35'6''	Designer
Auxiliary . . . . std	Thomas Gillmer
Yanmar . . . . . 22 hp	Builder . . Roughwater
Diesel	First Built 1974
Fuel Cap . . . . . . 40 gal	No. Built 40
	Price $61,000
	with sails

ROUGHWATER BOAT SALES
13442 Bali Way
Marina Del Rey, CA 90291
(213) 823-8288

Pearson 323

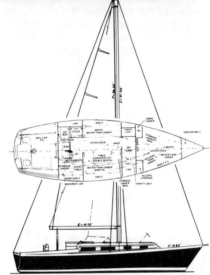

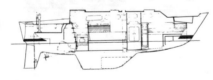

LOD . . . . 32'3''	Hull . . . . FRP
LWL . . . . 27'6''	Deck . . . . FRP
Beam . . . . 10'3''	Spar . . . . Alum
Draft . . . . 4'5''	Cockpit . . . . 8'
Disp . . . . . 12,800 lbs	SA/Disp 14
Ballast . . . . 4500 lbs	Disp/LWL 275
Sail Area	Blst/Disp . . . . . 35 %
Sloop . . . . 478 sq ft	Designer William Shaw
Mast Ht . . . . . . 45'4''	Price $66,301
Auxiliary . . . . std	with sails
Diesel	

PEARSON YACHTS
West Shore Rd.
Portsmouth, RI 02871
(401) 683-0100

Aloha 32

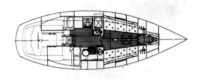

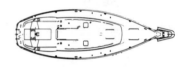

LOD . . . . 32'5''	Hull . . . . FRP
LWL . . . . 25'	Deck . . . . FRP
Beam . . . . 10'10''	Spar . . . . Alum
Draft . . . . 4'9''	SA/Disp 18.1
Disp . . . . . 9800 lbs	Disp/LWL 280
Ballast . . . . na	Designer . . Mark Ellis
Sail Area	Price . . . $65,611 Can
Sloop . . . . 518 sq ft	with sails
Auxiliary . . . . std	
Westerbeke . . 21 hp	
Diesel	

ALOHA YACHTS INT'L
1638 Charles St.
Whitby, Ontario
Canada Lin 1B9
(416) 686-2127

Sunbird 32

SwingWing

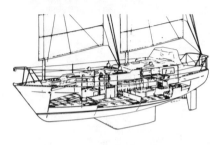

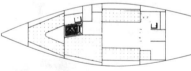

The Sunbird 32 has been carefully designed to suit the cruising family with an easily handled rig and spacious accommodation arranged for comfort and convenience both at sea and in harbour.

The Chinese lug rig has been proven over fourteen years on Western yachts and over several thousand years in the far east! Its principal advantage is the ease with which it can be handled by one person under all conditions (especially when reefing) and we believe that this is a considerable safety factor for a cruising family. The deck lay-out has been arranged so that the rig can be handled completely from the cockpit or the companion hatch which is protected by a spray hood. As an additional bonus, the rig allows a rigid or inflated dinghy to be carried on deck.

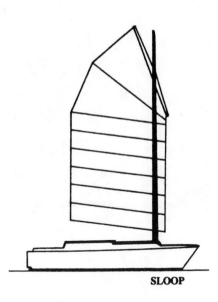

SLOOP

The Sunbird 32 can be bought with either a sloop rig with one mast and sail, or a schooner rig with two; and there is a choice between a fin keel with encapsulated cast iron ballast, or external cast iron bilge keels.

LOD	32'6"	Hull	FRP
LWL	26'1"	Deck	FRP
Beam	10'4"	Spar	Alum
Draft	4'	Cockpit	6'
Disp	10,100 lbs	Headroom	6'2"
Ballast	3650 lbs	Fr. Water	100 gal
Sail Area		SA/Disp	19.2
Swing-wing	560 sq ft	Disp/LWL	254
Junk	560 sq ft	Blst/Disp	36%
Sloop	560 sq ft	Designer	Alan Boswell
Mast	unstayed	First Built	1977
Auxiliary	std	No. Built	150
Volvo	25 hp	Kit	available
Diesel		Price	na
Fuel Cap	25 gal		

The Sunbird SwingWing is a completely new sailing rig which combines the easy handling and low stresses of the traditional junk rig with the superb windward performance of a modern wing sail with completely reversible camber.

It is this *combination* of desirable features that makes it so unusual. Other rigs have provided either easy handling, or good performance, or simplicity, or low stresses, but never before has there been a rig giving such a superb combination of these qualities.

SUNBIRD YACHTS LTD.

373 Huntspond Rd.
Titchfield
Fareham, Hants England PO14 4PB
Titchfield 0329 42613

Watkins 32

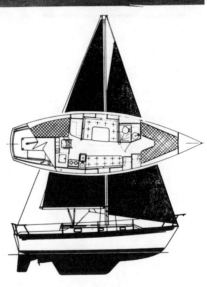

LOD	32'6"	Hull	FRP
LWL	26'7"	Deck	FRP
Beam	10'2"	Spar	Alum
Draft	4'	Headroom	6'5"
Disp	10,800 lbs	Fr. Water	40 gal
Ballast	5500 lbs	SA/Disp	15.4
Sail Area		Disp/LWL	257
Sloop	470 sq ft	Blst/Disp	51%
Mast Ht	43'	Price	$44,995
Auxiliary	std		with sails
Yanmar	15 hp		
Diesel			
Fuel Cap	30 gal		

WATKINS YACHTS INC.
12645 49th St. N.
Clearwater, FL 33520
(813) 577-3684

CS 33

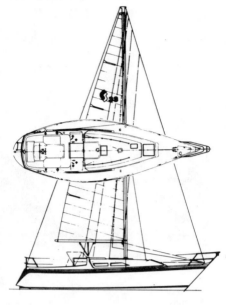

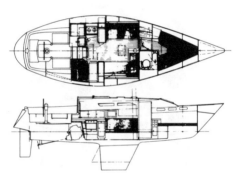

LOD	32'8"	Hull	FRP
LWL	26'5"	Deck	FRP
Beam	10'8"	Spar	Alum
Draft		Headroom	6'2"
Shoal	4'7"	Fr. Water	50 gal
Deep	5'9"	SA/Disp	17.3
Disp	10,000 lbs	Disp/LWL	242
Ballast	4200 lbs	Blst/Disp	42%
Sail Area		Designer	CS Yachts
Sloop	503 sq ft	First Built	1980
Mast Ht	47'6"	No. Built	125
Auxiliary	std	Price	$59,900
Bukh	20 hp		without sails
Diesel			
Fuel Cap	21 gal		

CS YACHTS LTD.
79 Bramsteele Rd.
Brampton, Ont. Canada
(416) 457-6713

Hans Christian 33

LOA	41'	Hull	FRP
LOD	32'9"	Deck	FRP/Teak
LWL	29'2"	Spar	Alum
Beam	11'8"	Cockpit	7'
Draft	5'6"	Headroom	6'6"
Disp	18,500 lbs	Fr. Water	100 gal
Ballast	6800 lbs	SA/Disp	14.6
Sail Area		Disp/LWL	332
Cutter	640 sq ft	Blst/Disp	37%
Mast Ht	49'3"	Designer	
Auxiliary	std		Harwood S. Ives
Yanmar	33 hp	First Built	1979
Diesel		No. Built	41
Fuel Cap	80 gal	Price	$87,500
			with sails

HANS CHRISTIAN YACHTS
6201 Bayshore Walk
Long Beach, CA 90803
(213) 434-2076

Rodgers 33

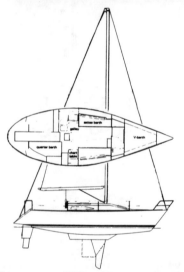

LOD . . . . 32'9"	Hull . . . . . FRP/Balsa
LWL . . . . 25'6"	Deck . . . . . FRP/Balsa
Beam . . . . 11'2"	Spar . . . . Alum
Draft	Fr. Water . . . . 25 gal
Deep . . . . 6'	SA/Disp 19.3
Shoal cb up . . 2'6"	Disp/LWL 240
Shoal cb dn . . . . 8'	Blst/Disp 51%
Disp . . . . . . 8900 lbs	Designer O.H. Rodgers
Ballast . . . . 4500 lbs	Price $54,995
Sail Area	without sails
Sloop . . . . 517 sq ft	
Auxiliary . . . . std	
Diesel . . . . . . 15 hp	
Fuel Cap . . . . . . 14 gal	

RODGERS YACHT & DESIGN
4501 Ulmerton Rd.
Clearwater, FL 33702
(813) 577-2662

BB 10

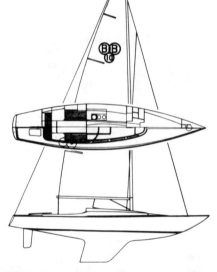

LOD . . . . 32'10"	Hull . . . FRP/Klegecell
LWL . . . . 23'11"	Deck . . . . FRP
Beam . . . . 7'6"	Spar . . . . Alum
Draft . . . . 4'10"	Cockpit . . . . 7'
Disp . . . . . . 4956 lbs	Headroom . . . . . 4'9"
Ballast . . . . 2698 lbs	SA/Disp 21.2
Sail Area	Disp/LWL 161
Sloop . . . . 386 sq ft	Blst/Disp 54%
Auxiliary . . . . . . opt	Designer
BMW . . . . . . 7 hp	Borge Borreson
Diesel	No. Built 110
	Price $30,500
	with sails

BB 10 MANUFACTURING INC.
222 Severn Ave.
Annapolis, MD 21403
(301) 267-0990

Nautilus 33

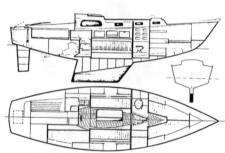

LOD . . . . 32'10"	Hull . . . . Steel
LWL . . . . 27'7"	Deck . . . . Steel
Beam . . . . 9'10"	Spar . . . . Alum
Draft . . . . 5'6"	Cockpit . . . . 6'6"
Disp . . . 13,000 lbs	Headroom . . . . . 6'3"
Ballast . . . . 5730 lbs	Fr. Water . . . . 47.3 gal
Sail Area	SA/Disp 21
Sloop . . . . 727 sq ft	Disp/LWL 276
Mast Ht . . . . 43'	Blst/Disp 44%
Auxiliary . . . . opt	Designer Van De Stadt
25 hp	First Built 1982
inbd	No. Built 2
	Kit . . . . . $17,500 Can

ATELIER MARITIME DE L'EXOCET
P. O. Box 307
Lanoraie, Quebec
Canada J0K 1E0
(514) 887-2926

MS33   Cape Dory 33   Freedom 33

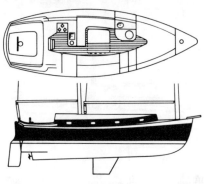

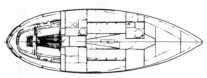

MS33	
LOD . . . . 32'11"	Hull . . . . FRP
LWL . . . . na	Deck . . . . FRP
Beam . . . . 10'6"	Spar . . . . Alum
Draft . . . . 4'5"	Fr. Water . . . 53 gal
Disp . . . . . 15,400 lbs	SA/Disp 11.1
Ballast . . . . . 5510 lbs	Blst/Disp 36%
Sail Area	Designer Eivind Amble
Sloop . . . . 430 sq ft	Builder Fjord, Norway
Auxiliary . . . . std	Price . . . . na
Perkins . . . . . 47 hp	
Diesel	
Fuel Cap . . . . . . 53 gal	

Cape Dory 33	
LOD . . . . 33'	Hull . . . . FRP
LWL . . . . 24'6"	Deck . . . . . FRP/Balsa
Beam . . . . 10'3"	Spar . . . . Alum
Draft . . . . 4'2"	Cockpit . . . . 7'7"
Disp . . . . . 13,300 lbs	Headroom . . . . . 6'5"
Ballast . . . . 5500 lbs	Fr. Water . . . 74 gal
Sail Area	SA/Disp 15.6
Sloop . . . . 546 sq ft	Disp/LWL 403
Mast Ht . . . . . 46'8"	Blst/Disp 41%
Auxiliary . . . . std	Designer . . Carl Alberg
Universal . . . 23 hp	First Built 1980
Diesel	No. Built 87
Fuel Cap . . . . . . 21 gal	Price . . . . na

Freedom 33	
LOD . . . . 33'	Hull . . . . . . FRP/Balsa
LWL . . . . 30'	Deck . . . . . FRP/Balsa
Beam . . . . 11'	Spar . . . Carbon Fiber
Draft	Cockpit . . . . 7'
Shoal cb up . . 3'6"	Headroom . . . . . 6'1"
Shoal cb dn . . . . 6'	Fr. Water . . . . . 83 gal
Deep . . . . 4'6"	SA/Disp 15.8
Disp . . . . 12,000 lbs	Disp/LWL 198
Ballast . . . . 3800 lbs	Blst/Disp 32%
Sail Area	Designer . . . . J. Paris
Cat Ketch . 516 sq ft	Builder
Mast Ht . . . . 46'	Tillotson-Pearson
Mast . . . . . . unstayed	First Built 1978
Auxiliary . . . . std	No. Built 74
Yanmar . . 22.5 hp	Price $78,500
Diesel	
Fuel Cap . . . . . . 25 gal	without sails

FJORD MOTORSAILERS
Eleven 42nd St. N.
St. Petersburg, FL 33713
(813) 327-2711

CAPE DORY YACHTS INC.
160 Middleboro Ave.
E. Taunton, MA 02718
(617) 823-6776

FREEDOM YACHTS
49 America's Cup Ave.
Newport, RI 02840
(401) 847-7475

Harmonie 11M

Newport 33

Offshore 33

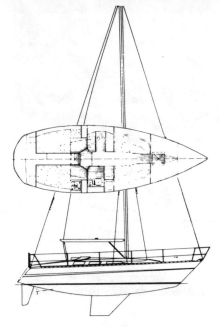

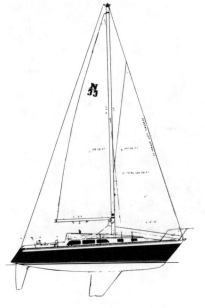

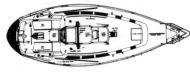

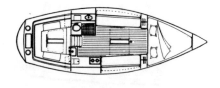

LOA	36'1"	Hull	Alum
LOD	33'	Deck	Alum
LWL	29'6"	Spar	Alum
Beam	12'2"	Pos Float	yes
Draft		Headroom	6'3"
Shoal	5'3"	Fr. Water	100 gal
Deep	5'11"	SA/Disp	16.5
Disp	14,400 lbs	Disp/LWL	250
Ballast	7000 lbs	Blst/Disp	49%
Sail Area		Designer	
Sloop	611 sq ft		Robert Dufour
Mast Ht	54'	First Built	1981
Auxiliary	std	No. Built	2
Bukh	20 hp	Price	$79,000
Diesel			with sails
Fuel Cap	30 gal		

LOD	33'	Hull	FRP
LWL	27'	Deck	FRP
Beam	10'10"	Spar	Alum
Draft		Headroom	6'4"
Shoal	4'	SA/Disp	16.6
Intermediate	5'2"	Disp/LWL	215
Deep	6'	Price	na
Disp	9500 lbs		
Ballast	na		
Sail Area			
Sloop	465 sq ft		
Auxiliary	std		
Diesel			
Fuel Cap	30 gal		

LOD	33'	Hull	FRP
LWL	26'9"	Deck	FRP
Beam	11'	Spar	Alum
Draft		Cockpit	6'
Shoal	4'	Headroom	6'3"
Deep	5'	Fr. Water	75 gal
Disp	13,000 lbs	SA/Disp	14.6
Ballast	5000 lbs	Disp/LWL	303
Sail Area		Blst/Disp	38%
Sloop	506 sq ft	First Built	1979
Mast Ht	46'2"	No. Built	50
Auxiliary	std	Price	$47,045
Universal	16 hp		with sails
Diesel			
Fuel Cap	30 gal		

HARMONIE ALUMINUM YACHTS
11368 Alfred
Montreal-Nord, Quebec
Canada H1G 5B9
(514) 322-3628

CAPITAL YACHTS INC.
25914 President Ave.
Harbor City, CA 90710
(213) 530-1311

CLEARWATER CUSTOM YACHT
4501 Ulmerton Road
Clearwater, FL 33520
(813) 577-7626

Soverel 33

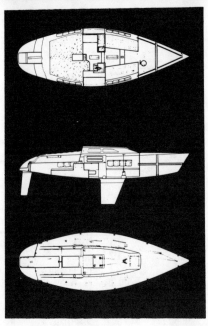

LOD . . . . 33'	Hull . . . FRP/Klegecell
LWL . . . . 30'6"	Deck . . FRP/Klegecell
Beam . . . . 11'	Spar . . . . Alum
Draft . . . . 6'	SA/Disp 26.6
Disp . . . . . . 5800 lbs	Disp/LWL 91
Ballast . . . . . 2800 lbs	Blst/Disp 48%
Sail Area	Price $33,990
Sloop . . . . 537 sq ft	without sails
Auxiliary . . . . opt	

SOVEREL MARINE
2385 P.G.A. Blvd.
Palm Beach Gardens, FL 33410
(305) 622-6910

Wings 33

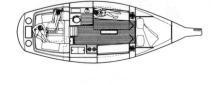

LOD . . . . 33'	Hull . . . . FRP
LWL . . . . 26'9"	Deck . . . . FRP
Beam . . . . 11'	Spar . . . . Alum
Draft	Cockpit . . . . 6'
Shoal . . . . 4'	Headroom . . . . . 6'3"
Deep . . . . 5'	Fr. Water . . . . . 75 gal
Disp . . . . . 13,000 lbs	SA/Disp 24.5
Ballast . . . . . 5000 lbs	Disp/LWL 303
Sail Area	Blst/Disp 38%
Cat Ketch . 845 sq ft	Price $54,245
Mast . . . . . . unstayed	with sails
Auxiliary . . . . std	
Universal . . . 16 hp	
Diesel	
Fuel Cap . . . . . . 30 gal	

CLEARWATER CUSTOM YACHT
4501 Ulmerton Road
Clearwater, FL 33520
(813) 577-7626

Chapman 33

LOD . . . . 33'1"	Hull . . . . FRP
LWL . . . . 27'6"	Deck . . . . FRP
Beam . . . . 10'8"	Spar . . . . Alum
Draft . . . . 4'9"	Fr. Water . . . . 110 gal
Disp . . . . . 13,500 lbs	SA/Disp 16.9
Ballast . . . . . 4700 lbs	Disp/LWL 289
Sail Area	Blst/Disp 35%
Cutter . . . 600 sq ft	Designer
Auxiliary . . . . std	Raymond H. Richards
Universal . . . 27 hp	First Built 1975
Diesel	No. Built 75
Fuel Cap . . . . . . 40 gal	1 Design . . . . yes
	Kit $9,100
	Price $67,300
	with sails

CHAPMAN YACHT CORP.
5201 Argosy Drive
Huntington Beach, CA 92649
(714) 891-3428

Wings 33

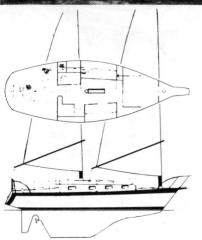

LOD	33'1"	Hull	FRP
LWL	26'9"	Deck	FRP
Beam	11'	Spar	Carb Fib
Draft		Headroom	6'2"
Shoal	4'	Fr. Water	75 gal
Deep	5'	SA/Disp	14.5
Disp	13,000 lbs	Disp/LWL	303
Ballast	5000 lbs	Blst/Disp	38%
Sail Area		Price	na
Cat ketch	500 sq ft		
Auxiliary	std		
Universal	16 hp		
Diesel			
Fuel Cap	30 gal		

OFFSHORE YACHTS
P. O. Box 6
Cos Cob, CT 06807
(203) 869-8054

Nauticat 33 Ketch

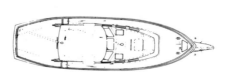

LOD	33'2"	Hull	FRP
LWL	28'3"	Deck	FRP
Beam	10'8"	Spar	Alum
Draft	5'1"	Headroom	6'7"
Disp	29,670 lbs	Fr. Water	66 gal
Ballast	4840 lbs	SA/Disp	9.5
Sail Area		Disp/LWL	587
Ketch	567 sq ft	Blst/Disp	16%
Mast Ht	46'11"	Builder	Siltala
Mast	unstayed		Yachts Oy Finland
Auxiliary	std	Price	na
Ford	80 hp		
Diesel			
Fuel Cap	140 gal		

NAUTICAT INC.
Box 809, Tucker's Wharf
Marblehead, MA 01945
(617) 631-8491

R & L 33

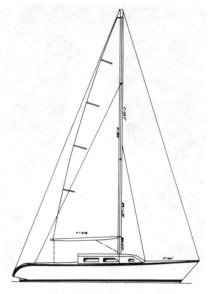

LOD	33'2"	Hull	Wood
LWL	27'1"	Deck	Wood
Beam	11'2"	Spar	Alum
Draft	5'11"	Headroom	6'
Disp	9200 lbs	Fr. Water	25 gal
Ballast	4600 lbs	SA/Disp	18.8
Sail Area		Disp/LWL	207
Sloop	515 sq ft	Blst/Disp	50%
Mast Ht	50'	Designer	
Auxiliary	std		Graham & Schlageter
Diesel		First Built	1979
		No. Built	7
		Price	$80,000 Can
			with sails

R&L YACHT CONSULTANTS
217 George St.
Toronto, Ontario
Canada M5A 2M9
(416) 922-9443

Tartan Ten

LOD	33'2"	Hull .... FRP
LWL	27'	Deck .... FRP
Beam	9'3"	Spar .... Alum
Draft	5'10"	Fr. Water .... 19 gal
Disp	6700 lbs	SA/Disp 21.9
Ballast	3340 lbs	Disp/LWL 152
Sail Area		Blst/Disp 50%
Sloop	486 sq ft	Designer
Auxiliary	std	Sparkman & Stephens
Universal	11 hp	Price .... na
Diesel		
Fuel Cap	10 gal	

TARTAN MARINE CO.
320 River St.
Grand River, OH 44045
(216) 354-5671

Abbott 33

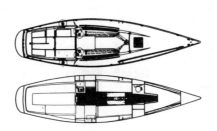

LOD	33'3"	Hull .... FRP
LWL	26'11"	Deck .... FRP
Beam	8'2"	Spar .... Alum
Draft	5'5"	Headroom ...... 5'2"
Disp	6057 lbs	Fr. Water .... 15 gal
Ballast	3304 lbs	SA/Disp 21.3
Sail Area		Disp/LWL 138
Sloop	443 sq ft	Blst/Disp 55%
Mast Ht	42'	1 Design .... yes
Auxiliary	std	Price $35,500
Volvo	7.5 hp	without sails
Diesel		
Fuel Cap	10 gal	

ABBOTT BOATS LTD.
1458 London Rd.
Sarnia, Ontario
Canada N7S 1P7
(519) 542-2771

Westerly Discus

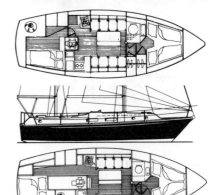

LOD	33'3"	Hull .... FRP
LWL	28'5"	Deck .... FRP
Beam	11'2"	Spar .... Alum
Draft		Headroom ...... 6'1"
Fixed	5'5"	Fr. Water .... 50 gal
Twin	4'4"	SA/Disp 14
Disp	14,800 lbs	Disp/LWL 288
Ballast	6000 lbs	Blst/Disp 41%
Sail Area		Designer
Sloop	527 sq ft	Laurent Giles
Ketch	510 sq ft	Builder
Mast Ht	46'6"	Westerly-England
Auxiliary	std	First Built 1978
Bukh	20 hp	No. Built 350
Diesel		Price $64,482
Fuel Cap	40 gal	with sails

ANDREW GEMENY & SONS
5809 Annapolis Rd.
Hyattsville, MD 20784
(301) 779-6190

Raider 33

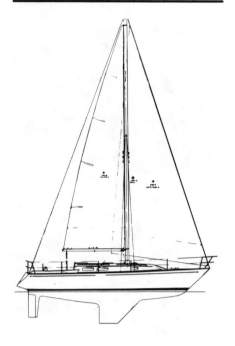

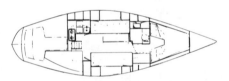

LOD .... 33'4"	Hull .... FRP
LWL .... 27'	Deck .... FRP
Beam .... 10'7"	Spar .... Alum
Draft	Headroom ..... 6'3"
Shoal ...... 4'6"	Fr. Water ..... 30 gal
Deep ...... 5'8"	SA/Disp 18
Disp ...... 9300 lbs	Disp/LWL 211
Ballast ..... 4100 lbs	Blst/Disp 44%
Sail Area	Designer
Sloop .... 498 sq ft	John Cherubini
Auxiliary .... std	Kit .... available
Yanmar ..... 15 hp	Price $56,900
Diesel	with sails
Fuel Cap ...... 12 gal	

Yamaha 33

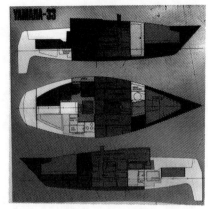

LOD .... 33'5"	Hull .... FRP
LWL .... 26'11"	Deck .... FRP
Beam .... 11'	Spar .... Alum
Draft .... 6'3"	Headroom ..... 6'3"
Disp .... 10,584 lbs	Fr. Water ..... 45 gal
Ballast .... 4410 lbs	SA/Disp 16.3
Sail Area	Disp/LWL 242
Sloop .... 492 sq ft	Blst/Disp 42%
Mast Ht ...... 46'7"	Builder Yamaha, Japan
Auxiliary .... std	Price .... na
Yanmar ..... 15 hp	
Diesel	
Fuel Cap ...... 19 gal	

Ericson 33

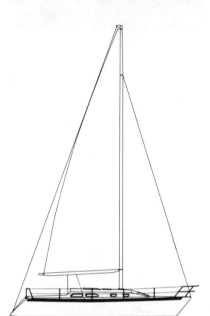

LOD .... 33'6"	Hull .... FRP
LWL .... 26'10"	Deck .... FRP
Beam .... 11'2"	Spar .... Alum
Draft .... 5'11"	Headroom ..... 6'2"
Disp ...... 9500 lbs	SA/Disp 20.4
Ballast ..... 3950 lbs	Disp/LWL 220
Sail Area	Blst/Disp 42%
Sloop .... 573 sq ft	Designer Ron Holland
Auxiliary .... std	Price .... na
Universal ... 11 hp	
Diesel	

RAIDER YACHTS
Box 365, A1, RD1
Medford, NJ 08055
(609) 267-2230

YAMAHA SAILBOATS U.S.A.
6555 Katella Ave.
Cypress, CA 90630
(714) 761-7609

ERICSON YACHTS INC.
1931 Deere Ave.
Irvine, CA 92714
(714) 540-8001

Sabre 34

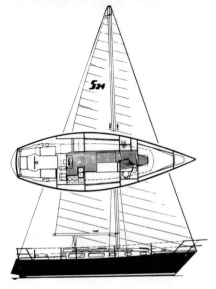

LOD	33'8''	Hull	FRP
LWL	26'3''	Deck	FRP
Beam	10'6''	Spar	Alum
Draft		Cockpit	7'2''
Shoal cb up	3'11''	Headroom	6'3''
Shoal cb dn	7'9''	Fr. Water	44 gal
Deep	5'6''	SA/Disp	15.7
Disp		Disp/LWL	289
Shoal	11,700 lbs	Blst/Disp	42%
Deep	11,400 lbs	Designer	
Ballast			Sabre Design Team
Shoal	4900 lbs	First Built	1976
Deep	4600 lbs	No. Built	175
Sail Area		Price	$68,500
Sloop	507 sq ft		without sails
Mast Ht	48'6''		
Auxiliary	std		
Westerbeke	27 hp		
Diesel			
Fuel Cap	20 gal		

SABRE YACHTS
Hawthorne Rd.
S. Casco, ME 04077
(207) 655-3831

Show 34

LOD	33'8''	Hull	FRP
LWL	27'2''	Deck	FRP
Beam	11'2''	Spar	Alum
Draft	6'	Fr. Water	24 gal
Disp	10,780 lbs	SA/Disp	16
Ballast	4400 lbs	Disp/LWL	240
Sail Area		Blst/Disp	41%
Sloop	487 sq ft	Designer	
Auxiliary	std		Barberis/Franco
Bukh	20 hp	Builder	Barberis-
Diesel			Cantieri, Italy
		Price	$64,500
			with sails

SATELLITE MANAGEMENT INC.
P. O. Box 357
Larchmont, NY 10538
(914) 833-0043

Tartan 33

LOD	33'8''	Hull	FRP
LWL	28'10''	Deck	FRP
Beam	10'11''	Spar	Alum
Draft		Fr. Water	60 gal
Shoal	4'5''	SA/Disp	18.3
Deep	6'3''	Disp/LWL	186
Disp	10,000 lbs	Blst/Disp	44%
Ballast	4400 lbs	Designer	
Sail Area			Sparkman & Stephens
Sloop	531 sq ft	Price	na
Auxiliary	std		
Universal	24 hp		
Diesel			
Fuel Cap	26 gal		

TARTAN MARINE CO.
320 River St.
Grand River, OH 44045
(216) 354-5671

Pearson 34

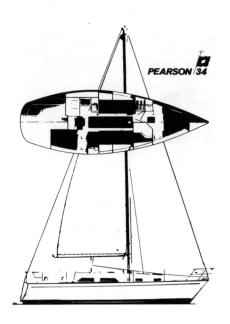

LOD	33'9"	Hull	FRP
LWL	28'1"	Deck	FRP
Beam	11'2"	Spar	Alum
Draft		Fr. Water	50 gal
Shoal cb up	3'10"	SA/Disp	17
Shoal cb dn	7'6"	Disp/LWL	237
Deep	5'11"	Blst/Disp	40%
Disp		Price	na
Shoal	11,750 lbs		
Deep	11,240 lbs		
Ballast			
Shoal	4700 lbs		
Deep	4250 lbs		
Sail Area			
Sloop	550 sq ft		
Mast Ht	48'9"		
Auxiliary	std		
Diesel			
Fuel Cap	22 gal		

PEARSON YACHTS
West Shore Rd.
Portsmouth, RI 02871
(401) 683-0100

S2 10.3

LOD	33'9"	Hull	FRP/Balsa
LWL	28'	Deck	FRP/Balsa
Beam	11'4"	Spar	Alum
Draft		Cockpit	8'1"
Shoal	4'11"	Headroom	6'2"
Deep	6'11"	Fr. Water	42 gal
Disp	10,500 lbs	SA/Disp	18.5
Ballast	4350 lbs	Disp/LWL	214
Sail Area		Blst/Disp	41%
Sloop	553 sq ft	Designer	G & S
Mast Ht	49'6"	Price	$67,500
Auxiliary	std		with sails
Yanmar	15 hp		
Diesel			
Fuel Cap	23 gal		

S2 YACHTS INC.
725 E. 40th St.
Holland, MI 49423
(616) 392-7163

Wylie 34

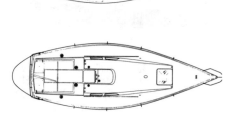

LOD	33'9"	Hull	FRP/Balsa
LWL	25'9"	Deck	FRP/Balsa
Beam	10'10"	Spar	Alum
Draft	6'	Headroom	6'2"
Disp	7800 lbs	Fr. Water	20 gal
Ballast	3235 lbs	SA/Disp	20.5
Sail Area		Disp/LWL	203
Sloop	503 sq ft	Blst/Disp	41%
Auxiliary	std	Price	$67,500
BMW			without sails
Diesel			
Fuel Cap	16 gal		

NORTH COAST YACHTS INC.
2100 Clement Ave.
Alameda, CA 94501
(415) 523-8330

San Juan 34

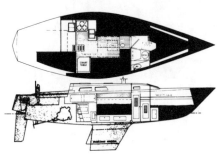

LOD	33'10''	Hull	FRP
LWL	27'11''	Deck	FRP
Beam	10'11''	Spar	Alum
Draft		Cockpit	8'
Shoal	4'9''	Headroom	6'1''
Deep	5'11''	Fr. Water	50 gal
Disp	10,500 lbs	SA/Disp	18.3
Ballast		Disp/LWL	215
Shoal	5300 lbs	Blst/Disp	46%
Deep	4800 lbs	Designer	
Sail Area			Hein Dreyhausen
Sloop	548 sq ft	First Built	1976
Mast Ht	48'	No. Built	60
Auxiliary	std	Price	$55,495
Yanmar	20 hp		with sails
Diesel			
Fuel Cap	22 gal		

CLARK BOAT CO.
25-37th St. NE
Auburn, WA 98002
(206) 854-5400

Sea Sprite 34

LOD	33'10''	Hull	FRP/Airex
LWL	24'	Deck	FRP/Balsa
Beam	10'3''	Spar	Alum
Draft	5'	Cockpit	7'
Disp	12,800 lbs	Headroom	6'3''
Ballast	5000 lbs	Fr. Water	70 gal
Sail Area		SA/Disp	15.6
Sloop	532 sq ft	Disp/LWL	413
Mast Ht	49'	Blst/Disp	39%
Auxiliary	std	Designer	Bill Luders
Universal	24 hp	First Built	1981
Diesel		No. Built	22
Fuel Cap	18 gal	Kit	available
		Price	na

C.E. RYDER CORP.
47 Gooding Ave.
Bristol, RI 02809
(401) 253-8554

Aloha 10.4

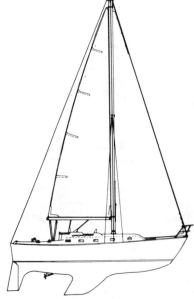

LOD	34'	Hull	FRP
LWL	28'8''	Deck	FRP
Beam	11'2''	Spar	Alum
Draft	5'6''	Headroom	6'3''
Disp	13,600 lbs	Fr. Water	60 gal
Ballast	4700 lbs	SA/Disp	12.5
Sail Area		Disp/LWL	257
Sloop	445 sq ft	Blst/Disp	35%
Auxiliary	std	Designer	
Universal	24 hp		Brewer & Wallstrom
Diesel		Price	$78,589 Can
Fuel Cap	26 gal		with sails

ALOHA YACHTS INT'L
1638 Charles St.
Whitby, Ontario
Canada L1N 1B9
(416) 686-2127

O'Day 34

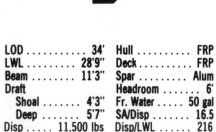

LOD . . . . 34'	Hull . . . . FRP
LWL . . . . 28'9"	Deck . . . . FRP
Beam . . . . 11'3"	Spar . . . . Alum
Draft	Headroom . . . . 6'
Shoal . . . . . . 4'3"	Fr. Water . . . . 50 gal
Deep . . . . 5'7"	SA/Disp 16.5
Disp . . . . . 11,500 lbs	Disp/LWL 216
Ballast . . . . 4650 lbs	Blst/Disp 40%
Sail Area	Designer
Sloop . . 524.3 sq ft	C. R. Hunt Assoc.
Mast Ht . . . . . . 47'2"	First Built 1980
Auxiliary . . . . std	No. Built 141
Universal . . . 25 hp	1 Design . . . . yes
Diesel	Price . . . . na
Fuel Cap . . . . . . 30 gal	

BANGOR PUNTA MARINE
848 Airport Rd.
Box 991
Fall River, MA 02722
(617) 678-5291

Seidelmann 34

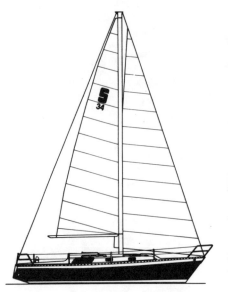

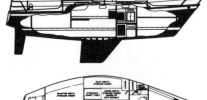

LOD . . . . 34'	Hull . . . . FRP
LWL . . . . 26'6"	Deck . . . . FRP
Beam . . . . . . 11'10"	Spar . . . . Alum
Draft	Cockpit . . . . 8'
Shoal . . . . . . 3'11"	Headroom . . . . . 6'7"
Deep . . . . 5'5"	Fr. Water . . . . 70 gal
Disp . . . 11,000 lbs	SA/Disp 16.7
Ballast . . . . . 5000 lbs	Disp/LWL 264
Sail Area	Blst/Disp 45%
Sloop . . . . 516 sq ft	Designer
Mast Ht . . . . . . 46'6"	Bob Seidelmann
Auxiliary . . . . std	First Built 1982
Yanmar . . 23.5 hp	No. Built 23
Diesel	Price $74,700
Fuel Cap . . . . . . 18 gal	with sails

SEIDELMANN YACHTS
Cushman Ave., P. O. Box 2529
Berlin, NJ 08009
(609) 768-1707

Westerly Vulcan

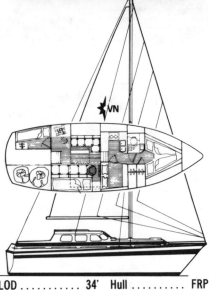

LOD . . . . 34'	Hull . . . . FRP
LWL . . . . 28'5"	Deck . . . . FRP
Beam . . . . 11'9"	Spar . . . . Alum
Draft	Headroom . . . . . 6'1"
Fixed . . . . 5'	SA/Disp 12.8
Twin . . . . . . 4'3"	Disp/LWL 303
Disp . . . . 15,571 lbs	Blst/Disp 46%
Ballast	Designer
Fixed . . . . 7200 lbs	Laurent Giles
Twin . . . . 6945 lbs	Builder
Sail Area	Westerly-England
Sloop . . . . 500 sq ft	First Built 1980
Mast Ht . . . . 44'	No. Built 40
Auxiliary . . . . std	Price $86,055
Volvo . . . . . 60 hp	with sails
Diesel	
Fuel Cap . . . . . . 70 gal	

ANDREW GEMENY & SONS
5809 Annapolis Rd.
Hyattsville, MD 20784
(301) 779-6190

Alberg 34

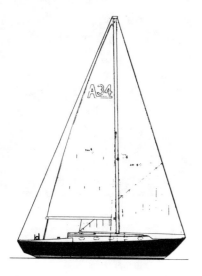

LOD . . . . 34'1"	Hull . . . . FRP
LWL . . . . 25'6"	Deck . . . . FRP
Beam . . . . 10'1"	Spar . . . . Alum
Draft . . . . 5'3"	Cockpit . . . . 8'6"
Disp . . . . 14,000 lbs	Headroom . . . . . 6'3"
Ballast . . . . . 6500 lbs	Fr. Water . . . . 50 gal
Sail Area	SA/Disp 15.5
Sloop . . . . 563 sq ft	Disp/LWL 377
Auxiliary . . . . std	Blst/Disp 46%
Yanmar . . . . . 22 hp	Designer
Diesel	Carl A. Alberg
Fuel Cap . . . . . 18 gal	First Built 1983
	1 Design . . . . yes
	Kit . . . . available
	Price $75,000
	without sails

NYE YACHTS
25 Dundas St. W.
Belleville, Ontario
Canada K8P 3M7

Gale Force 34

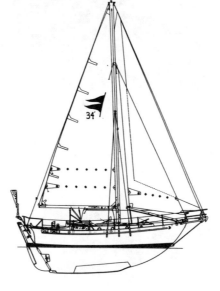

LOA . . . . 39'6"	Hull . . . . FRP
LOD . . . . 34'1"	Deck . . . . FRP
LWL . . . . 27'6"	Spar . . . . Alum
Beam . . . . 10'6"	Cockpit . . . . 6'6"
Draft . . . . 5'2"	Fr. Water . . . . 90 gal
Disp . . . . 18,000 lbs	Disp/LWL 386
Ballast . . . . na	Price $130,000
Sail Area	with sails
Cutter . . . . na	
Auxiliary . . . . std	
Westerbeke . . 40 hp	
Diesel	
Fuel Cap . . . . . . 48 gal	

KAISER YACHTS
1122 E. 7th St.
Wilmington, DE 19801

Vixen 34

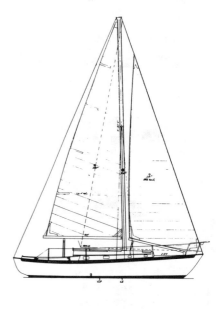

LOD . . . . 34'4"	Hull . . . . FRP
LWL . . . . 27'5"	Deck . . . . FRP
Beam . . . . 10'6"	Spar . . . . Alum
Draft . . . . 5'2"	Cockpit . . . . 9'
Disp . . . . 12,000 lbs	Headroom . . . . . 6'4"
Ballast . . . . . 5500 lbs	Fr. Water . . . . 45 gal
Sail Area	SA/Disp 16.5
Sloop . . . . 540 sq ft	Disp/LWL 259
Ketch . . . . 579 sq ft	Blst/Disp 46%
Mast Ht . . . . 46'	Designer Thomas Hale
Auxiliary . . . . std	First Built 1977
Pathfinder . . 50 hp	No. Built 20
Diesel	1 Design . . . . yes
	Price $91,000
	with sails

MARTHA'S VINEYARD SHIPYARD
Beach Rd., Box 1236
Vineyard Haven, MA 02568
(617) 693-0400

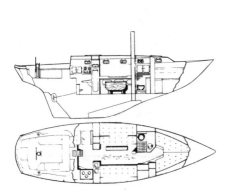

Hunter 34

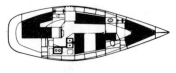

LOD	34'5''	Hull	FRP
LWL	28'3''	Deck	FRP
Beam	11'7''	Spar	Alum
Draft		Fr. Water	65 gal
Shoal	4'3''	SA/Disp	17.9
Deep	5'6''	Disp/LWL	220
Disp		Blst/Disp	43%
Shoal	11,120 lbs	Designer	
Deep	10,900 lbs		Cortland Steck
Ballast		Price	$44,900
Shoal	4760 lbs		with sails
Deep	4540 lbs		
Sail Area			
Sloop	557 sq ft		
Mast Ht	51'6''		
Auxiliary	std		
Westerbeke			
Diesel			
Fuel Cap	25 gal		

HUNTER MARINE
Box 1030, Hwy 441
Alachua, FL 32601
(904) 462-3077

Tanzer 10.5

LOD	34'5''	Hull	FRP
LWL	27'6''	Deck	FRP
Beam	11'6''	Spar	Alum
Draft		Cockpit	6'
Swing keel up	2'1''	headroom	6'2''
Swing keel dn	6'6''	Fr. Water	70 gal
Fixed	5'11''	SA/Disp	17.1
Disp	13,000 lbs	Disp/LWL	279
Ballast	5700 lbs	Blst/Disp	44%
Sail Area		Designer	Dick Carter
Sloop	592 sq ft	First Built	1982
Mast Ht	48'6''	No. Built	15
Auxiliary	std	Price	$72,500
Yanmar	30 hp		with sails
Diesel			
Fuel Cap	35 gal		

TANZER INDUSTRIES
P. O. Box 67
Dorion, PQ Canada J7V 5V8
(514) 455-5681

Young Sun 35

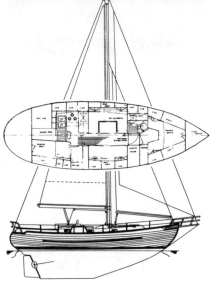

LOA	39'	Hull	FRP
LOD	34'6''	Deck	FRP
LWL	29'	Spar	Alum
Beam	11'	Fr. Water	75 gal
Draft	5'4''	SA/Disp	15.4
Disp	19,100 lbs	Disp/lwl	349
Ballast	6700 lbs	Blst/Disp	35%
Sail Area		Designer	
Cutter	688 sq ft		Robert H. Perry
Auxiliary	std	Builder	
Yanmar	36 hp		Young Sun, Taiwan
Diesel		Price	$69,900
Fuel Cap	60 gal		with sails

EASTPORT YACHT MFG. INC.
222 Severn Ave.
Annapolis, MD 21403
(301) 269-6042

WONDERLAND INTERNATIONAL
P. O. Box 676
Syosset, NY 11791
(516) 689-8481

Irwin 34

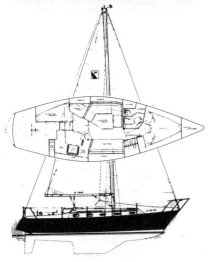

LOD . . . . 34'7"	Hull . . . . FRP/Coremat
LWL . . . . 27'4"	Deck . . . . FRP
Beam . . . . 11'3"	Spar . . . . Alum
Draft	Fr. Water . . . . . 80 gal
Shoal cb up . . . . 4'	SA/Disp 16.9
Shoal cb dn . . 8'1"	Disp/LWL 251
Deep . . . . 5'4"	Blst/Disp 39%
Disp . . . . 11,500 lbs	Price $46,950
Ballast	with sails
Shoal . . . . 4500 lbs	
Deep . . . . 4100 lbs	
Sail Area	
Sloop . . . . 538 sq ft	
Mast Ht . . . . 46'1"	
Auxiliary . . . . std	
Yanmar . . . . . 15 hp	
Diesel	
Fuel Cap . . . . . . 31 gal	

IRWIN YACHTS
13055 49th St. N.
Clearwater, FL 33520
(813) 577-4581

C & C 35

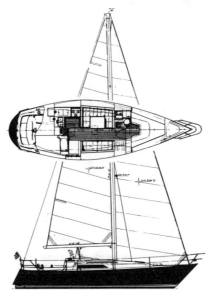

LOD . . . . 34'8"	Hull . . . . . FRP/Balsa
LWL . . . . 28'	Deck . . . . FRP/Balsa
Beam . . . . 11'2"	Spar . . . . Alum
Draft . . . . 6'5"	Headroom . . . . 6'3"
Disp . . . . 10,800 lbs	Fr. Water . . . . 32 gal
Ballast . . . . . 4350 lbs	SA/Disp 18.7
Sail Area	Disp/LWL 219
Sloop . . . . 570 sq ft	Blst/Disp 40%
Auxiliary . . . . std	Price $76,950
Yanmar . . . . . 22 hp	without sails
Diesel	
Fuel Cap . . . . . . 20 gal	

C&C YACHTS
55 Port Street East
Mississauga, Ontario
Canada L5G 4P3
(416) 274-7131

Nightwind 35

LOD . . . . 34'8"	Hull . . . . . . FRP/Airex
LWL . . . . 28'1"	Deck . . . . . FRP/Airex
Beam . . . . 11'6"	Spar . . . . Alum
Draft	Cockpit . . . . 8'
cb up . . . . 2'9"	Fr. Water . . . . . 50 gal
cb dn . . . . 7'3"	SA/Disp 19.7
Disp . . . . 11,900 lbs	Disp/LWL 239
Ballast . . . . 5500 lbs	Blst/Disp 46%
Sail Area	Designer . Bruce Kirby
Sloop . . . . 642 sq ft	Price $75,000
Auxiliary . . . . std	with sails
Pathfinder . . 42 hp	
Diesel	
Fuel Cap . . . . . . 35 gal	

ARKADY MARINE INC.
122 N. Madison St.
Box 1386
Green Bay, WI 54305
(414) 432-6090

Allmand 35
Raised Cabin

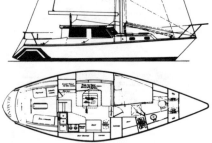

LOD	34'9"	Hull	FRP
LWL	28'2"	Deck	FRP
Beam	11'8"	Spar	Alum
Draft		Headroom	6'8"
Shoal	3'11"	Fr. Water	125 gal
Deep	4'11"	SA/Disp	16
Disp	12,000 lbs	Disp/LWL	239
Ballast	4300 lbs	Blst/Disp	36%
Sail Area		Designer . Walter Scott	
Sloop	525 sq ft		& T. R. Allmand
Auxiliary	std	Price	$81,500
Universal			with sails
Diesel			
Fuel Cap	40 gal		

ALLMAND BOATS INC.
P. O. Drawer 4910
Hialeah, FL 33014
(305) 821-4070

Allmand 35
Tri-Cabin

LOD	34'9"	Hull	FRP
LWL	29'7"	Deck	FRP
Beam	11'8"	Spar	Alum
Draft	5'2"	Fr. Water	95 gal
Disp	15,100 lbs	SA/Disp	14.4
Ballast	4300 lbs	Disp/LWL	260
Sail Area		Blst/Disp	28%
Sloop	550 sq ft	Price	$72,500
Auxiliary	std		with sails
Universal			
Diesel			
Fuel Cap	40 gal		

ALLMAND BOATS INC.
P. O. Drawer 4910
Hialeah, FL 33014
(305) 821-4070

Island Trader 35
Trawl'r Sailer

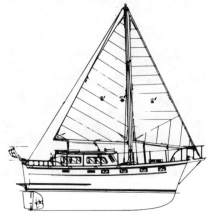

LOD	34'9"	Hull	FRP
LWL	31'6"	Deck	Teak
Beam	12'6"	Spar	Wood
Draft	4'	Cockpit	6'11"
Disp	na	Headroom	6'8"
Ballast	6000 lbs	Fr. Water	250 gal
Sail Area		Designer . Floyd Ayers	
Sloop	453 sq ft	First Built	1983
Mast Ht	38'2"	No. Built	0
Auxiliary	std	1 Design	yes
Lehman/Ford 120 hp		Price	na
Diesel			
Fuel Cap	250 gal		

MARINE TRADING
INTERNATIONAL
Box 1232
Point Pleasant Beach, NJ 08742
(201) 899-6800

Contest 35

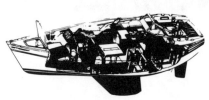

LOD	34'11"	Hull	FRP
LWL	29'2"	Deck	FRP
Beam	11'8"	Headroom	6'3"
Draft		Fr. Water	55 gal
Shoal	5'5"	SA/Disp	16.6
Deep	6'3"	Disp/LWL	273
Disp		Blst/Disp	46%
Shoal	15,212 lbs	Designer	Dick Zaal
Deep	14,881 lbs	Builder	
Ballast			Conyplex, Holland
Shoal	6944 lbs	Price	na
Deep	6613 lbs		
Sail Area			
Sloop	636 sq ft		
Mast Ht	56'5"		
Auxiliary	std		
Volvo Penta			
Diesel			
Fuel Cap	33 gal		

HOLLAND YACHTS
Box 129
Solomons, MD 20688
(301) 326-3960

Dufour 35 Valentijn

Aft Cabin

Offshore

LOD	34'11"	Hull	FRP
LWL	27'7"	Deck	FRP
Beam	11'1"	Spar	Alum
Draft		Headroom	6'2"
Shoal	4'11"	Fr. Water	35 gal
Deep	6'	Disp/LWL	225
Disp	10,579 lbs	Blst/Disp	49%
Ballast	5150 lbs	Designer	
Sail Area			Johan Valentijn
Sloop	na	Builder	
Auxiliary	std		Dufour, France
Volvo	25 hp	Price	na
Diesel			
Fuel Cap	25 gal		

EURO SAILBOATS LTD.
131 Boston Post Road
Mamaroneck, NY 10543
(914) 381-4500

Cal 35

CAL 35
MARK II

LOD	35'	Hull	FRP
LWL	18'9"	Deck	FRP
Beam	10'11"	Spar	Alum
Draft		Cockpit	7'7"
Shoal	5'	Headroom	6'3"
Deep	6'	Fr. Water	90 gal
Disp	13,000 lbs	SA/Disp	17.2
Ballast	5200 lbs	Disp/LWL	880
Sail Area		Blst/Disp	40%
Sloop	595 sq ft	Designer	
Mast Ht	52'6"		Bill Lapworth
Auxiliary	std	First Built	1973
Universal	32 hp	No. Built	53
Diesel		1 Design	yes
Fuel Cap	33 gal	Price	na

BANGOR PUNTA MARINE
848 Airport Rd.
Box 991
Fall River, MA 02722
(617) 678-5291

Departure 35

INBOARD PROFILE

STANDARD ARRANGEMENT

BLUEWATER ARRANGEMENT

LOD	35'	Hull	Steel
LWL	29'	Deck	Steel
Beam	11'	Spar	Alum
Draft	5'	SA/Disp	14.8
Disp	16,480 lbs	Disp/LWL	301
Ballast	na	Designer	
Sail Area			Charles Wittholz
Cutter	600 sq ft	Price	na

MOONEY MARINE INC.
Rt. 33, Box 208
Deltaville, VA 23043
(804) 776-6392

Friendship 35

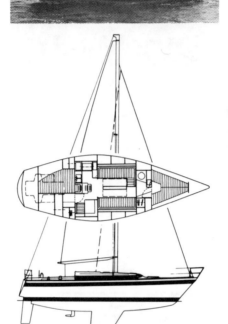

LOD	35'	Hull	FRP
LWL	28'3"	Deck	FRP/Balsa
Beam	11'5"	Spar	Alum
Draft		Pos Float	yes
Shoal cb up	3'11"	Cockpit	8'9"
Shoal cb dn	7'2"	Headroom	6'4"
Intermediate	5'3"	Fr. Water	45 gal
Deep Deep	6'3"	SA/Disp	21.4
Disp	12,750 lbs	Disp/LWL	252
Ballast		Blst/Disp	43%
Shoal	5500 lbs	Designer	
Deep	4800 lbs		Jac De Ridder
Sail Area		Builder	
Sloop (MH)	730 sq ft		Meijer, Holland
Sloop (FR)	730 sq ft	First Built	1982
Mast Ht		No. Built	27
Sloop (MH)	53'	Price	$79,500
Sloop (FR)	52'		with sails
Auxiliary	std		
Volvo Penta	25 hp		
Diesel			
Fuel Cap	25 gal		

SAILSPIRIT
P. O. Box 340007
Miami, FL 33114
(305) 441-9193

Santana 35

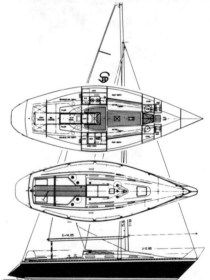

LOD	35'	Hull	FRP
LWL	26'6"	Deck	FRP
Beam	11'11"	Spar	Alum
Draft	6'3"	Headroom	6'2"
Disp	8500 lbs	Fr. Water	20 gal
Ballast	3300 lbs	SA/Disp	21.1
Sail Area		Disp/LWL	204
Sloop	550 sq ft	Blst/Disp	39%
Auxiliary	std	Designer	Shad Turner
Volvo Penta	13 hp	Price	$68,500
Diesel			with sails
Fuel Cap	20 gal		

W. D. SCHOCK CORP.
3502 S. Greenville St.
Santa Ana, CA 92704
(714) 549-2277

Skipjack 35

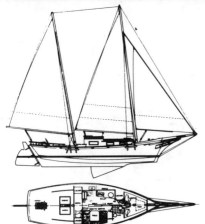

LOA	47'	Hull	FRP
LOD	35'	Deck	FRP
LWL	32'	Spar	Alum
Beam	11'8"	Cockpit	4'6"
Draft		Headroom	6'3"
cb up	2'4"	Fr. Water	50 gal
cb dn	5'8"	SA/Disp	19.8
Disp	12,000 lbs	Disp/LWL	163
Ballast	na	Designer	
Sail Area			Howard Chapelle
Ketch	650 sq ft	First Built	1966
Mast Ht	40'	Kit	available
Auxiliary	opt	Price	$58,000
Diesel	30 hp		with sails

KENNER MFG. CO. INC.
P. O. Box "H"
Knoxville, AK 71845
(501) 885-3171

Niagara 35

LOD	35'1"	Hull	FRP/Balsa
LWL	26'8"	Deck	FRP/Balsa
Beam	11'5"	Spar	Alum
Draft	5'2"	Cockpit	6'
Disp	15,000 lbs	Headroom	6'4"
Ballast	5500 lbs	Fr. Water	80 gal
Sail Area		SA/Disp	15.7
Sloop	598 sq ft	Disp/LWL	353
Mast Ht	50'	Blst/Disp	37%
Auxiliary	std	Designer	Mark Ellis
Westerbeke	29 hp	First Built	1978
Diesel		No. Built	160
Fuel Cap	30 gal	Price	$72,500
			without sails

HINTERHOELLER YACHTS LTD.
8 Keefer Rd., St. Catharines,
Ontario L2M 7N9, Canada
(416) 937-4440

Cooper 353

LOD	35'3"	Hull	FRP
LWL	28'6"	Deck	FRP
Beam	12'	Spar	Alum
Draft	5'10"	Cockpit	6'
Disp	13,250 lbs	Headroom	6'2"
Ballast	5250 lbs	Fr. Water	100 gal
Sail Area		SA/Disp	16
Sloop	561 sq ft	Disp/LWL	255
Auxiliary	std	Blst/Disp	40%
Volvo	23 hp	Designer	
Diesel			S. Huntingford
Fuel Cap	50 gal	First Built	1980
		No. Built	30
		Price	$73,900
			with sails

COOPER ENTERPRISES LTD.
1642 Langan Ave.
Port Coquituam, B.C.
Canada V3C 1K5
(604) 942-5945

Nicholson 35   Southern Cross 35   Comet 11

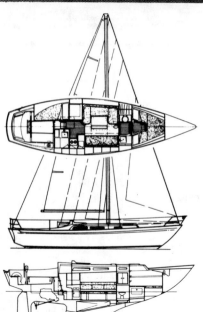 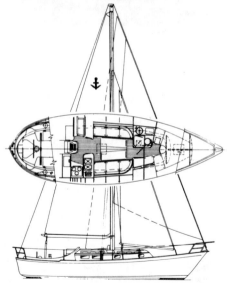 

Nicholson 35

LOD	35'3"	Hull	FRP
LWL	26'9"	Deck	FRP
Beam	10'5"	Spar	Alum
Draft	5'6"	SA/Disp	18.7
Disp	15,800 lbs	Disp/LWL	368
Ballast	7000 lbs	Blst/Disp	44%
Sail Area		Builder	England
Sloop	736 sq ft	Price	$61,200
Auxiliary	std		with sails
Petter	36 hp		
Diesel			

CAMPER & NICHOLSONS
Box 3296
Annapolis, MD 21403
(301) 267-0933

Southern Cross 35

LOD	35'3"	Hull	FRP/Airex
LWL	28'	Deck	FRP/Balsa
Beam	11'5"	Spar	Alum
Draft	4'11"	Cockpit	8'
Disp	14,461 lbs	Headroom	6'4"
Ballast	5750 lbs	Fr. Water	90 gal
Sail Area		SA/Disp	17
Cutter	632 sq ft	Disp/LWL	294
Mast Ht	49'	Blst/Disp	40%
Auxiliary	std	Designer	Tom Gillmer
Universal	24 hp	First Built	1982
Diesel		No. Built	6
		Kit	available
		Price	na

C.E. RYDER CORP.
47 Gooding Ave.
Bristol, RI 02809
(401) 253-8554

Comet 11

LOD	35'5"	Hull	FRP
LWL	29'6"	Deck	FRP/Balsa
Beam	11'10"	Spar	Alum
Draft		Fr. Water	100 gal
Shoal	5'3"	Disp/LWL	226
Deep	6'7"	Blst/Disp	35%
Disp	13,000 lbs	Designer	
Ballast	4600 lbs		Groupe Finot
Sail Area		Builder	Comar Italy
Sloop	na	Price	na
Auxiliary	std		
Volvo	25 hp		
Diesel			
Fuel Cap	37 gal		

COMAR USA
149 Shaw Ave.
Irvington, NJ 07111

Endeavour 35   J—35   Bristol 35.5

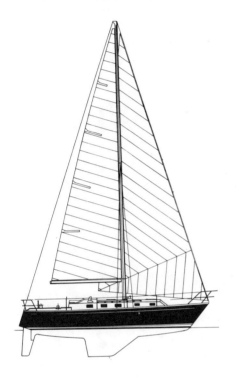

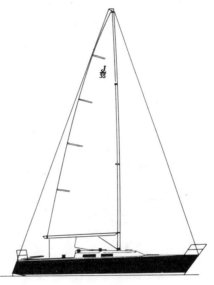

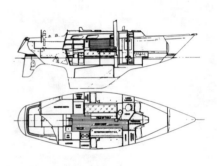

Endeavour 35

LOD	35'5"	Hull	FRP
LWL	29'6"	Deck	FRP
Beam	12'2"	Spar	Alum
Draft	4'11"	SA/Disp	19.2
Disp	13,250 lbs	Disp/LWL	230
Ballast	5630 lbs	Blst/Disp	42%
Sail Area		Designer	Bruce Kelley
Sloop	671 sq ft	Price	$64,900
Auxiliary	std		without sails
Diesel			

J—35

LOD	35'5"	Hull	FRP
LWL	30'	Deck	FRP
Beam	11'9"	Spar	Alum
Draft	6'11"	Disp/LWL	165
Disp	10,000 lbs	Blst/Disp	44%
Ballast	4400 lbs	Designer	
Sail Area			Rod Johnstone
Sloop	na	First Built	1983
Auxiliary	std	1 Design	yes
Diesel	22.5 hp	Price	na

Bristol 35.5

LOD	35'6"	Hull	FRP
LWL	27'6"	Deck	FRP/Balsa
Beam	10'10"	Spar	Alum
Draft		Pos Float	yes
Shoal cb up	3'9"	Headroom	6'5"
Shoal cb dn	7'9"	Fr. Water	90 gal
Deep	5'9"	SA/Disp	15.5
Disp	15000 lbs	Disp/LWL	321
Ballast		Blst/Disp	47%
Shoal	7000 lbs	Designer	Ted Hood
Deep	6500 lbs	First Built	1977
Sail Area		No. Built	116
Sloop	589 sq ft	Price	$75,816
Auxiliary	std		without sails
Universal	24 hp		
Diesel			
Fuel Cap	36 gal		

ENDEAVOUR YACHT CORP.
11700 S. Belcher Rd.
Largo, FL 33543
(813) 541-3553

J BOATS INC.
24 Mill St.
Newport, RI 02840
(401) 846-8410

BRISTOL YACHT CO.
Franklin St.
Bristol, RI 02890
(401) 253-5200

Sceptre 36

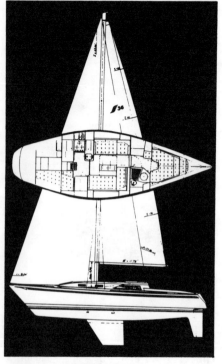

LOD	35'6"	Hull	FRP
LWL	29'1"	Deck	FRP
Beam	11'5"	Spar	Alum
Draft	6'	Cockpit	8'
Disp	12,000 lbs	Headroom	6'2"
Ballast	5500 lbs	Fr. Water	72 gal
Sail Area		SA/Disp	18.2
Sloop	597 sq ft	Disp/LWL	218
Mast Ht	52'6"	Blst/Disp	46%
Auxiliary	std	Designer	
Yanmar	22.5 hp		H. W. Driehuyzen
Diesel		First Built	1979
		No. Built	35
		Price	$78,500
			with sails

SCEPTRE YACHTS LTD.
4720 Cowley Cresc.
Richmond, B.C.
Canada V7B 1C2
(604) 273-1308

Catalina 36

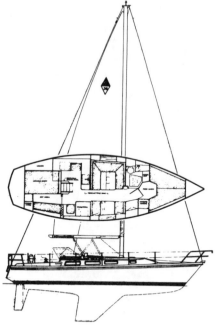

LOD	35'7"	Hull	FRP
LWL	30'3"	Deck	FRP
Beam	11'11"	Spar	Alum
Draft	5'5"	Headroom	6'7"
Disp	15,000 lbs	Fr. Water	48 gal
Ballast	6000 lbs	SA/Disp	14.6
Sail Area		Disp/LWL	241
Sloop	555 sq ft	Blst/Disp	40%
Mast Ht	54'6"	Designer	Frank Butler
Auxiliary	std	First Built	1982
Universal	25 hp	No. Built	36
Diesel		Price	$54,475
Fuel Cap	33 gal		without sails

CATALINA YACHTS
21200 Victory Blvd.
Woodland Hills, CA 91367
(213) 884-7700

Ericson 36

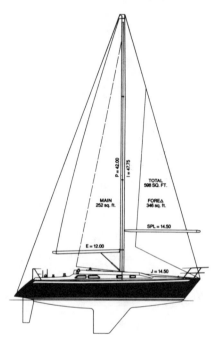

LOD	35'7"	Hull	FRP
LWL	29'	Deck	FRP
Beam	11'10"	Spar	Alum
Draft	6'3"	Headroom	6'3"
Disp	11,600 lbs	SA/Disp	18.7
Ballast	5230 lbs	Disp/LWL	212
Sail Area		Blst/Disp	45%
Sloop	598 sq ft	Designer	Ron Holland
Auxiliary	std	Price	na
Universal	24 hp		
Diesel			

ERICSON YACHTS INC.
1931 Deere Ave.
Irvine, CA 92714
(714) 540-8001

Southerly 105

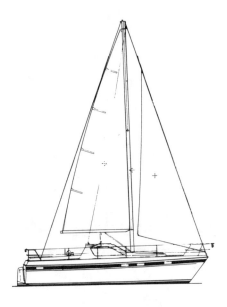

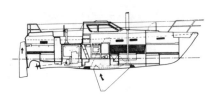

LOD . . . . 35'7"	Hull . . . . FRP
LWL . . . . 27'6"	Deck . . . . . FRP/Balsa
Beam . . . . 11'11"	Spar . . . . Alum
Draft	Cockpit . . . . 5'3"
Swing keel up . 2'3"	Headroom . . . . . 6'6"
Swing keel dn . 6'8"	Fr. Water . . . . . 72 gal
Disp . . . . . 14,600 lbs	SA/Disp 12.9
Ballast . . . . . 4962 lbs	Disp/lwl 313
Sail Area	Blst/Disp 34%
Sloop . . . . 480 sq ft	Designer . . Dick Carter
Mast Ht . . . . . . 44'6"	Builder
Auxiliary . . . . std	Northshore, England
Bukh . . . . . 36 hp	First Built 1979
Diesel	No. Built . . . . . 100+
Fuel Cap . . . . . 60 gal	1 Design . . . . yes
	Price $63,700
	with sails

PARKER YACHTS
South Freeport, ME 04078
(207) 865-6692

New York 36

LOD . . . . 35'8"	Hull . . . . FRP
LWL . . . . 29'6"	Deck . . . . FRP
Beam . . . . 11'8"	Spar . . . . Alum
Draft . . . . 6'4"	Fr. Water . . . . . 20 gal
Disp . . . . 10,500 lbs	SA/Disp 21.7
Ballast . . . . . 4200 lbs	Disp/LWL 183
Sail Area	Blst/Disp 40%
Sloop . . . . 650 sq ft	Designer William Cook
Auxiliary . . . . std	1 Design . . . . yes
Volvo Penta . 13 hp	Price $84,950
Diesel	with sails
Fuel Cap . . . . . 20 gal	

W. D. SCHOCK CORP.
3502 S. Greenville St.
Santa Ana, CA 92704
(714) 549-2277

Freeport 36

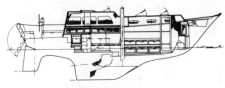

LOD . . . . 35'9"	Hull . . . . FRP
LWL . . . . 27'6"	Deck . . . . FRP
Beam . . . . 12'	Spar . . . . Alum
Draft . . . . 5'3"	Fr. Water . . . . 120 gal
Disp . . . . . 17,000 lbs	SA/Disp 15.8
Ballast . . . . . 6300 lbs	Disp/LWL 364
Sail Area	Blst/Disp 37%
Sloop . . . . 653 sq ft	Designer Robert Perry
Mast Ht . . . . 53'	Price . . . . na
Auxiliary . . . . std	
Pathfinder . . 42 hp	
Diesel	
Fuel Cap . . . . . 50 gal	

ISLANDER YACHTS
1922 Barranca Rd.
Irvine, CA 92714
(714) 549-8526

Westerly Conway   # J—36   # White Wing 36

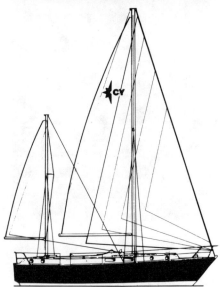

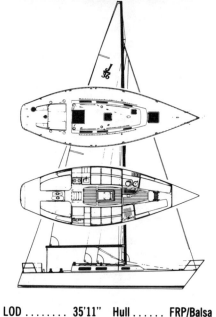

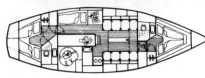

LOD . . . . 35'9''	Hull . . . . FRP
LWL . . . . 30'3''	Deck . . . . . FRP/Balsa
Beam . . . . 11'2''	Spar . . . . Alum
Draft	Headroom . . . . 6'1''
Fixed . . . . 6'	Fr. Water . . . . 70 gal
Twin . . . . 4'6''	SA/Disp 12.6
Disp . . . . . 16,128 lbs	Disp/LWL 260
Ballast . . . . . 7168 lbs	Blst/Disp 44%
Sail Area	Designer
Sloop . . . . 502 sq ft	Laurent Giles
Ketch . . . . 528 sq ft	Builder
Mast Ht	Westerly-England
Sloop . . . . 50'5''	First Built 1975
Ketch . . . . 46'7''	No. Built 400
Auxiliary . . . . std	Price $90,020
Volvo . . . . . . 36 hp	with sails
Diesel	
Fuel Cap . . . . . . 40 gal	

LOD . . . . 35'11''	Hull . . . . . . FRP/Balsa
LWL . . . . 30'6''	Deck . . . . . FRP/Balsa
Beam . . . . 11'9''	Spar . . . . Alum
Draft . . . . 6'7''	Cockpit . . . . 10'6''
Disp . . . . 10,570 lbs	Headroom . . . . . 6'1''
Ballast . . . . . 4600 lbs	Fr. Water . . . . 30 gal
Sail Area	SA/Disp 22.4
Sloop . . . . 675 sq ft	Disp/LWL 166
Mast Ht . . . . 56'	Blst/Disp 44%
Auxiliary . . . . std	Designer
Yanmar . . . . 22 hp	Rodney Johnstone
Diesel	Builder
Fuel Cap . . . . . 21 gal	Tillitson Pearson
	First Built 1981
	No. Built 60
	1 Design . . . . yes
	Price $84,500
	without sails

LOD . . . . 35'11''	Hull . . . . . . FRP/Balsa
LWL . . . . 30'	Deck . . . . . FRP/Balsa
Beam . . . . 11'8''	Spar . . . . Alum
Draft . . . . 5'6''	Cockpit . . . . 8'
Disp . . . . 17,900 lbs	Headroom . . . . . 6'3''
Ballast . . . . . 6179 lbs	Fr. Water . . . . 106 gal
Sail Area	SA/Disp 15.9
Cutter . . . 678 sq ft	Disp/LWL 296
Mast Ht . . . . 53'	Blst/Disp 35%
Auxiliary . . . . std	Designer Robert Perry
Pathfinder . . 42 hp	First Built 1982
Diesel	No. Built 2
Fuel Cap . . . . . . 60 gal	Price $114,000
	with sails

ANDREW GEMENY & SONS
5809 Annapolis Rd.
Hyattsville, MD 20784
(301) 779-6190

J BOATS INC.
24 Mill St.
Newport, RI 02840
(401) 846-8410

WHITE WING YACHTS
1800 Westlake N. #201
Seattle, WA 98109
(206) 285-0602

Yamaha 36

Cascade 36

Morgan 36

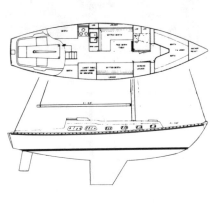

LOD .... 35'11"	Deck .... FRP
LWL .... 29'1"	Spar .... Alum
Beam .... 11'10"	Headroom ..... 6'4"
Draft .... 6'7"	Fr. Water .... 106 gal
Disp ..... 14,333 lbs	SA/Disp 16.6
Ballast ..... 5610 lbs	Disp/LWL 260
Sail Area	Blst/Disp 39%
Sloop .... 611 sq ft	Builder Yamaha, Japan
Mast Ht ...... 51'10"	Price .... na
Auxiliary .... std	
Yanmar ..... 22 hp	
Diesel	
Fuel Cap ...... 26 gal	

LOD .... 36'	Hull .... FRP
LWL .... 29'	Deck ... FRP/Plywood
Beam .... 10'	Spar .... Alum
Draft .... 5'6"	Cockpit .... 7'
Disp .... 13,000 lbs	Headroom ..... 6'4"
Ballast .... 4455 lbs	Fr. Water .... 70 gal
Sail Area	SA/Disp 17.1
Sloop .... 590 sq ft	Disp/LWL 238
Cutter ... 590 sq ft	Blst/Disp 34%
Mast Ht .... 48'	Designer
Auxiliary .... std	Robert A. Smith
Farymann ... 24 hp	First Built 1967
Diesel	No. Built 154
Fuel Cap ..... 42 gal	Kit $45,000

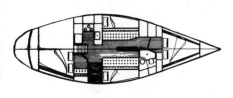

LOD .... 36'	Hull .... FRP
LWL .... 27'6"	Deck .... FRP
Beam .... 11'10"	Spar .... Alum
Draft	SA/Disp 19.8
Deep .... 6'6"	Disp/LWL 236
Shoal cb up .. 4'6"	Blst/Disp 50%
Shoal cb dn .. 6'6"	Price .... na
Disp ..... 11,000 lbs	
Ballast ..... 5500 lbs	
Sail Area	
Sloop .... 612 sq ft	
Auxiliary .... std	

YAMAHA SAILBOATS U.S.A.
6555 Katella Ave.
Cypress, CA 90630
(714) 761-7609

YACHT CONSTRUCTORS INC.
7030 N.E. 42nd Ave.
Portland, OR 97218
(503) 287-5794

MORGAN YACHT INC.
7200 Bryan Dairy Rd.
Largo, FL 33543
(813) 544-6681

Nonsuch 36

S2 11.0A

S2 11-OC

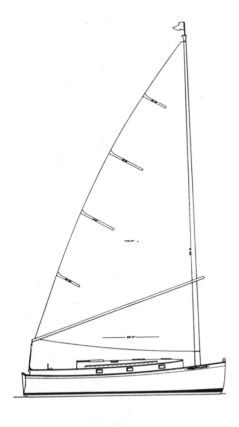

LOD	36'	Hull	FRP/Balsa
LWL	33'9"	Deck	FRP/Balsa
Beam	12'8"	Spar	alum
Draft	5'6"	Cockpit	7'
Disp	17,000 lbs	Headroom	6'6"
Ballast	6700 lbs	Fr. Water	100 gal
Sail Area		SA/Disp	18
Cat	742 sq ft	Disp/LWL	197
Mast Ht	62'	Blst/Disp	39%
Mast	unstayed	Designer	Mark Ellis
Auxiliary	std	First Built	1983
Westerbeke	52 hp	Price	$103,000
Diesel			without sails
Fuel Cap	45 gal		

LOD	36'	Hull	FRP
LWL	28'3"	Deck	FRP/Balsa
Beam	11'11"	Spar	Alum
Draft		Cockpit	9'
Shoal	4'8"	Headroom	6'3"
Deep	5'6"	Fr. Water	80 gal
Disp	15,000 lbs	SA/Disp	16.4
Ballast	6000 lbs	Disp/LWL	297
Sail Area		Blst/Disp	40%
Sloop	625 sq ft	Designer	
Mast Ht	49'		Arthur Edmunds
Auxiliary	std		
Universal	32 hp	Price	$84,900
Diesel			with sails
Fuel Cap	50 gal		

LOD	36'	Hull	FRP
LWL	28'3"	Deck	FRP/Balsa
Beam	11'11"	Spar	Alum
Draft		Cockpit	7'
Shoal	4'8"	Headroom	6'3"
Deep	5'6"	Fr. Water	80 gal
Disp	15,000 lbs	SA/Disp	16.4
Ballast	6000 lbs	Disp/LWL	297
Sail Area		Blst/Disp	40%
Sloop	625 sq ft	Designer	
Mast Ht	49'		Arthur Edmunds
Auxiliary	std	Price	$94,150
Universal	32 hp		with sails
Diesel			
Fuel Cap	70 gal		

HINTERHOELLER YACHTS LTD.
8 Keefer Rd., St. Catharines,
Ontario L2M 7N9, Canada
(416) 937-4440

S2 YACHTS INC.
725 E. 40th St.
Holland, MI 49423
(616) 392-7163

S2 YACHTS INC.
725 E. 40th St.
Holland, MI 49423
(616) 392-7163

Vancouver 36   Watkins 36   Cape Dory 36

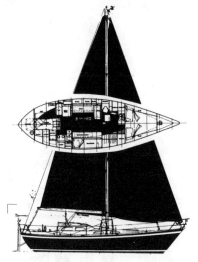

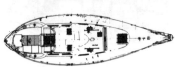

LOD .... 36'	Hull ..... FRP/Airex	
LWL .... 27'11"	Deck .. FRP/Klegecell	
Beam .... 11'	Spar .... Alum	
Draft .... 5'	Cockpit .... 6'6"	
Disp ..... 18,000 lbs	Headroom ..... 6'4"	
Ballast ..... 7600 lbs	Fr. Water .... 140 gal	
Sail Area	SA/Disp 16.3	
Cutter ... 700 sq ft	Disp/LWL 369	
Mast Ht ...... 52'10"	Blst/Disp 42%	
Auxiliary .... std	Designer	
Volvo-Penta . 36 hp	Robert B. Harris	
Diesel	First Built 1980	
Fuel Cap ..... 50 gal	No. Built 15	
	Kit $23,000	
	Price $121,000	
	without sails	

LOA .... 37'9"	Hull .... FRP
LOD .... 36'	Deck .... FRP
LWL .... 29'4"	Spar .... Alum
Beam .... 10'6"	Headroom ..... 6'3"
Draft .... 4'6"	Fr. Water .... 45 gal
Disp .... 17,000 lbs	SA/Disp 12.7
Ballast .... 6000 lbs	Disp/LWL 301
Sail Area	Blst/Disp 35%
Sloop .... 526 sq ft	Price $83,995
Mast Ht .... 45'	with sails
Auxiliary .... std	
Diesel ...... 40 hp	
Fuel Cap ..... 40 gal	

LOD .... 36'1"	Hull .... FRP
LWL .... 27'	Deck ..... FRP/Balsa
Beam .... 10'8"	Spar .... Alum
Draft .... 5'	Cockpit .... 7'7"
Disp .... 16,100 lbs	Headroom ..... 6'4"
Ballast .... 6050 lbs	Fr. Water .... 110 gal
Sail Area	SA/Disp 15.6
Cutter ... 622 sq ft	Disp/LWL 365
Mast Ht ...... 46'6"	Blst/Disp 38%
Auxiliary .... std	Designer .. Carl Alberg
Perkins ..... 50 hp	First Built 1978
Diesel	No. Built 85
Fuel Cap ..... 43 gal	1 Design .... yes
	Price .... na

Gulfstar 36

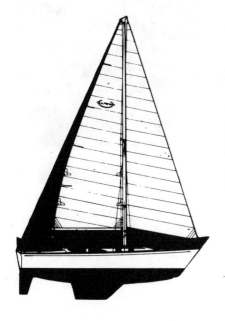

LOD	36'1"	Hull	FRP/Balsa
LWL	30'4"	Deck	FRP/Balsa
Beam	12'	Spar	Alum
Draft	4'9"	Fr. Water	80 gal
Disp	13,900 lbs	SA/Disp	16.8
Ballast	5500 lbs	Disp/LWL	222
Sail Area		Blst/Disp	40%
Sloop	608 sq ft	Designer	Dick Lazzara
Auxiliary	std	Price	$74,900
Westerbeke	27 hp		without sails
Diesel			
Fuel Cap	50 gal		

GULFSTAR INC.
6101 45th St. N.
St. Petersburg, FL 33714
(813) 527-7251

Islander 36

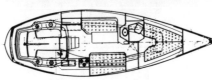

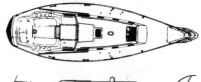

LOD	36'1"	Hull	FRP
LWL	28'3"	Deck	FRP
Beam	11'2"	Spar	Alum
Draft		Fr. Water	54 gal
Deep	6'	SA/Disp	16.3
Shoal	4'9"	Disp/LWL	266
Disp		Blst/Disp	41%
Deep	13,450 lbs	Designer	Alan Gurney
Shoal	13,600 lbs	Price	na
Ballast			
Deep	5450 lbs		
Shoal	5600 lbs		
Sail Area			
Sloop	575 sq ft		
Mast Ht	49'		
Auxiliary	std		
Pathfinder	42 hp		
Diesel			
Fuel Cap	32 gal		

ISLANDER YACHTS
1922 Barranca Rd.
Irvine, CA 92714
(714) 549-8526

Rajo—Sailer 37

LOA	41'7"	Hull	Steel
LOD	36'1"	Deck	Steel
LWL	32'1"	Spar	Alum
Beam	12'	Pos Float	yes
Draft	4'11"	Cockpit	6'
Disp	28,671 lbs	Headroom	6'6"
Ballast	8822 lbs	Fr. Water	132 gal
Sail Area		SA/Disp	13
Cutter	763 sq ft	Disp/LWL	388
Ketch	711 sq ft	Blst/Disp	31%
Mast Ht		Designer	M. Bekebrede
Cutter	50'	First Built	1975
Ketch	46'	No. Built	45
Auxiliary	std	Price	$111,500
Volvo	62 hp		with sails
Diesel			
Fuel Cap	79 gal		

RAJO—WATERSPORT BV
Werfweg 2 — 8243 PG Lelystad
Industrieterrein Noordersluis
Holland
(03200) 60929/60979

Lancer 36

LANCER YACHTS

LOD .... 36'2"	Hull .... FRP
LWL .... 29'	Deck .... FRP
Beam .... 11'9"	Spar .... Alum
Draft	Cockpit .... 8'
Shoal ...... 4'11"	Headroom .... 6'
Deep .... 6'2"	Fr. Water .... 40 gal
Disp ..... 10,500 lbs	SA/Disp 19.6
Ballast ..... 4000 lbs	Disp/LWL 192
Sail Area	Blst/Disp 38%
Sloop .... 588 sq ft	Designer
Sloop .... 705 sq ft	Bill Lee/Bruce Farr
Mast Ht .... 47'	First Built 1978
Auxiliary .... std	1 Design ...... yes
Yanmar ..... 22 hp	Price $81,158
Diesel	with sails
Fuel Cap ...... 30 gal	

LANCER YACHT CORP.
1939 Deere Ave.
Irvine, CA 92714
(714) 751-7220

Comet 111

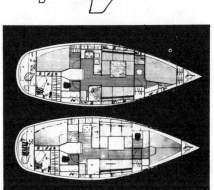

LOD .... 36'3"	Hull .... FRP
LWL .... 29'7"	Deck ..... FRP/Balsa
Beam .... 11'3"	Spar .... Alum
Draft	Fr. Water .... 75 gal
Shoal ...... 5'3"	Disp/LWL 238
Deep .... 6'7"	Blst/Disp 37%
Disp ..... 13,860 lbs	Designer Groupe Finot
Ballast ..... 5060 lbs	Builder ... Comar Italy
Sail Area	Price .... na
Sloop .... na	
Auxiliary .... std	
Volvo ...... 25 hp	
Diesel	
Fuel Cap ...... 35 gal	

COMAR USA
149 Shaw Ave.
Irvington, NJ 07111

F3

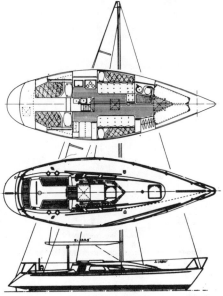

LOD .... 36'3"	Hull ...... FRP/Balsa
LWL .... 29'6"	Deck ..... FRP/Balsa
Beam .... 11'10"	Spar .... Alum
Draft .... 6'9"	Cockpit .... 8'
Disp .... 10,900 lbs	Headroom ..... 6'2"
Ballast .... 5700 lbs	Fr. Water .... 40 gal
Sail Area	SA/Disp 20.3
Sloop .... 625 sq ft	Disp/LWL 189
Mast Ht .... 52'	Blst/Disp 52%
Auxiliary .... std	Designer German Frers
Westerbeke .. 29 hp	Builder
Diesel	Hinterhoeller Yachts
Fuel Cap ..... 25 gal	First Built 1982
	No. Built 25
	Price $86,795
	with sails

NEW WAVE MARKETING
29 Touro Street
Newport, RI 02840
(401) 849-2450 (800) 556-7708

Pearson 36

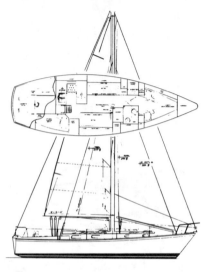

LOD	36'5''	Hull	FRP
LWL	30'	Deck	FRP
Beam	11'5''	Spar	Alum
Draft	5'6''	Cockpit	8'
Disp	17,700 lbs	Headroom	6'3''
Ballast	7300 lbs	Fr. Water	150 gal
Sail Area		SA/Disp	14.1
Cutter	599 sq ft	Disp/LWL	293
Mast Ht	47'4''	Blst/Disp	41%
Auxiliary	std	Designer	William Shaw
Diesel		Price	$81,650
Fuel Cap	50 gal		with sails

PEARSON YACHTS
West Shore Rd.
Portsmouth, RI 02871
(401) 683-0100

CS 36

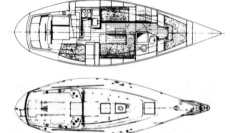

LOD	36'6''	Hull	FRP
LWL	29'3''	Deck	FRP
Beam	11'6''	Spar	Alum
Draft		Headroom	6'2''
Shoal	4'11''	Fr. Water	83 gal
Deep	6'3''	SA/Disp	16.5
Disp	15,500 lbs	Disp/LWL	277
Ballast	6500 lbs	Blst/Disp	42%
Sail Area		Designer	
Sloop	640 sq ft		CS Yachts Ltd.
Mast Ht	52'10''	First Built	1978
Auxiliary	std	No. Built	175
Westerbeke	30 hp	Price	$79,900
Diesel			without sails
Fuel Cap	35 gal		

CS YACHTS LTD.
79 Bramsteele Rd.
Brampton, Ont. Canada
(416) 457-6713

Banner 37

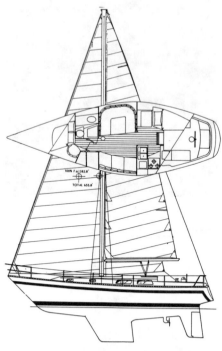

LOD	36'7''	Hull	FRP
LWL	28'10''	Deck	FRP
Beam	12'	Spar	Alum
Draft	5'10''	Cockpit	8'
Disp	13,500 lbs	Headroom	6'4''
Ballast	5550 lbs	Fr. Water	50 gal
Sail Area		SA/Disp	18.5
Sloop	655 sq ft	Disp/LWL	251
Auxiliary	std	Blst/Disp	41%
Volvo	23 hp	Designer	
Diesel			S. Huntingford
Fuel Cap	50 gal	First Built	1981
		No. Built	7
		Price	$68,500
			with sails

COOPER ENTERPRISES LTD.
1642 Langan Ave.
Port Coquituam, B.C.
Canada V3C 1K5
(604) 942-5945

Performance 36　Pipedream 36.6　Scheel 36

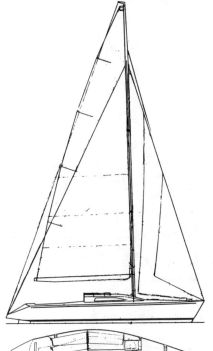

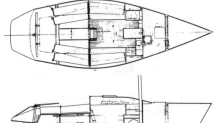

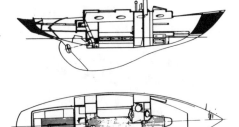

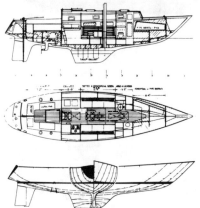

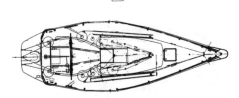

LOD	36'7"	Hull ..... FRP/Foam
LWL	30'8"	Deck ..... FRP/Foam
Beam	12'5"	Spar ..... Alum
Draft	6'10"	SA/Disp 23.1
Disp	10,361 lbs	Disp/LWL 160
Ballast	4817 lbs	Blst/Disp 46%
Sail Area		Designer .. Bruce Farr
Sloop .... 687 sq ft		Price $99,000
		without sails

LOD	36'7"	Hull ..... FRP
LWL	25'6"	Deck ..... FRP
Beam	10'7"	Spar ..... Alum
Draft	5'9"	Headroom ..... 6'
Disp	14,000 lbs	Fr. Water .... 50 gal
Ballast	6200 lbs	SA/Disp 22.5
Sail Area		Disp/LWL 377
Sloop	816 sq ft	Blst/Disp 44%
Mast Ht	49'	Designer
Auxiliary	std	Francis Kinney
Universal	25 hp	First Built 1982
		Kit ..... available
		Price $54,000
		without sails

LOD	36'8"	Hull ..... Wood
LWL	30'	Deck ... FRP/Plywood
Beam	na	Spar ..... Alum
Draft	4'8"	Cockpit ..... 7'
Disp	11,000 lbs	Headroom ..... 6'4"
Ballast	5400 lbs	Fr. Water ..... 80 gal
Sail Area		SA/Disp 19.5
Cutter	604 sq ft	Disp/LWL 182
Sloop	na	Blst/Disp 49%
Mast Ht	47'	Designer
Auxiliary	std	Henry A. Scheel
Diesel		First Built 1983
		Price ..... na

PERFORMANCE YACHTS INC.
P. O. Box 13505
Tampa, FL 33681
(813) 447-7852

G. A. PATTEN
RR # Box 559
Kittery, ME 03904
(207) 439-3967

ROGERS MARINE INC.
P. O. Box 684
Rockland, ME 04841
(207) 594-7215

Seafarer 37

Tayana 37

Slocum 37

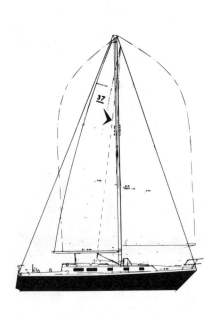

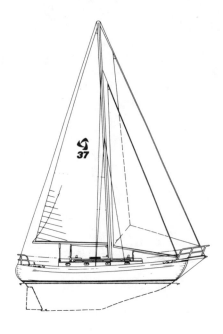

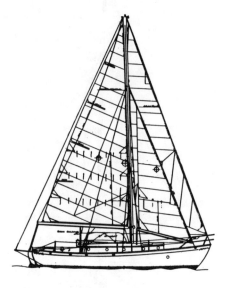

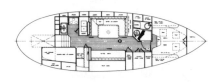

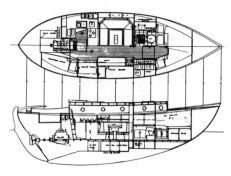

LOD . . . . 36'8"	Hull . . . . FRP
LWL . . . . 31'3"	Deck . . . . FRP
Beam . . . . 11'9"	Spar . . . . Alum
Draft	Cockpit . . . . 8'3"
Shoal . . . . 5'	Headroom . . . . . 6'5"
Deep . . . . . . 6'3"	Fr. Water . . . . 150 gal
Disp . . . . . 16,500 lbs	SA/Disp 18.6
Ballast . . . . . 6675 lbs	Disp/LWL 241
Sail Area	Blst/Disp 40%
Sloop . . . . 752 sq ft	Designer
Mast Ht . . . . . . 50'	McCurdy/Rhodes
Auxiliary . . . . std	First Built 1980
Yanmar . . . 22.5 hp	No. Built 25
Diesel	Price $84,000
Fuel Cap . . . . . 20 gal	with sails

LOA . . . . 42'2"	Hull . . . . FRP
LOD . . . . 36'8"	Deck . . . . FRP
LWL . . . . 30'10"	Spar . . . Alum or wood
Beam . . . . 11'6"	Cockpit . . . . 4'6"
Draft . . . . 5'8"	Headroom . . . . . 6'3"
Disp . . . . . 22,500 lbs	Fr. Water . . . 100 gal
Ballast . . . . 7340 lbs	SA/Disp 17.3
Sail Area	Disp/LWL 343
Cutter . . . 864 sq ft	Blst/Disp 33%
Ketch . . . . 768 sq ft	Designer Robert Perry
Mast Ht	Builder . . . . . Ta Yang
Cutter . . . . . . 54'6"	First Built 1975
Ketch . . . . 48'	No. Built 376
Auxiliary . . . . std	Price $74,000
Yanmar . . . . . 30 hp	with sails
Diesel	
Fuel Cap . . . . . . 90 gal	

LOD . . . . 36'9"	Hull . . . . . . FRP/Airex
LWL . . . . 32'	Deck . . . . . FRP/Balsa
Beam . . . . 11'8"	Spar . . . . Alum
Draft . . . . 6'	Pos Float . . . . yes
Disp . . . . . 27,000 lbs	Cockpit . . . . 6'
Ballast . . . 12,000 lbs	Headroom . . . . . 6'5"
Sail Area	Fr. Water . . . . 200 gal
Cutter . . . 802 sq ft	SA/Disp 14.3
Auxiliary . . . . std	Disp/LWL 367
Volvo . . . . . . 36 hp	Blst/Disp 44%
Diesel	Designer
	Stan Huntingford
	First Built 1978
	No. Built 52
	Price $85,000
	with sails

SEAFARER YACHTS INC.
760 Park Ave.
Huntington, NY 11743
(516) 427-6670

SOUTHERN OFFSHORE YACHTS
Box 6
Tarpon Springs, FL 33589
(813) 937-3188

CRUISING YACHTS INT'L.
12530 Olympia Dr.
Houston, TX 77077
(713) 497-6958

Sea Bird 37

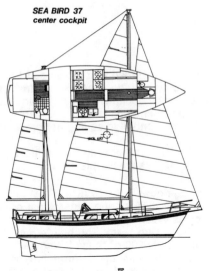

SEA BIRD 37
center cockpit

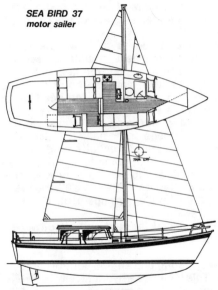

SEA BIRD 37
motor sailer

LOA	38'10''	Hull	FRP
LOD	36'10''	Deck	FRP
LWL	32'6''	Spar	Alum
Beam	11'8''	Cockpit	6'
Draft	4'	Headroom	6'2''
Disp	18,000 lbs	Fr. Water	100 gal
Ballast	6000 lbs	SA/Disp	14.4
Sail Area		Disp/LWL	234
Sloop	620 sq ft	Blst/Disp	33%
Cutter	639 sq ft	Designer	
Ketch	650 sq ft		Cooper Yachts
Auxiliary	std	First Built	1975
Lehman	46 hp	No. Built	54
Diesel		Price	$74,750
Fuel Cap	90 gal		with sails

COOPER ENTERPRISES LTD.
1642 Langan Ave.
Port Coquituam, B.C.
Canada V3C 1K5
(604) 942-5945

Seidelmann 37

LOD	36'10''	Hull	FRP
LWL	29'6''	Deck	FRP
Beam	12'	Spar	Alum
Draft		Cockpit	8'
Shoal	4'	Headroom	6'7''
Deep	5'11''	Fr. Water	70 gal
Disp		SA/Disp	17.8
Shoal	13,900 lbs	Disp/LWL	242
Deep	13,500 lbs	Blst/Disp	46%
Ballast		Designer	
Shoal	6400 lbs		Bob Seidelmann
Deep	6000 lbs	First Built	1981
Sail Area		No. Built	71
Sloop	643 sq ft	Price	$83,350
Mast Ht	53'2''		with sails
Auxiliary	std		
Yanmar	23.5 hp		
Diesel			
Fuel Cap	18 gal		

SEIDELMANN YACHTS
Cushman Ave., P. O. Box 2529
Berlin, NJ 08009
(609) 768-1707

Swan 371

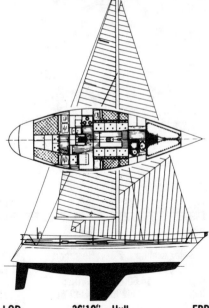

LOD	36'10''	Hull	FRP
LWL	29'9''	Deck	FRP
Beam	11'4''	Spar	Alum
Draft	6'10''	Disp/LWL	261
Disp	15400 lbs	Blst/Disp	37%
Ballast	5700 lbs	Designer	Ron Holland
Sail Area		Builder	
Sloop	na		Nautor, Finland
Auxiliary	std	Price	$97,000
Bukh	20 hp		with sails
Diesel			

NAUTOR EAST
55 America's Cup Avenue
Newport, RI 02840
(401) 846-8404

Southerly 115

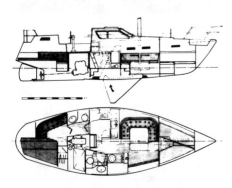

The SOUTHERLY 115 is a brand new boat, designed and developed to fill the gap for the yachtsman who wants to combine both deep and shoal draft (1), dual cockpit and interior steering controls (2), center cockpit, large aft cabin suite with walk-through with its own toilet compartment (3), large galley area up where the view and the company are (4), with lively and high sailing performance, built to the very highest quality standards.

(1) Go-anywhere cruising   (2) All-weather sailing in comfort
(3) Privacy   (4) Cooks are people, too!

Unique features explained:

Although she is new for 1983, her heritage goes back to lifting/keel ocean racing craft like "NORYEMA VG" and "RED ROOSTER," the sensational cruising/racing boat which collected a lot of Cowes Week trophies, won the Fastnet race and was top boat of the winning Admiral's Cup team. The builders of the SOUTHERLYS developed and have now built nearly 200 of these lifting keel go-anywhere cruising yachts. Their experience with this break-through type is unique and invaluable. They have built many times more of these very successful boats than any other builder in the world. with the keel fully raised, she can cruise and sail and moor in less than 2½ feet of water!

The airfoil cast iron keel, weighing about a ton, is fully retractable and swings up and down without any side play from a very heavy stainless steel pivot fitted into a substantial boss at the forward end of a cast iron keel grounding plate that weighs nearly a ton and a half. The keel plate is one of the most important features that makes the SOUTHERLY unique; it is the heart of her difference. The whole cast iron keel assembly fits and bolts into a recess molded into the bottom of the hull. It acts as transverse stiffening at the keel slot and enables the boat to ground out, level, without damage or the need for bilge keels, props or cradle. The keel and plate assembly can readily be unbolted and removed if this should ever be needed. With the keel up, her bottom is fair. With the keel down, the keel casting has a fairing flange molded in to eliminate trunk aperture drag for best performance. To provide any draft between 2'6" and 6'8", the keel is raised and lowered by a ram hydraulic and dual pulley arrangement. There is a cushioned safety down-stop built into the system.

The large, low aspect ratio rudder is balanced for light and effective helm response and mounts from a metal reinforced skeg-keel shoe that provides a protected propellor aperture.

In addition to the usual cockpit wheel steering and engine controls, another complete helm station is provided below. This includes a hydraulically controlled steering wheel that can be clutched out, and full engine controls. Visibility at this station, out of the weather, is excellent. A windshield wiper is provided. The navigation/helmsman's seat is adjustable for height.

The very private aft cabin suite is reachable by below decks walk-through. It provides 6' headroom, quite unusual in a boat of her size. There is a large double berth, big hanging locker and a comfortable settee. A head, with toilet and wash basin, is located off the passage, with two sets of folding doors that allow closing off in either or both directions to provide a large head-dressing room area.

Yet another unique feature is the location of the galley area. It's large and bright, with fine visibility out, and yet close by the cockpit and main cabin/saloon. Six window/deadlights are set right into the hull for keeping up with the passing scene, even while seated in the main and forward cabins.

Last, but by no means the least of the SOUTHERLY 115's unique features, is her quality. She's the pride of a British yard that molds to Lloyds specifications for Camper & Nicholsons and builds the beautiful FISHER yachts. Lloyds certificates available. That says it all!

LOD	36'10"	Hull	FRP
LWL	27'6"	Deck	FRP/Balsa
Beam	11'11"	Spar	Alum
Draft		Cockpit	5'6"
Swing keel up .	2'3"	Headroom	6'
Swing keel dn .	6'8"	Fr. Water	72 gal
Disp	14,600 lbs	SA/Disp	13.6
Ballast	4962 lbs	Disp/LWL	313
Sail Area		Blst/Disp	34%
Sloop	509 sq ft	Designer .	Northshore
Mast Ht	48'6"		Yacht Yards, England
Auxiliary	std	Builder ..	Northshore
Bukh	36 hp		Yacht Yards, England
Diesel		First Built	1982
Fuel Cap	60 gal	No. Built	2
		1 Design	yes
		Price	$77,600
			with sails

PARKER YACHTS
South Freeport, ME 04078
(207) 865-6692

Crealock 37

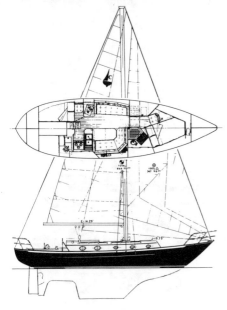

LOD	36'11"	Hull	FRP
LWL	27'9"	Deck	FRP/Plywood
Beam	10'10"	Spar	Alum
Draft		Cockpit	6'10"
Shoal	4'4"	Headroom	6'4"
Deep	5'4"	Fr. Water	100 gal
Disp	16,000 lbs	SA/Disp	14.4
Ballast	6200 lbs	Disp/LWL	334
Sail Area		Blst/Disp	39%
Sloop	573 sq ft	Designer	
Cutter	708 sq ft		W. I. B. Crealock
Yawl	619 sq ft	No. Built	50
Mast Ht	47'6"	Kit	$19,400
Auxiliary	std	Price	$88,800
Universal	32 hp		without sails
Diesel			
Fuel Cap	47 gal		

PACIFIC SEACRAFT CORP.
3301 S. Susan St.
Santa Ana, CA 92704
(714) 751-1343

Pearson 37

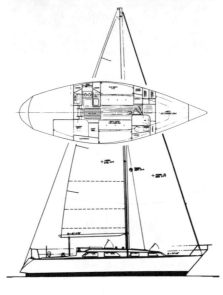

LOD	36'11"	Hull	FRP
LWL	30'1"	Deck	FRP
Beam	11'10"	Spar	Alum
Draft		Cockpit	8'6"
Shoal	4'11"	Headroom	6'3"
Deep	6'6"	Fr. Water	70 gal
Disp		SA/Disp	
Ballast	na	Disp/LWL	
Sail Area		Designer	William Shaw
Sloop	639 sq ft	Price	$85,850
Mast Ht	52'11"		with sails
Auxiliary	std		
Universal	23 hp		
Diesel			
Fuel Cap	22 gal		

PEARSON YACHTS
West Shore Rd.
Portsmouth, RI 02871
(401) 683-0100

Dickerson 37

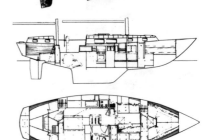

LOD	37'	Hull	FRP
LWL	28'10"	Deck	FRP
Beam	11'6"	Spar	Alum
Draft	4'6"	Cockpit	7'
Disp	16,000 lbs	Headroom	6'3"
Ballast	5900 lbs	Fr. Water	90 gal
Sail Area		SA/Disp	17.0
Sloop	675 sq ft	Disp/LWL	297
Cutter	675 sq ft	Blst/Disp	37%
Ketch	675 sq ft	Designer	George Hazen
Mast Ht		First Built	1981
Sloop	51'	No. Built	15
Cutter	51'	Price	$99,500
Ketch	49'		without sails
Auxiliary	std		
Perkins	40 hp		
Diesel			
Fuel Cap	40 gal		

DICKERSON BOATBUILDERS
Route 2 Box 92
Trappe, MD 21673
(301) 822-8556

Dockrell 37

LOD . . . . 37'	Hull . . . . FRP
LWL . . . . 30'	Deck . . . . FRP
Beam . . . . 10'2"	Spar . . . . Alum
Draft	Cockpit . . . . 9'3"
cb up . . . . 3'9"	Headroom . . . . 6'2"
cb dn . . . . . . 8'4"	SA/Disp 18.8
Disp . . . . . 11,500 lbs	Disp/LWL 190
Ballast . . . . 5500 lbs	Blst/Disp 48%
Sail Area	Builder
Cutter . . . 600 sq ft	Dockrell Yachts, England
Auxiliary . . . . std	Price $49,995
Ford	with sails
Diesel	

DOCKRELL YACHTS
1839 Route 46
Parsippany, NJ 07054
(201) 226-3200

Espirit 37

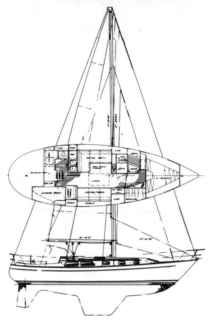

LOD . . . . 37'	Hull . . . . FRP
LWL . . . . 31'8"	Deck . . . . FRP
Beam . . . . 11'6"	Spar . . . . Alum
Draft . . . . 5'9"	Fr. Water . . . . 100 gal
Disp . . . . 17,000 lbs	SA/Disp 16.1
Ballast . . . . 6700 lbs	Disp/LWL 239
Sail Area	Blst/Disp 39%
Cutter . . . 667 sq ft	Designer Robert Perry
Auxiliary . . . . std	Price $135,000
Westerbeke	with sails
Diesel	
Fuel Cap . . . . . . 40 gal	

VALIANT YACHTS CORP.
2000 Westlake Ave. North
Seattle, WA 98109
(206) 284-7943

Hunter 37

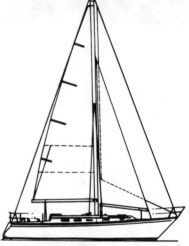

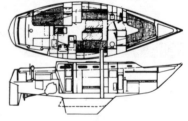

LOD . . . . 37'	Hull . . . . FRP
LWL . . . . 30'	Deck . . . . FRP
Beam . . . . 11'10"	Spar . . . . Alum
Draft	Fr. Water . . . . 100 gal
Shoal . . . . 4'	SA/Disp 16.7
Deep . . . . 5'1"	Disp/LWL 294
Disp . . . . 17,800 lbs	Blst/Disp 40%
Ballast	Price $62,190
Shoal . . . . 7150 lbs	with sails
Deep . . . . 6850 lbs	
Sail Area	
Cutter . . . 710 sq ft	
Mast Ht . . . . 50'	
Auxiliary . . . . std	
Yanmar . . . . . 30 hp	
Diesel	
Fuel Cap . . . . . . 44 gal	

HUNTER MARINE
Box 1030, Hwy 441
Alachua, FL 32601
(904) 462-3077

Irwin 37

LOD	37'	Hull	FRP/Coremat
LWL	30'	Deck	FRP
Beam	11'6"	Spar	Alum
Draft		Fr. Water	187 gal
Shoal cb up	4'	SA/Disp	13.6
Shoal cb dn	8'	DISP/LWL	330
Deep	5'6"	Blst/Disp	39%
Disp	20,000 lbs	Price	$69,950
Ballast	7800 lbs		with sails
Sail Area			
Sloop	624 sq ft		
Ketch	593 sq ft		
Mast Ht	46'		
Auxiliary	std		
Perkins			
Diesel			
Fuel Cap	85 gal		

IRWIN YACHTS
13055 49th St. N.
Clearwater, FL 33520
(813) 577-4581

Lancer 40

LOD	37'	Hull	FRP
LWL	31'8"	Deck	FRP
Beam	12'	Spar	Alum
Draft		Cockpit	6'6"
Shoal	4'11"	Headroom	6'
Deep	6'3"	Fr. Water	140 gal
Disp	15,000 lbs	SA/Disp	19.1
Ballast	4000 lbs	Disp/LWL	210
Sail Area		Blst/Disp	27%
Sloop	727 sq ft	Designer	Herb David
Mast Ht	54'	First Built	1981
Auxiliary	std	1 Design	yes
Volvo	35 hp	Price	$129,900
Diesel			with sails
Fuel Cap	60 gal		

LANCER YACHT CORP.
1939 Deere Ave.
Irvine, CA 92714
(714) 751-7220

Northern 37

LOD	37'	Hull	FRP
LWL	28'11"	Deck	FRP
Beam	11'	Spar	Alum
Draft		Cockpit	6'6"
Shoal	5'8"	Headroom	6'3"
Deep	5'10"	Fr. Water	100 gal
Disp	14,950 lbs	SA/Disp	15.8
Ballast	6165 lbs	Disp/LWL	276
Sail Area		Blst/Disp	41%
Ketch	600 sq ft	Designer	
Sloop	572 sq ft		Northern Yachts
Mast Ht	52'	Builder	
Auxiliary	std		Northern Yachts
Perkins 108		First Built	1977
Diesel		No. Built	18
Fuel Cap	45 gal	Kit	available
		price	$75,000
			with sails

NORTHERN YACHTS
395 Francom St.
Ajax, Ontario
Canada L1S 1R4
(416) 683-5980

O'Day 37   Oceanic 37   Peterson 37

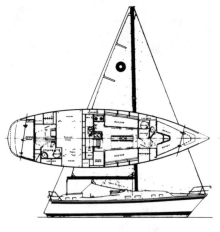

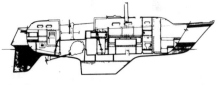

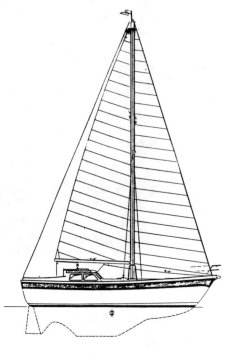

LOD	37'	Hull	FRP
LWL	30'4"	Deck	FRP
Beam	11'2"	Spar	Alum
Draft	4'9"	Headroom	6'1"
Disp	14,000 lbs	Fr. Water	150 gal
Ballast	5800 lbs	SA/Disp	16.4
Sail Area		Disp/LWL	223
Sloop	594 sq ft	Blst/Disp	41%
Mast Ht	47'	Designer	
Auxiliary	std		C. R. Hunt Assoc.
Universal	32 hp	First Built	1978
Diesel		No. Built	204
Fuel Cap	40 gal	1 Design	yes
		Price	na

LOD	37'	Hull	FRP
LWL	31'4"	Deck	FRP/Wood
Beam	11'8"	Spar	Alum
Draft	5'6"	Fr. Water	180 gal
Disp	18,000 lbs	SA/Disp	16.3
Ballast	6500 lbs	Disp/LWL	261
Sail Area		Blst/Disp	36%
Sloop	698 sq ft	Designer	Ted Brewer
Auxiliary	std	Price	$80,000
Yanmar	30 hp		with sails
Diesel			
Fuel Cap	120 gal		

LOD	37'	Hull	FRP/Balsa
LWL	30'10"	Deck	FRP/Balsa
Beam	11'11"	Cockpit	8'
Draft	6'8"	Headroom	6'2"
Disp	12,000 lbs	Fr. Water	40 gal
Ballast	na	Disp/LWL	183
Sail Area		Designer	
Sloop	na		Doug Peterson
Auxiliary	std	First Built	1982
Universal	25 hp	No. Built	2
Diesel		1 Design	yes
Fuel Cap	16	Kit	available
		Price	$93,000 Can
			without sails

BANGOR PUNTA MARINE
848 Airport Rd.
Box 991
Fall River, MA 02722
(617) 678-5291

PAN—OCEANIC MARINE
619 NW 12th Ave.
Miami, FL 33136
(305) 324-0088

WIGGERS CUSTOM YACHTS
200 Valencia Rd.
Oshawa, Ontario
Canada L1J 1P3
(416) 723-0370

Reliance 37

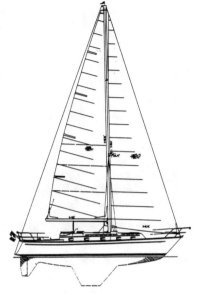

LOD . . . . 37'1"	Hull . . . . FRP
LWL . . . . 30'	Deck . . . . FRP
Beam . . . . 11'4"	Spar . . . . Alum
Draft . . . . 6'3"	Fr. Water . . 85 gal
Disp . . . . . 17,200 lbs	Disp/LWL 284
Ballast . . . . . 5542 lbs	Blst/Disp 32%
Sail Area	Designer
Sloop . . . . na	Robert H. Perry
Auxiliary . . . . std	First Built 1980
Izusu . . . . . . 42 hp	Kit $32,000
Diesel	Price $105,000
Fuel Cap . . . . . . 65 gal	with sails

MARKOS YACHTS LTD.
#3: 1210 Pipeline Rd.
Coquitlam, B.C. Canada V3B 4S1
(604) 464-7533

Alberg 37

LOD . . . . 37'2"	Hull . . . . FRP
LWL . . . . 26'6"	Deck . . . . FRP
Beam . . . . 10'2"	Spar . . . . Alum
Draft . . . . 5'6"	Fr. Water . . 60 gal
Disp . . . . . 16,800 lbs	SA/Disp 16.7
Ballast . . . . . 6500 lbs	Disp/LWL 403
Sail Area	Blst/Disp 39%
Yawl . . . . 686 sq ft	Price . . . $64,600 Can
Sloop . . . . 646 sq ft	without sails
Auxiliary . . . . std	
Volvo	
Diesel	
Fuel Cap . . . . . . 35 gal	

WHITBY BOAT WORKS LTD.
1710 Charles St.
Whitby, Ontario
Canada L1N 1C2
(416) 668-7755

Classic 37

Available in
KIT
or any stage of
completion.

LOD . . . . 37'3"	Hull . . . . FRP
LWL . . . . 26'3"	Deck . . . . FRP
Beam . . . . 10'2"	Spar . . . . Alum
Draft . . . . 5'10"	SA/Disp 15.6
Disp . . . . . 16,800 lbs	Disp/LWL 415
Ballast . . . . . 6800 lbs	Blst/Disp 40%
Sail Area	Kit . . . . . $14,500 Can
Sloop . . . . 639 sq ft	
Auxiliary . . . . std	

J & C FIBERCRAFT
P. O. Box 263
Barrie, Ontario
Canada L4M 4T2
(705) 326-8880

Contest 38 S

Tartan 37

Island Trader 38

Island Trader 38
Ketch

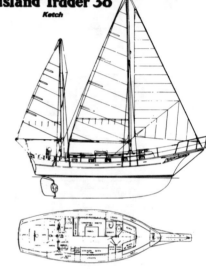

Contest 38 S

LOD	37'3"	Hull	FRP
LWL	29'10"	Deck	FRP
Beam	12'	Headroom	6'3"
Draft		Fr. Water	77 gal
Shoal	5'5"	SA/Disp	14.3
Deep	6'5"	Disp/LWL	324
Disp		Blst/Disp	43%
Shoal	19,285 lbs	Designer	Dick Zaal
Deep	18,603 lbs	Builder	
Ballast			Conyplex, Holland
Shoal	8230 lbs	Price	na
Deep	7593 lbs		
Sail Area			
Ketch	641 sq ft		
Mast Ht	48'9"		
Auxiliary	std		
Volvo Penta	36 hp		
Diesel			
Fuel Cap	44 gal		

Tartan 37

LOD	37'3"	Hull	FRP
LWL	28'6"	Deck	FRP
Beam	11'9"	Spar	Alum
Draft		Fr. Water	90 gal
Shoal cb up	4'2"	SA/Disp	16.1
Shoal cb dn	7'9"	Disp/LWL	299
Deep	6'7"	Blst/Disp	48%
Disp	15,500 lbs	Designer	
Ballast			Sparkman & Stephens
Shoal	7500 lbs	Price	na
Deep	7200 lbs		
Sail Area			
Sloop	625 sq ft		
Auxiliary	std		
Westerbeke	41 hp		
Diesel			
Fuel Cap	50 gal		

Island Trader 38

LOD	37'4"	Hull	FRP
LWL	30'4"	Deck	Teak
Beam	12'	Spar	Wood
Draft	4'6"	Cockpit	6'4"
Disp	26,400 lbs	Headroom	6'4"
Ballast	7000 lbs	SA/Disp	10.2
Sail Area		Disp/LWL	422
Ketch	567 sq ft	Blst/Disp	27%
Mast Ht	42'3"	Designer	Floyd Ayers
Auxiliary	std	1 Design	yes
		Price	$72,500
			with sails

HOLLAND YACHTS
Box 129
Solomons, MD 20688
(301) 326-3960

TARTAN MARINE CO.
320 River St.
Grand River, OH 44045
(216) 354-5671

**MARINE TRADING
INTERNATIONAL**
Box 1232
Point Pleasant Beach, NJ 08742
(201) 899-6800

Endeavour 37

E37 Ketch

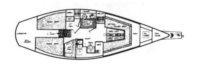

LOD .... 37'5"	Hull .... FRP
LWL .... 30'	Deck .... FRP
Beam .... 11'7"	Spar .... Alum
Draft .... 4'6"	Headroom ..... 6'6"
Disp ..... 21,000 lbs	SA/Disp 12.2
Ballast ..... 9000 lbs	Disp/LWL 347
Sail Area	Blst/Disp 43%
Sloop .... 580 sq ft	Price $77,900
Ketch .... 640 sq ft	without sails
Mast Ht .... 49'	
Auxiliary .... std	
Diesel ..... 50 hp	

ENDEAVOUR YACHT CORP.
11700 S. Belcher Rd.
Largo, FL 33543
(813) 541-3553

Nauticat 38 Ketch

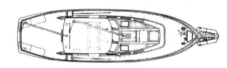

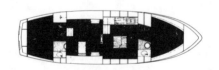

LOD .... 37'6"	Hull .... FRP
LWL .... 30'4"	Deck .... FRP
Beam .... 11'1"	Spar .... Alum
Draft .... 5'11"	Fr. Water ..... 66 gal
Disp ... 24,200 lbs	SA/Disp 15.8
Ballast ..... 6835 lbs	disp/LWL 387
Sail Area	Blst/Disp 28%
Ketch .... 827 sq ft	Builder
Mast Ht ...... 46'11"	Siltala Yachts Oy Finland
Auxiliary .... std	Price .... na
Ford .... 80 hp	
Diesel	
Fuel Cap ..... 160 gal	

NAUTICAT INC.
Box 809, Tucker's Wharf
Marblehead, MA 01945
(617) 631-8491

C & C 37

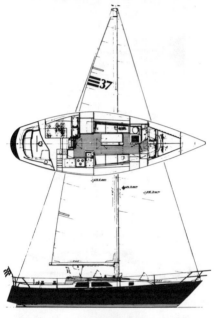

LOD .... 37'7"	Hull ...... FRP/Balsa
LWL .... 28'9"	Deck ..... FRP/Balsa
Beam .... 11'8"	Spar .... Alum
Draft .... 6'7"	Fr. Water ..... 60 gal
Disp .... 14,300 lbs	SA/Disp 18.2
Ballast ..... 6000 lbs	Disp/LWL 268
Sail Area	Blst/Disp 42%
Sloop .... 670 sq ft	Price $93,950
Mast Ht .... 55'1"	without sails
Auxiliary .... std	
Yanmar	
Diesel	
Fuel Cap ..... 20 gal	

C&C YACHTS
55 Port Street East
Mississauga, Ontario
Canada L5G 4P3
(416) 274-7131

Ericson 38

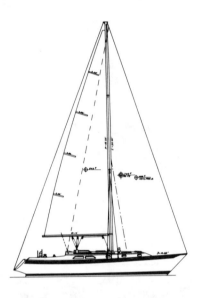

LOD . . . . 37'8"	Hull . . . . FRP
LWL . . . . 30'6"	Deck . . . . FRP
Beam . . . . 12'	Spar . . . . Alum
Draft	Headroom . . . . 6'4"
Shoal . . . . . 4'11"	SA/Disp 18.8
Deep . . . . 6'6"	Disp/LWL 234
Disp . . . . 14,850 lbs	Blst/Disp 42%
Ballast . . . . . 6200 lbs	Designer . . Bruce King
Sail Area	Price . . . . na
Sloop . . . . 709 sq ft	
Auxiliary . . . . std	
Universal . . . 32 hp	
Diesel	

Liberty 38

No Photo
or
Line Drawing
Available

LOD . . . . 37'8"	Hull . . . . FRP
LWL . . . . 30'8"	Deck . . . . FRP
Beam . . . . 11'6"	Spar . . . . Alum
Draft . . . . 4'9"	Cockpit . . . . 8'
Disp . . . . 20,000 lbs	Headroom . . . . 6'5"
Ballast . . . . . 8000 lbs	Disp/LWL 309
Cutter . . . . na	Blst/Disp 40%
Ketch . . . . na	Designer
Auxiliary . . . . std	J. W. Fennell
Diesel . . . . . 40 hp	First Built 1983
	Kit . . . . available
	Price $110,000
	with sails

Dartsailer 38

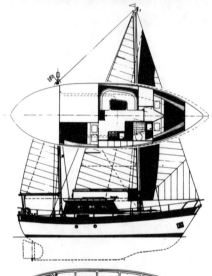

LOD . . . . 37'9"	Hull . . . . FRP
LWL . . . . 31'6"	Deck . . . . FRP
Beam . . . . 12'4"	Spar . . . . Alum
Draft . . . . 4'11"	Cockpit . . . . 7'5"
Disp . . . . 28,600 lbs	Headroom . . . . . 6'5"
Ballast . . . 11,000 lbs.	Fr. Water . . . 119 gal
Sail Area	SA/Disp 10.1
Ketch . . . . 589 sq ft	Disp/LWL 408
Mast Ht . . . . . . 45'7"	Blst/Disp 38%
Auxiliary . . . . std	Designer
Volvo . . . . . . 85 hp	W. De Vries Lentsch
Diesel	Builder
	Neptunus, Holland
	First Built 1978
	Price $81,000
	with sails

38 Mark II

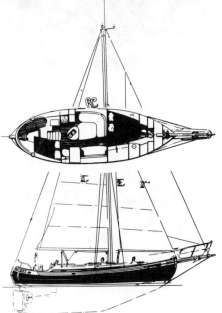

LOA . . . . 46'	Hull . . . . FRP
LOD . . . . 37'9"	Deck . . . . . FRP/Teak
LWL . . . . 33'	Spar . . . . Alum
Beam . . . . 12'6"	Cockpit . . . . 8'
Draft . . . . 6'	Headroom . . . . 6'4"
Disp . . . . . 27,500 lbs	Fr. Water . . . . 170 gal
Ballast . . 10,300 lbs	SA/Disp 15.2
Sail Area	Disp/LWL 341
Cutter . . . 867 sq ft	Blst/Disp 37%
Mast Ht . . . . . . 58'	Designer
Auxiliary . . . . std	Harwood S. Ives
Diesel	First Built 1978
Fuel Cap . . . . . 145 gal	No. Built 70
	Price $113,000
	with sails

HANS CHRISTIAN YACHTS
6201 Bayshore Walk
Long Beach, CA 90803
(213) 434-2076

39 Pilot House

LOA . . . . 46'	Hull . . . . FRP
LOD . . . . 37'9"	Deck . . . . . FRP/Teak
LWL . . . . 33'	Spar . . . . Alum
Beam . . . . 12'6"	Cockpit . . . . 8'
Draft . . . . 6'	Headroom . . . . 6'6"
Disp . . . . 27,585 lbs	Fr. Water . . . . 200 gal
Ballast . . 10,287 lbs	SA/Disp 15.2
Sail Area	Disp/LWL 342
Cutter . . . 867 sq ft	Blst/Disp 37%
Mast Ht . . . . . . 57'6"	Designer
Auxiliary . . . . std	Harwood S. Ives
Diesel . . . . 60 hp	First Built 1980
Fuel Cap . . . . . 250 gal	No. Built 10
	Price $130,000
	with sails

HANS CHRISTIAN YACHTS
6201 Bayshore Walk
Long Beach, CA 90803
(213) 434-2076

Shannon 38

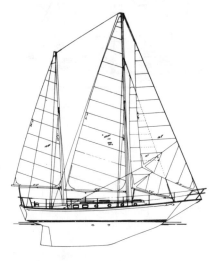

LOA . . . . 42'	Hull . . . . FRP
LOD . . . . 37'9"	Deck . . . . . FRP/Balsa
LWL . . . . 30'10"	Spar . . . . Alum
Beam . . . . 11'6"	Cockpit . . . . 10'
Draft . . . . 5'	Headroom . . . . . 6'5"
Disp . . . . 18,500 lbs	Fr. Water . . . . 120 gal
Ballast . . . . 6300 lbs	SA/Disp 17.2
Sail Area	Disp/LWL 282
Ketch . . . 751 sq ft	Blst/Disp 34%
Cutter . . . 703 sq ft	Designer
Mast Ht	Schultz & Stadel
Ketch . . . . 48'	First Built 1975
Cutter . . . . 50'	No. Built 82
Auxiliary . . . . std	Price $177,330
Perkins . . . . . 40 hp	with sails
Diesel	
Fuel Cap . . . . . . 70 gal	

SHANNON BOAT CO. INC.
19 Broad Common Rd.
Bristol, RI 02809
(401) 253-2441

Shannon Pilot 38

LOA	42'	Hull	FRP
LOD	37'9"	Deck	FRP/Balsa
LWL	30'10"	Spar	Alum
Beam	11'6"	Cockpit	6'6"
Draft	5'	Headroom	6'5"
Disp	18,500 lbs	Fr. Water	120 gal
Ballast	6300 lbs	SA/Disp	16.1
Sail Area		Disp/LWL	282
Cutter	703 sq ft	Blst/Disp	34%
Mast Ht	50'	Designer	
Auxiliary	std		Schulz & Stadel
Perkins	40 hp	First Built	1979
Diesel		No. Built	9
Fuel Cap	75 gal	Price	$187,530
			with sails

SHANNON BOAT CO. INC.
19 Broad Common Rd.
Bristol, RI 02809
(401) 253-2441

Sabre 38

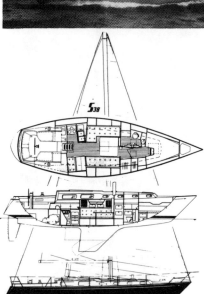

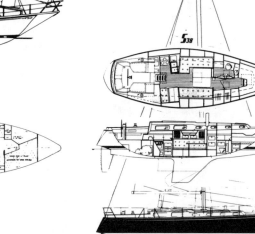

LOD	37'10"	Hull	FRP
LWL	31'2"	Deck	FRP
Beam	11'6"	Spar	Alum
Draft		Cockpit	8'
Shoal cb up	4'3"	Headroom	6'3"
Shoal cb dn	8'	Fr. Water	94 gal
Deep	6'6"	SA/Disp	17.6
Disp		Disp/LWL	230
Shoal	15,600 lbs	Blst/Disp	44%
Deep	15,200 lbs	Designer	
Ballast			Sabre Design Team
Shoal	6800 lbs	First Built	1981
Deep	6400 lbs	No. Built	25
Sail Area		Price	$97,900
Sloop	688 sq ft		without sails
Mast Ht	54'6"		
Auxiliary	std		
Westerbeke	33 hp		
Diesel			
Fuel Cap	30 gal		

SABRE YACHTS
Hawthorne Rd.
S. Casco, ME 04077
(207) 655-3831

38 Traditional

LOA	48'	Hull	FRP
LOD	37'11"	Deck	FRP/Teak
LWL	33'	Spar	Alum
Beam	12'4"	Cockpit	7'
Draft	6'	Headroom	6'6"
Disp	26,500 lbs	Fr. Water	100 gal
Ballast	9500 lbs	SA/Disp	14.2
Sail Area		Disp/LWL	329
Cutter	791 sq ft	Blst/Disp	36%
Mast Ht	54'6"	Designer	Harwood Ives
Auxiliary	std	First Built	1975
Diesel	60 hp	No. Built	85
Fuel Cap	100 gal	Price	$113,000
			with sails

HANS CHRISTIAN YACHTS
6201 Bayshore Walk
Long Beach, CA 90803
(213) 434-2076

Chapman 38

LOD . . . . 38'	Hull . . . . FRP
LWL . . . . 32'7"	Deck . . . . FRP
Beam . . . . 11'6"	Spar . . . . Alum
Draft . . . . 5'7"	Headroom . . . . 6'
Disp . . . . . 27,000 lbs	Fr. Water . . . . 100 gal
Ballast . . . 10,000 lbs	SA/Disp 15.6
Sail Area	Disp/LWL 348
Cutter . . . 880 sq ft	Blst/Disp 37%
Auxiliary . . . . std	Designer Don Chapman
Perkins . . . . . 50 hp	First Built 1972
Diesel	No. Built 100
Fuel Cap . . . . . . 75 gal	Kit $13,740
	Price $104,760
	with sails

CHAPMAN YACHT CORP.
5201 Argosy Drive
Huntington Beach, CA 92649
(714) 891-3428

Little Harbor 38

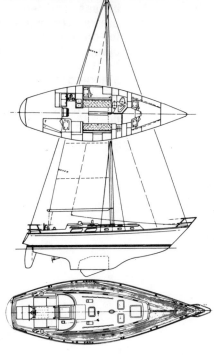

LOD . . . . 38'	Hull . . . . . FRP/Airex
LWL . . . . 31'11"	Deck . . . . FRP/Balsa
Beam . . . . . . 11'10"	Spar . . . . Alum
Draft	Headroom . . . . . 6'7"
cb up . . . . . . 4'8"	Fr. Water . . . . 100 gal
cb dn . . . . . 11'3"	SA/Disp 14.9
Disp . . . . 22,500 lbs	Disp/LWL 308
Ballast . . . . 8500 lbs	Blst/Disp 38%
Sail Area	Designer . . Ted Hood
Sloop . . . . 744 sq ft	Builder . . . Lhien Wha
Mast Ht . . . . 55'	First Built 1980
Auxiliary . . . . std	No. Built 22
Perkins . . . . . 38 hp	Price $121,000
Diesel	with sails
Fuel Cap . . . . . . 55 gal	

LITTLE HARBOR CUSTOM YACHTS
Little Harbor Way
Marblehead, MA 01945
(617) 631-8840

Nereia

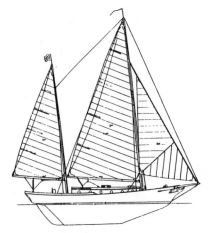

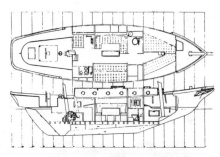

LOA . . . . 43'	Hull . . . . . . FRP/Airex
LOD . . . . 38'	Deck . . . . FRP
LWL . . . . 31'9"	Spar . . . . Alum
Beam . . . . 11'	Cockpit . . . . 7'
Draft . . . . 5'2"	Headroom . . . . . 6'2"
Disp . . . 23,000 lbs	Fr. Water . . . 100 gal
Ballast . . . 12,000 lbs	SA/Disp 13.3
Sail Area	Disp/LWL 321
Ketch . . . 673 sq ft	Blst/Disp 52%
Cutter . . . 620 sq ft	Designer
Mast Ht 47	L. F. Herreshoff
Auxiliary . . . . std	First Built 1981
Perkins . . . . 50 hp	No. Built 1
Diesel	1 Design . . . . yes
Fuel Cap . . . . . 50 gal	Kit . . . . available
	Price . . . . na

NEREIA YACHTS
5316 Denee Dr.
Wilmington, NC 28405
(919) 675-0923

Vancouver 38

The VANCOUVER 38 is Robert Harris's latest design. Built in epoxylined steel for ultimate strength and durability, she retains the ocean proven concepts that made the VANCOUVERs safe and comfortable passage makers. Long keel for stability, well supported rudder, highly efficient sail plan and many other built in features contributing to comfort at sea and ease of handling for short handed crews. The standard and custom all teak interior lay-outs include 3 seaworthy berths, 3 separate cabins, shower, full sit at navigation station and a huge galley. She comes with an exhaustive list of standard equipment including anchor and mooring tackle.

The VANCOUVER 38 is superbly suitable as a live aboard and for chartering.

NEW

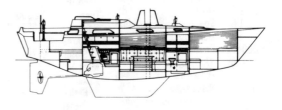

LOD	38'	Hull	Steel
LWL	30'	Deck	Steel & Wood
Beam	11'8"	Spar	Alum
Draft	5'6"	Headroom	6'8"
Disp	23,000 lbs	Fr. Water	70 gal
Ballast	10,000 lbs	SA/Disp	16.8
Sail Area		Disp/LWL	380
Cutter	850 sq ft	Blst/Disp	43%
Mast Ht	48'	Designer	
Auxiliary	std		Robert Harris
Bukh	36 hp	Builder	
Diesel			Pheon Yachts U.K.
		First Built	1983
		Price	$120,000
			with sails

RAY G. VANHEUSDEN TREMAYNE CORPORATION

1611 N. Kent Street, Suite 801
Arlington, VA 22209
(703) 522-3355

North American 40

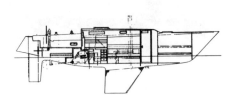

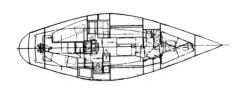

LOA . . . . 40'	Hull . . . . . . FRP/Airex
LOD . . . . 38'	Deck . . . . FRP
LWL . . . . 32'	Spar . . . . Alum
Beam . . . . 12'8"	Cockpit . . . . 12'
Draft . . . . . . 6'10"	Headroom . . . . . 6'2"
Disp . . . . . 17,000 lbs	Fr. Water . . . . 60 gal
Ballast . . . . . 7900 lbs	SA/Disp 18.8
Sail Area	Disp/LWL 231
Sloop . . . . 776 sq ft	Blst/Disp 46%
Mast Ht . . . . 54'	Designer . R. E. Carter
Auxiliary . . . . std	Builder . Morgan Yacht
Perkins . . . . . 50 hp	First Built 1978
Diesel	No. Built 45
Fuel Cap . . . . . 27 gal	1 Design . . . . yes
	Price $75,000
	with sails

NORTH AMERICAN OFFSHORE
840 W. Milwaukee Ave.
Detroit, MI 48202

Baltic 38 DP

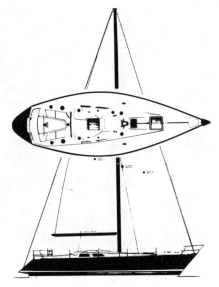

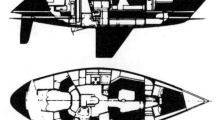

LOD . . . . 38'1"	Hull . . . . FRP
LWL . . . . 31'6"	Deck . . . . FRP
Beam . . . . 12'4"	Spar . . . . Alum
Draft . . . . 7'4"	Fr. Water . . . . 48 gal
Disp . . . . 14,300 lbs	Disp/LWL 204
Ballast . . . . . 6503 lbs	Blst/Disp 45%
Sail Area	Designer
Sloop . . . . na	Doug Peterson
Auxiliary . . . . std	Builder
Yanmar . . . . . 30 hp	Baltic Finland
Diesel	Price . . . . na
Fuel Cap . . . . . 30 gal	

BALTIC YACHTS
NORTH AMERICA
Box 832
Tucker's Wharf
Marblehead, MA 01945
(617) 639-0590

Baltic 39

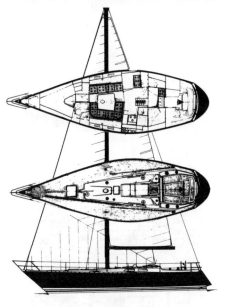

LOD . . . . 38'1"	Hull . . . . FRP
LWL . . . . 32'8"	Deck . . . . FRP
Beam . . . . 12'7"	Spar . . . . Alum
Draft . . . . 6'11"	Fr. Water . . . . 475 gal
Disp . . . . 18,000 lbs	Disp/LWL 230
Ballast . . . . . 7800 lbs	Blst/Disp 43%
Sail Area	Designer
Sloop . . . . na	C&C Design Group
Auxiliary . . . . std	Builder
Volvo . . . . . 23 hp	Baltic Finland
Diesel	Price . . . . na
Fuel Cap . . . . 264 gal	

BALTIC YACHTS
NORTH AMERICA
Box 832
Tucker's Wharf
Marblehead, MA 01945
(617) 639-0590

Irwin 38

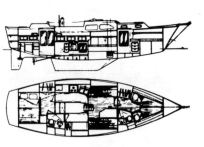

LOA	40'1"	Hull	FRP/Coremat
LOD	38'2"	Deck	FRP
LWL	32'6"	Spar	Alum
Beam	12'3"	Fr. Water	145 gal
Draft		SA/Disp	16.9
Shoal	4'6"	Disp/LWL	260
Deep	6'3"	Blst/Disp	35%
Disp	20,000 lbs	Price	$82,950
Ballast	7000 lbs		with sails
Sail Area			
Sloop	776 sq ft		
Mast Ht	54'		
Auxiliary	std		
Perkins			
Diesel			
Fuel Cap	230 gal		

IRWIN YACHTS
13055 49th St. N.
Clearwater, FL 33520
(813) 577-4581

Krogen 38' Cutter

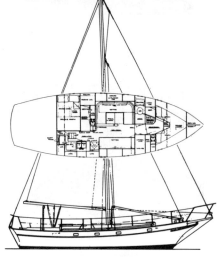

LOD	38'2"	Hull	FRP
LWL	32'1"	Deck	FRP
Beam	12'8"	Spar	Alum
Draft		Cockpit	8'6"
Shoal cb up	3'	Headroom	6'3"
Shoal cb dn	6'7"	Fr. Water	150 gal
Deep	5'	SA/Disp	17.6
Disp	21,700 lbs	Disp/LWL	293
Ballast	7000 lbs	Blst/Disp	32%
Sail Area		Designer James Krogen
Cutter	858 sq ft	First Built	1980
Mast Ht	52'	No. Built	39
Auxiliary	std	Price	$89,500
Perkins	50 hp		without sails
Diesel			
Fuel Cap	80 gal		

KADEY-KROGEN YACHTS INC.
3315 Rice St., Suite 7
Miami, FL 33133
(305) 446-3281

Bristol 38.8

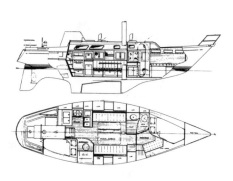

LOD	38'3"	Hull	FRP
LWL	30'7"	Deck	FRP/Balsa
Beam	12'2"	Spar	Alum
Draft		Pos Float	yes
cb up	4'6"	Headroom	6'5"
cb dn	10'	Fr. Water	90 gal
Disp	19,150 lbs	SA/Disp	17.1
Ballast	9000 lbs	Disp/LWL	298
Sail Area		Blst/Disp	47%
Sloop	766 sq ft	Designer	Ted Hood
Auxiliary	std	First Built	1982
Universal	44 hp	No. Built	5
Diesel		Price	$107,715
Fuel Cap	36 gal		without sails

BRISTOL YACHT CO.
Franklin St.
Bristol, RI 02809
(401) 253-5200

Catalina 38

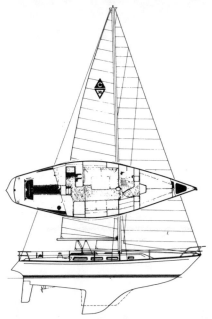

LOD	38'3"	Hull	FRP
LWL	30'3"	Deck	FRP
Beam	11'10"	Spar	Alum
Draft	6'9"	Headroom	6'3"
Disp	15,900 lbs	Fr. Water	41 gal
Ballast	6850 lbs	SA/Disp	16.2
Sail Area		Disp/LWL	256
Sloop	639 sq ft	Blst/Disp	43%
Mast Ht	56'	Designer	Frank Butler
Auxiliary	std	First Built	1978
Atomic	30 hp	No. Built	222
Diesel		1 Design	yes
Fuel Cap	36 gal	Price	$51,950
			without sails

CATALINA YACHTS
21200 Victory Blvd.
Woodland Hills, CA 91367
(213) 884-7700

Triade 38

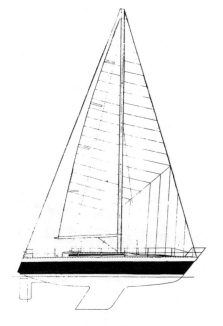

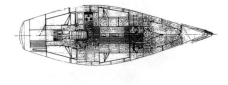

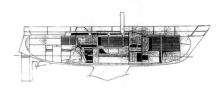

LOD	38'3"	Hull	Steel
LWL	32'6"	Deck	Steel
Beam	12'	Spar	Alum
Draft	6'7"	Cockpit	6'7"
Disp	18,960 lbs	Headroom	6'1"
Ballast	7496 lbs	Fr. Water	53 gal
Sail Area		SA/Disp	21.3
Sloop	947 sq ft	Disp/LWL	246
Mast Ht	55'9"	Blst/Disp	40%
Auxiliary	opt	Designer	
	50 hp		Sylvestre Langevin
	inbd	First Built	1982
		No. Built	1
		Kit	$26,500 Can

ATELIER MARITIME DE L'EXOCET
P. O. Box 307
Lanoraie, Quebec
Canada J0K 1E0
(514) 887-2926

Golden Wave 38

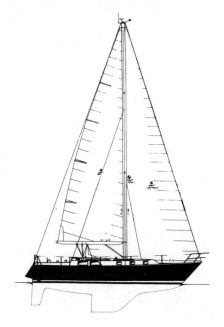

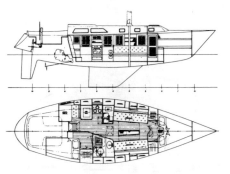

LOD	38'4"	Hull	FRP
LWL	30'10"	Deck	Teak
Beam	11'9"	Spar	Alum
Draft	6'	SA/Disp	16.2
Disp	19,025 lbs	Disp/LWL	290
Ballast	7250 lbs	Blst/Disp	38%
Sail Area		Designer	Pedrick
Sloop	720 sq ft	Builder	Cheoy Lee
Auxiliary	std	First Built	1983
Diesel		Price	$110,000
			with sails

REX YACHT SALES
2152 S.E. 17th St.
Ft. Lauderdale, FL 33315
(305) 463-8810

Morgan 38

LOD	38'4"	Hull	FRP
LWL	30'6"	Deck	FRP
Beam	12'	Spar	Alum
Draft	5'	Fr. Water	90 gal
Disp	18,000 lbs	SA/Disp	15.8
Ballast	6800 lbs	Disp/LWL	283
Sail Area		Blst/Disp	38%
Sloop	680 sq ft	Designer	Ted Brewer
Mast Ht	54'6"	Price	na
Auxiliary	std		
Perkins			
Diesel			
Fuel Cap	40 gal		

MORGAN YACHT INC.
7200 Bryan Dairy Rd.
Largo, FL 33543
(813) 544-6681

Westerly Sealord

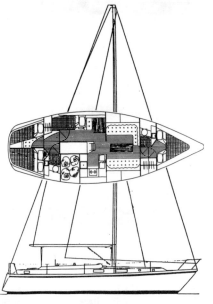

LOD	38'6"	Hull	FRP
LWL	32'6"	Deck	FRP
Beam	13'2"	Spar	Alum
Draft	5'6"	Headroom	6'2"
Disp	18,500 lbs	Fr. Water	110 gal
Ballast	8000 lbs	SA/Disp	17.5
Sail Area		Disp/LWL	240
Sloop	764 sq ft	Blst/Disp	43%
Ketch	776 sq ft	Designer	Ed Dubois
Auxiliary	std	Builder	
Volvo	36 hp		Westerly-England
Diesel		First Built	1982
Fuel Cap	50 gal	Price	$108,000
			with sails

ANDREW GEMENY & SONS
5809 Annapolis Rd.
Hyattsville, MD 20784
(301) 779-6190

O'Day 39

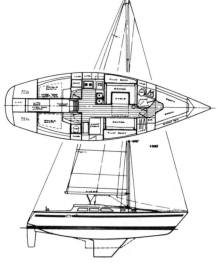

LOD	38'7"	Hull	FRP
LWL	33'6"	Deck	FRP
Beam	12'7"	Spar	Alum
Draft		Cockpit	8'9"
Shoal	4'11"	Headroom	6'
Deep	6'4"	Fr. Water	110 gal
Disp	18,000 lbs	SA/Disp	15.9
Ballast		Disp/LWL	213
Shoal	7385 lbs	Blst/Disp	41%
Deep	7200 lbs	Designer	
Sail Area			Phillipe Briand
Sloop	681 sq ft	First Built	1982
Auxiliary	std	No. Built	16
Universal	44 hp	1 Design	yes
Diesel		Price	na
Fuel Cap	40 gal		

BANGOR PUNTA MARINE
848 Airport Rd.
Box 991
Fall River, MA 02722
(617) 678-5291

Southern Cross 39   Corbin 39   Westsail 39

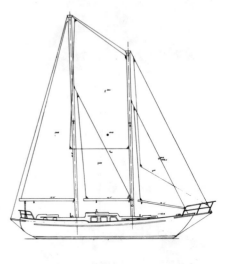

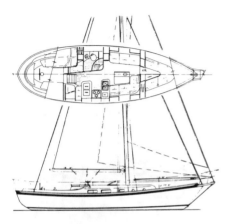

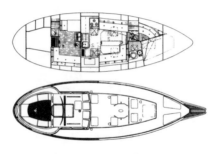

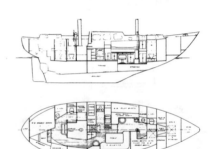

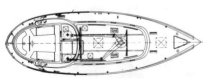

LOA	43'	Hull	FRP/Airex
LOD	38'7''	Deck	FRP/Balsa
LWL	31'	Spar	Alum
Beam	12'1''	Cockpit	9'
Draft	6'4''	Headroom	6'4''
Disp	21,000 lbs	Fr. Water	120 gal
Ballast	7676 lbs	SA/Disp	17.6
Sail Area		Disp/LWL	315
Cutter	835 sq ft	Blst/Disp	37%
Mast Ht	55'3''	Designer	Tom Gillmer
Auxiliary	std	First Built	1979
Perkins	50 hp	No. Built	6
Diesel		Kit	available
Fuel Cap	50 gal	Price	na

C.E. RYDER CORP.
47 Gooding Ave.
Bristol, RI 02809
(401) 253-8554

LOA	41'8''	Hull	FRP/Airex
LOD	38'8''	Deck	FRP
LWL	31'11''	Spar	Alum
Beam	12'2''	Cockpit	6'6''
Draft	5'6''	Headroom	6'3''
Disp	22,000 lbs	Fr. Water	130 gal
Ballast	9200 lbs	SA/Disp	16.7
Sail Area		Disp/LWL	302
Cutter	818 sq ft	Blst/Disp	42%
Ketch	785 sq ft	Designer	
Mast Ht			Dufour & Corbin
Cutter	54'	First Built	1979
Ketch	51'	No. Built	135
Auxiliary	std	Kit	$19,900
Westerbeke	33 hp	Price	$134,000
Diesel			without sails
Fuel Cap	105 gal		

CORBIN LES BATEAUX INC.
2 Rang Cyr, C.P. 669
Napierville, Quebec
Canada JOJ 1LO
(514) 245-3358

LOD	38'8''	Hull	FRP
LWL	32'6''	Deck	FRP
Beam	11'10''	Spar	Alum
Draft	6'	Cockpit	6'
Disp	19,200 lbs	Headroom	6'2''
Ballast	8000 lbs	Fr. Water	100+ gal
Sail Area		SA/Disp	16.1
Cutter	722 sq ft	Disp/LWL	250
Schooner	910 sq ft	Blst/Disp	42%
Auxiliary	std	Designer	Bob Perry
Diesel	40 hp	Builder	
		P&M and Worldcruiser	
		First Built	1978
		Kit	available
		Price	$140,000
			with sails

WORLDCRUISER YACHT CO.
1300 Logan St.
Costa Mesa, CA 92626
(714) 549-9331

Cal 39

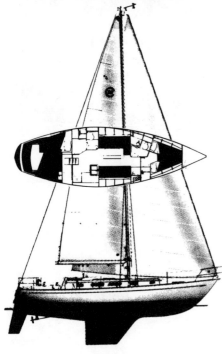

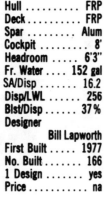

LOD . . . . 39'	Hull . . . . FRP
LWL . . . . 32'1"	Deck . . . . FRP
Beam . . . . 12'	Spar . . . . Alum
Draft	Cockpit . . . . 8'
Shoal . . . . . . 5'6"	Headroom . . . . 6'3"
Deep . . . . 6'8"	Fr. Water . . . . 152 gal
Disp . . . . 19,000 lbs	SA/Disp 16.2
Ballast . . . . 7000 lbs	Disp/LWL 256
Sail Area	Blst/Disp 37%
Sloop . . . . 720 sq ft	Designer
Sloop (tall) 776 sq ft	Bill Lapworth
Mast Ht	First Built 1977
Sloop . . . . 55'	No. Built 166
Sloop (tall) . . . 59'	1 Design . . . . . . yes
Auxiliary . . . . std	Price . . . . na
Universal . . . 44 hp	
Diesel	
Fuel Cap . . . . . 45 gal	

BANGOR PUNTA MARINE
848 Airport Rd.
Box 991
Fall River, MA 02722
(617) 678-5291

Freedom 39

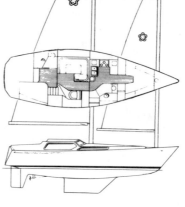

LOD . . . . 39'	Hull . . . . . . FRP/Balsa
LWL . . . . 31'	Deck . . . . . FRP/Balsa
Beam . . . . 12'10"	Spar . . . Carbon Fiber
Draft . . . . 5'6"	Cockpit . . . . 9'
Disp . . . . 18,500 lbs	Headroom . . . . 6'2"
Ballast . . . . . 6000 lbs	Fr. Water . . . . 160 gal
Sail Area	SA/Disp 17
Cat Scnr . . 744 sq ft	Disp/LWL 277
Mast . . . . . unstayed	Blst/Disp 32%
Auxiliary . . . . std	Designer Ron Holland
Perkins . . . . . 50 hp	Builder
Diesel	Tillotson-Pearson
Fuel Cap . . . . . 100 gal	First Built 1982
	No. Built 8
	Price $136,500
	without sails

FREEDOM YACHTS
49 America's Cup Ave.
Newport, RI 02840
(401) 847-7475

Nautical 39

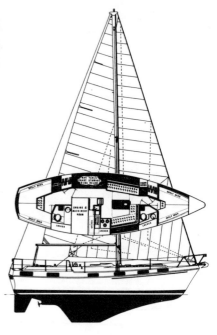

LOD . . . . 39'	Hull . . . . FRP
LWL . . . . 32'6"	Deck . . . . FRP
Beam . . . . 12'	Spar . . . . Alum
Draft . . . . 5'4"	Fr. Water . . . . 200 gal
Disp . . . . 22,500 lbs	SA/Disp 13.6
Ballast . . . . . 6000 lbs	Disp/LWL 292
Sail Area	Blst/Disp 27%
Sloop . . . . 677 sq ft	Designer
Auxiliary . . . . std	Morgan/Warren
Diesel . . . . . 50 hp	Price $96,500
Fuel Cap . . . . . 60 gal	without sails

NAUTICAL DEVELOPMENT CORP.
2055 34th Way
Largo, FL 33541
(813) 531-4674

Nicholson 39

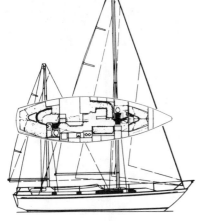

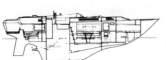

LOD . . . . 39'	Hull . . . . FRP
LWL . . . . 28'4"	Deck . . . . FRP
Beam . . . . 11'6"	Spar . . . . Alum
Draft . . . . 5'6"	Fr. Water . . . . 100 gal
Disp . . . 18,000 lbs	SA/Disp 20.5
Ballast . . . . . 7000 lbs	Disp/LWL 353
Sail Area	Blst/Disp 39%
Ketch . . . . 878 sq ft	Builder . . . . . England
Auxiliary . . . . std	Price $126,400
Ford . . . . . . 58 hp	with sails
Diesel	
Fuel Cap . . . . . . 60 gal	

CAMPER & NICHOLSONS
Box 3296
Annapolis, MD 21403
(301) 267-0933

MC 39

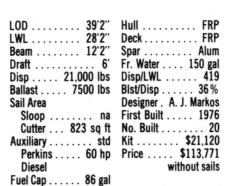

LOD . . . . 39'2"	Hull . . . . FRP
LWL . . . . 28'2"	Deck . . . . FRP
Beam . . . . 12'2"	Spar . . . . Alum
Draft . . . . 6'	Fr. Water . . . . 150 gal
Disp . . . 21,000 lbs	Disp/LWL 419
Ballast . . . . . 7500 lbs	Blst/Disp 36%
Sail Area	Designer . A. J. Markos
Sloop . . . . na	First Built 1976
Cutter . . . 823 sq ft	No. Built 20
Auxiliary . . . . std	Kit $21,120
Perkins . . . . . 60 hp	Price $113,771
Diesel	without sails
Fuel Cap . . . . . . 86 gal	

MARKOS YACHTS LTD.
#3: 1210 Pipeline Rd.
Coquitlam, B.C. Canada V3B 4S1
(604) 464-7533

Island Trader 40
Trawl'r Sailer

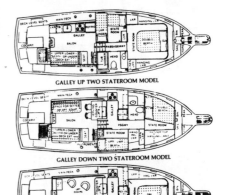

GALLEY UP TWO STATEROOM MODEL

GALLEY DOWN TWO STATEROOM MODEL

GALLEY DOWN SINGLE STATEROOM MODEL

LOD . . . . 39'4"	Hull . . . . FRP
LWL . . . . 34'3"	Deck . . . . Teak
Beam . . . . 13'4"	Spar . . . . Wood
Draft . . . . 4'9"	Cockpit . . . . 6'9"
Disp . . . . 34,400 lbs	Headroom . . . . 6'9"
Ballast . . . . . 7000 lbs	Fr. Water . . . . 300 gal
Sail Area	SA/Disp 7
Sloop . . . . 462 sq ft	Disp/LWL 382
Mast Ht . . . . . . 38'	Blst/Disp 20%
Auxiliary . . . . std	Designer . Floyd Ayers
Lehman/Ford 120 hp	1 Design . . . . . yes
Diesel	Price $92,500
Fuel Cap . . . . . 300 gal	with sails

MARINE TRADING
INTERNATIONAL
Box 1232
Point Pleasant Beach, NJ 08742
(201) 899-6800

Passport 40

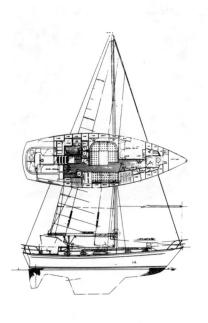

LOD . . . . 39'5"	Hull . . . . FRP
LWL . . . . 33'5"	Deck . . . . FRP
Beam . . . . 12'8"	Spar . . . . Alum
Draft	Fr. Water . . . 140 gal
Shoal . . . . . . 5'3"	SA/Disp 18.5
Deep . . . . . . 5'9"	Disp/LWL 272
Disp . . . . 22,771 lbs	Designer Robert Perry
Ballast . . . . na	Price $105,000
Sail Area	with sails
Sloop . . . . 931 sq ft	
Auxiliary . . . . std	

PASSPORT YACHTS
2900 Westlake Ave. North
Seattle, WA 98109
(206) 282-0401

Bayfield 40

LOA . . . . 45'6"	Hull . . . . FRP
LOD . . . . 39'6"	Deck . . . . FRP
LWL . . . . 30'6"	Spar . . . . Alum
Beam . . . . 12'	SA/Disp 21.2
Draft . . . . 4'11"	Disp/LWL 330
Disp . . . . 21,000 lbs	Blst/Disp 39%
Ballast . . . . . 8200 lbs	Price . . . . na
Sail Area	
Ketch . . . 1009 sq ft	
Auxiliary . . . . std	
Westerbeke . . 52 hp	
Diesel	

BAYFIELD BOAT YARD LTD.
Box 1076
Clinton, Ontario
Canada N0M 1L0
(519) 482-3425

Concept 40

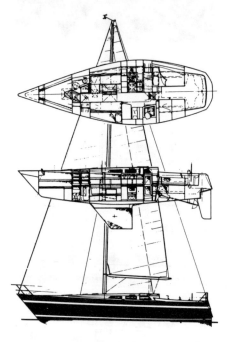

LOD . . . . 39'6"	Hull . . . . FRP
LWL . . . . 31'10"	Deck . . . . FRP
Beam . . . . 12'9"	Spar . . . . Alum
Draft . . . . 6'	Fr. Water . . . 150 gal
Disp . . . 16,600 lbs	SA/Disp 18.8
Ballast . . . . . 8500 lbs	Disp/LWL 229
Sail Area	Blst/Disp 51%
Sloop . . . . 766 sq ft	Designer . . . Gary Mull
Auxiliary . . . . std	Builder
Pathfinder . . 42 hp	Hyundai, Korea
Diesel	Price $100,000
Fuel Cap . . . . . . 80 gal	without sails

HYUNDAI CORP.
One Bridge Plaza North
Suite 600
Fort Lee, JN 07024
(201) 592-7766

Fast Passage 39

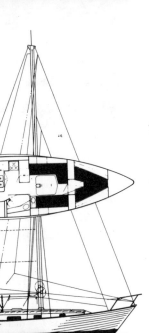

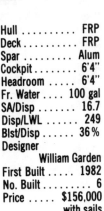

LOD	39'6"	Hull	FRP
LWL	33'6"	Deck	FRP
Beam	11'10"	Spar	Alum
Draft	5'6"	Cockpit	6'4"
Disp	21,000 lbs	Headroom	6'4"
Ballast	7500 lbs	Fr. Water	100 gal
Sail Area		SA/Disp	16.7
Cutter	795 sq ft	Disp/LWL	249
Mast Ht	56'8"	Blst/Disp	36%
Auxiliary	std	Designer	
Perkins	50 hp		William Garden
Diesel		First Built	1982
Fuel Cap	53 gal	No. Built	6
		Price	$156,000
			with sails

TOLLYCRAFT
2200 Clinton Ave.
Kelso, WA 98626
(206) 423-5160

Islander 40

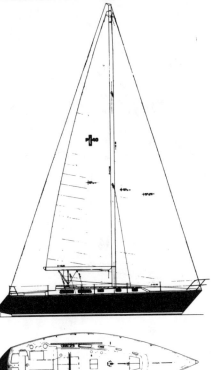

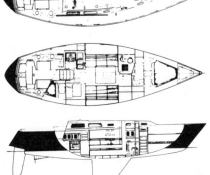

LOD	39'6"	Hull	FRP
LWL	30'10"	Deck	FRP
Beam	11'10"	Spar	Alum
Draft		Fr. Water	60 gal
Shoal	5'1"	SA/Disp	17.8
Deep	7'2"	Disp/LWL	258
Disp	17,000 lbs	Blst/Disp	45%
Ballast	7700 lbs	Designer	
Sail Area			Doug Peterson
Sloop	734 sq ft	Price	na
Mast Ht	58'		
Auxiliary	std		
Pathfinder	42 hp		
Diesel			
Fuel Cap	35 gal		

ISLANDER YACHTS
1922 Barranca Rd.
Irvine, CA 92714
(714) 549-8526

C & C 40

LOD	39'7"	Hull	FRP/Balsa
LWL	31'4"	Deck	FRP/Balsa
Beam	12'8"	Spar	Alum
Draft		Headroom	6'2"
Deep	7'	Fr. Water	60 gal
Shoal cb up	4'9"	SA/Disp	17.9
Shoal cb dn	8'6"	Disp/LWL	248
Disp		Blst/Disp	46%
Deep	17,100 lbs	Price	$127,750
Shoal	17,985 lbs		without sails
Ballast			
Deep	7910 lbs		
Shoal	8795 lbs		
Sail Area			
Sloop	743 sq ft		
Sloop (tall)	780 sq ft		
Mast Ht	56'10"		
Auxiliary	std		
Westerbeke 30	25 hp		
Diesel			
Fuel Cap	20 gal		

C&C YACHTS
55 Port Street East
Mississauga, Ontario
Canada L5G 4P3
(416) 274-7131

Horizon 39

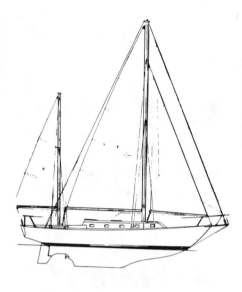

LOA .... 43'7"	Hull .... FRP
LOD .... 39'7"	Deck .... FRP
LWL .... 29'6"	Spar .... Alum
Beam .... 11'2"	Cockpit .... 7'4"
Draft	Headroom ..... 6'5"
cb up .... 4'	Fr. Water .... 120 gal
cb dn .... 10'	SA/Disp 14.7
Disp ..... 18,700 lbs	Disp/LWL 325
Ballast .... 8000 lbs	Blst/Disp 43%
Sail Area	First Built 1981
Sloop.... 648 sq ft	No. Built 17
Cutter 678 sq ft	Kit .... available
Ketch .... 747 sq ft	Price $89,000
Mast Ht	with sails
Sloop ...... 50'3"	
Cutter ...... 50'3"	
Ketch ...... 46'7"	
Auxiliary .... std	
Yanmar ..... 33 hp	
Diesel	
Fuel Cap ...... 50 gal	

HORIZON YACHT
4451 112th Terrace North
Clearwater, FL 33520
(813) 577-0624

Offshore 40

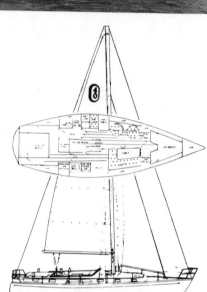

LOD .... 39'7"	Hull .... FRP
LWL .... 35'	Deck .... FRP
Beam .... 13'3"	Spar .... Alum
Draft .... 5'2"	Cockpit .... 6'
Disp ..... 21,500 lbs	Headroom ..... 6'5"
Ballast ..... 9000 lbs	Fr. Water .... 150 gal
Sail Area	SA/Disp 15.9
Sloop.... 766 sq ft	Disp/LWL 223
Cutter .... na	Blst/Disp 42%
Mast Ht ...... 56'6"	Designer
Auxiliary .... std	Creekmore/Lippincott
Universal .. 50 hp	First Built 1983
Diesel	1 Design ...... yes
Fuel Cap ...... 75 gal	Price $104,950
	without sails

CLEARWATER CUSTOM YACHT
4501 Ulmerton Road
Clearwater, FL 33520
(813) 577-7626

Sailmaster 39

LOA .... 39'7"	Hull ...... FRP/Balsa
LOD .... 39'7"	Deck ..... FRP/Balsa
LWL .... 32'4"	Spar .... Alum
Beam .... 12'1"	Fr. Water .... 150 gal
Draft .... 4'9"	SA/Disp 16.4
Disp .... 19,000 lbs	Disp/LWL 250
Ballast .... 8200 lbs	Blst/Disp 43%
Sail Area	Designer
Sloop.... 728 sq ft	R. C. Lazzara
Auxiliary .... std	Price $109,900
Perkins ..... 50 hp	without sails
Diesel	
Fuel Cap ...... 80 gal	

GULFSTAR INC.
6101 45th St. N.
St. Petersburg, FL 33714
(813) 527-7251

Nordic 40

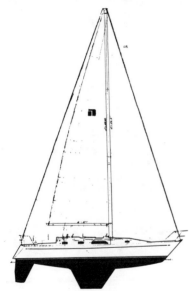

LOD	39'8"	Hull	FRP
LWL	32'6"	Deck	FRP/Balsa
Beam	12'5"	Spar	Alum
Draft		Fr. Water	130 gal
Shoal	5'2"	SA/Disp	17.6
Deep	6'4"	Disp/LWL	234
Disp	18,000 lbs	Blst/Disp	39%
Ballast	7091 lbs	Designer	Robert Perry
Sail Area		Price	$142,000
Sloop	756 sq ft		without sails
Auxiliary	std		
Universal	32 hp		
Diesel			
Fuel Cap	55 gal		

NORDIC YACHTS INC.
Box 964
Bellingham, WA 98227
(206) 398-1090

Irwin 40 MK II

LOD	39'9"	Hull	FRP/Coremat
LWL	31'2"	Deck	FRP
Beam	12'2"	Spar	Alum
Draft		Fr. Water	100 gal
Shoal cb up	4'3"	SA/Disp	17.9
Shoal cb dn	9'6"	Disp/LWL	249
Deep	6'3"	Blst/Disp	41%
Disp	16,890 lbs	Price	$72,950
Ballast			with sails
Shoal	7000 lbs		
Deep	6500 lbs		
Sail Area			
Sloop	737 sq ft		
Mast Ht	54'8"		
Auxiliary	std		
Yanmar			
Diesel			
Fuel Cap	40 gal		

IRWIN YACHTS
13055 49th St. N.
Clearwater, FL 33520
(813) 577-4581

Swan 391

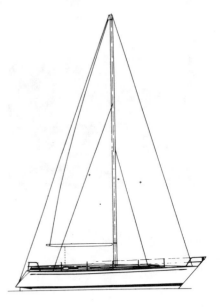

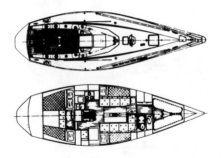

LOD	39'11"	Hull	FRP
LWL	33'1"	Deck	FRP
Beam	12'6"	Spar	Alum
Draft	7'2"	Disp/LWL	233
Disp	18900 lbs	Blst/Disp	32%
Ballast	6000 lbs	Designer	Ron Holland
Sail Area		Builder	
Sloop	na		Nautor, Finland
Auxiliary	std	Price	$131,000
Diesel	40 hp		with sails

NAUTOR EAST
55 America's Cup Avenue
Newport, RI 02840
(401) 846-8404

Valiant 40　　Avance 40　　Endeavour 40

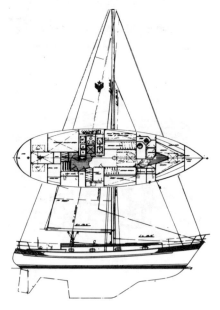

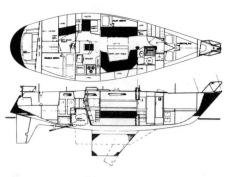

LOD . . . . 39'11"	Hull . . . . FRP
LWL . . . . 34'	Deck . . . . FRP
Beam . . . . 12'4"	Spar . . . . Alum
Draft	Fr. Water . . . . 150 gal
Shoal . . . . . 4'11"	SA/Disp 15.5
Deep . . . . 6'	Disp/LWL 256
Disp . . . . 22,500 lbs	Blst/Disp 34%
Ballast . . . . . 7700 lbs	Designer Robert Perry
Sail Area	Price $180,000
Cutter . . . 772 sq ft	with sails
Auxiliary . . . . std	
Westerbeke	

VALIANT YACHTS CORP.
2000 Westlake Ave. North
Seattle, WA 98109
(206) 284-7943

LOD . . . . 40'	Hull . . . . FRP
LWL . . . . 32'	Deck . . . . FRP
Beam . . . . 12'6"	Spar . . . . Alum
Draft	Cockpit . . . . 6'
Shoal cb up . 4'11"	Headroom . . . . . . 6'4"
Shoal cb dn . . . . na	Fr. Water . . . 100 gal
Deep . . . . 7'	SA/Disp 18.2
Disp . . . . 19,600 lbs	Disp/LWL 267
Ballast . . . . 8400 lbs	Blst/Disp 43%
Sail Area	Designer
Sloop . . . . 825 sq ft	Sparkman & Stephens
Mast Ht . . . . 63'	Builder . . . . . . Avance
Auxiliary . . . . std	First Built 1982
Bukh . . . . . . 36 hp	No. Built 3
Diesel	Price . . . . na
Fuel Cap . . . . . . 30 gal	

SPARKMAN & STEPHENS
79 Madison Ave.
New York, NY 10016
(212) 689-3880

LOD . . . . 40'	Hull . . . . FRP
LWL . . . . 32'	Deck . . . . FRP
Beam . . . . 13'	Spar . . . . Alum
Draft . . . . 5'	Headroom . . . . . 6'4"
Disp . . . . 25,000 lbs	Fr. Water . . . . 135 gal
Ballast . . . . 9000 lbs	SA/Disp 14.8
Sail Area	Disp/LWL 340
Ketch . . . . 789 sq ft	Blst/Disp 36%
Sloop . . . . 743 sq ft	Price $106,900
Mast Ht . . . . . . 54'5"	without sails
Auxiliary . . . . std	
Perkins . . . . 50 hp	
Diesel	
Fuel Cap . . . . . . 75 gal	

ENDEAVOUR YACHT CORP.
11700 S. Belcher Rd.
Largo, FL 33543
(813) 541-3553

Freedom 40

LOD .... 40'	Hull ...... FRP/Balsa
LWL .... 34'10"	Deck ..... FRP/Balsa
Beam .... 12'	Spar ... Carbon Fiber
Draft	Cockpit .... 8'
cb up .... 4'6"	Headroom .... 6'4"
cb dn .... 9'1"	Fr. Water .... 200 gal
Disp ..... 20,000 lbs	SA/Disp 18.2
Ballast ..... 6000 lbs	Disp/LWL 211
Sail Area	Blst/Disp 30%
Cat ketch . 836 sq ft	Designer
Mast ...... unstayed	Halsey Herreshoff
Auxiliary .... std	Builder
Perkins ..... 50 hp	Tillotson-Pearson
Diesel	First Built 1976
Fuel Cap ..... 107 gal	No. Built 63
	Price $142,000
	without sails

FREEDOM YACHTS
49 America's Cup Ave.
Newport, RI 02840
(401) 847-7475

Intrepid 40

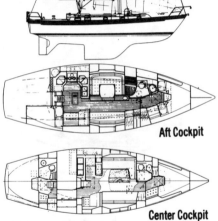

Aft Cockpit

Center Cockpit

LOD .... 40'	Hull ...... FRP/Airex
LWL .... 32'9"	Deck .. FRP/Klegecell
Beam .... 12'7"	Spar .... Alum
Draft	Headroom ..... 6'4"
Shoal .... 4'8"	Fr. Water .... 200 gal
Deep .... 5'8"	SA/Disp 16.8
Disp ..... 20,065 lbs	Disp/LWL 255
Ballast ..... 7422 lbs	Blst/Disp 37%
Sail Area	Designer . C. W. Paine
Sloop .... 775 sq ft	Builder ... Cape Dory
Ketch .... 775 sq ft	First Built 1981
Cutter ... 775 sq. ft	No. Built 4
Auxiliary .... std	Price $148,080
Perkins ..... 50 hp	with sails
Diesel	
Fuel Cap ...... 90 gal	

INTREPID YACHTS
160 Middleboro Ave.
E. Taunton, MA 02718
(617) 823-6776

Nicholson 40

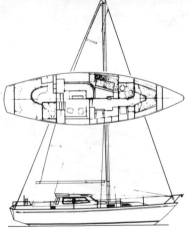

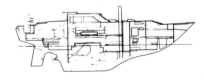

LOD .... 40'	Hull .... FRP
LWL .... 30'2"	Deck .... FRP
Beam .... 11'6"	Spar .... Alum
Draft .... 5'6"	Fr. Water .... 94 gal
Disp ..... 20,800 lbs	SA/Disp 16.9
Ballast ..... 7000 lbs	Disp/LWL 338
Sail Area	Blst/Disp 34%
Sloop .... 797 sq ft	Builder ...... C & N,
Auxiliary .... std	England
Diesel	Price $145,000
Fuel Cap ...... 75 gal	with sails

CAMPER & NICHOLSONS
Box 3296
Annapolis, MD 21403
(301) 267-0933

Nicholson 40AC | # Santa Cruz 40 | # Schucker 440

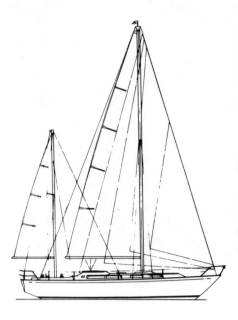

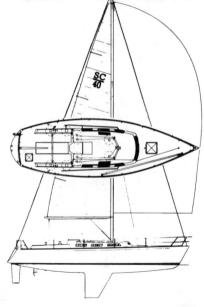

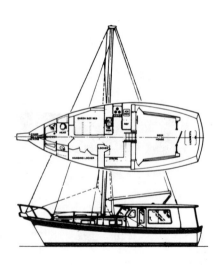

Nicholson 40AC			
LOD	40'	Hull	FRP
LWL	28'4"	Deck	FRP
Beam	11'6"	Spar	Alum
Draft	5'6"	Disp/LWL	353
Disp	18,000 lbs	Blst/Disp	60%
Ballast	10,800 lbs	Builder	England
Sail Area		Price	$140,000
Ketch	na		with sails
Auxiliary	std		
Diesel			

Santa Cruz 40			
LOD	40'	Hull	FRP/Klegecell
LWL	36'	Deck	FRP
Beam	12'	Spar	Alum
Draft	7'	Fr. Water	90 gal
Disp	10,500 lbs	SA/Disp	25.4
Ballast	5000 lbs	Disp/LWL	100
Sail Area		Blst/disp	48%
Sloop	760 sq ft	Designer	Bill Lee
Auxiliary	std	Price	$109,500
Trident	18 hp		without sails
Diesel			
Fuel Cap	40 gal		

Schucker 440			
LOD	40'	Hull	FRP
LWL	33'4"	Deck	FRP
Beam	14'	Spar	Alum
Draft	3'2"	Headroom	6'5"
Disp	26,000 lbs	Fr. Water	200 gal
Ballast	7000 lbs	SA/Disp	13.7
Sail Area		Disp/LWL	313
Cutter	750 sq ft	Blst/Disp	27%
Mast Ht	47'	Price	$133,000
Auxiliary	std		with sails
Perkins	85 hp		
Diesel			
Fuel Cap	200 gal		

CAMPER & NICHOLSONS
Box 3296
Annapolis, MD 21403
(301) 267-0933

BILL LEE YACHTS INC.
3700-B Hilltop Road
Soquel, CA 95073
(408) 475-9627

SCHUCKER YACHT CORP.
950 S. E. 11th Ave.
Cape Coral, FL 33904
(813) 574-2446

Island Trader 41

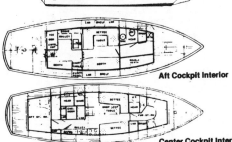

Aft Cockpit Interior

Center Cockpit Interior

LOD	40'3"	Hull	FRP
LWL	32'	Deck	Teak
Beam	12'	Spar	Wood
Draft	6'	Headroom	6'3"
Disp	29,000 lbs	SA/Disp	13.7
Ballast	9000 lbs	Disp/LWL	395
Sail Area		Blst/Disp	31%
Ketch	810 sq ft	Designer	Floyd Ayers
Mast Ht	50'4"	1 Design	yes
Auxiliary	std	Price	$85,900
			with sails

MARINE TRADING INTERNATIONAL
Box 1232
Point Pleasant Beach, NJ 08742
(201) 899-6800

Olson 40

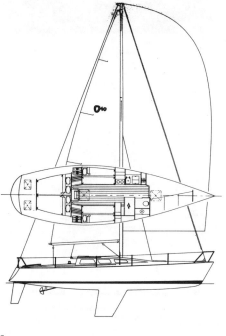

LOD	40'4"	Hull	FRP/Balsa
LWL	36'	Deck	FRP/Balsa
Beam	11'4"	Spar	Alum
Draft	6'6"	Cockpit	8'
Disp	10,350 lbs	Headroom	6'1"
Ballast	5500 lbs	Fr. Water	60 gal
Sail Area		SA/Disp	24
Sloop	712 sq ft	Disp/LWL	99
Auxiliary	std	Blst/Disp	53%
Trident	21 hp	Designer	George Olson
Diesel		First Built	1982
Fuel Cap	20 gal	No. Built	8
		Price	$95,000
			without sails

PACIFIC BOATS INC.
1041 17th Ave.
Santa Cruz, CA 95062
(408) 475-8586

Stevens Custom 40

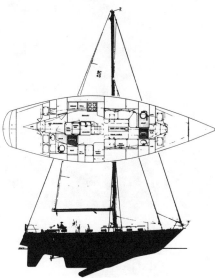

LOD	40'7"	Hull	FRP
LWL	31'4"	Deck	FRP
Beam	12'6"	Spar	Alum
Draft		Cockpit	6'
Shoal cb up	4'6"	Headroom	6'4"
Shoal cb dn	na	Fr. Water	200 gal
Deep	6'	SA/Disp	14.7
Disp	24,000 lbs	Disp/LWL	348
Ballast	8000 lbs	Blst/Disp	33%
Sail Area		Designer	
Cutter	767 sq ft	Sparkman & Stephens	
Sloop	na	First Built	1982
Mast Ht	56'	No. Built	6
Auxiliary	std	1 Design	yes
Universal	50 hp	Price	$165,000
Diesel			with sails
Fuel Cap	80 gal		

STEVENS YACHTS OF ANNAPOLIS
P. O. Box 129
Stevensville, MD 21666
(301) 269-0810

Bermuda 40

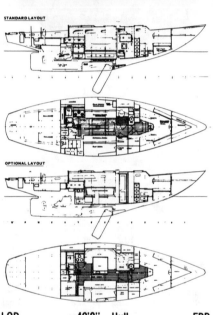

LOD	40'9"	Hull	FRP
LWL	27'10"	Deck	FRP
Beam	11'9"	Spar	Alum
Draft		Fr. Water	80 gal
cb up	4'3"	SA/Disp	15.8
cb dn	8'9"	Disp/LWL	414
Disp	20,000 lbs	Designer	
Ballast	na		Wm. H. Tripp Jr.
Sail Area		Price	$162,500
Sloop	727 sq ft		without sails
Yawl	776 sq ft		
Auxiliary	std		
Westerbeke	35 hp		
Diesel			
Fuel Cap	40 gal		

HENRY R. HINCKLEY & CO.
Southwest Harbor, ME 04679
(207) 244-5531

Irwin 41

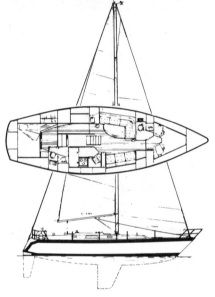

LOD	40'9"	Hull	FRP
LWL	33'4"	Deck	FRP
Beam	13'	Spar	Alum
Draft	7'3"	Fr. Water	40 gal
Disp	17,500 lbs	SA/Disp	18.7
Ballast	9500 lbs	Disp/LWL	210
Sail Area		Blst/Disp	54%
Sloop	787 sq ft	Price	$82,950
Mast Ht	58'3"		without sails
Auxiliary	std		
Yanmar	30 hp		
Diesel			
Fuel Cap	20 gal		

IRWIN YACHTS
13055 49th St. N.
Clearwater, FL 33520
(813) 577-4581

Rittun 41

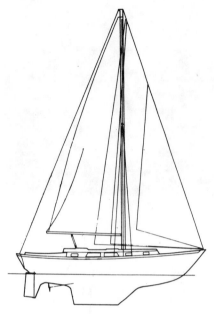

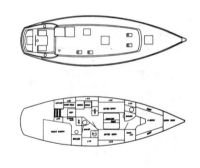

LOD	40'10"	Hull	FRP
LWL	33'10"	Deck	FRP
Beam	12'	Spar	Alum
Draft	6'	Fr. Water	140 gal
Disp	22,300 lbs	SA/Disp	15.4
Ballast	7600 lbs	Disp/lwl	257
Sail Area		Blst/Disp	34%
Sloop	765 sq ft	Designer	Robert Perry
Auxiliary	std	Builder	
Lehman Ford	65 hp		Rittun Marine, Taiwan
Diesel		Price	$65,500
Fuel Cap	180 gal		with sails

LITTON MARINE INC.
P. O. Box 600931
North Miami Beach, FL 33160
(305) 944-1556

C & C Custom 41

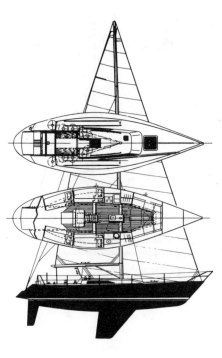

Freeport 41

Newport 41 MKII

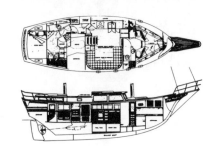

TRI CABIN

L SHAPED DINETTE

C & C Custom 41

LOD	41'	Headroom	6'2"
LWL	33'7"	SA/Disp	19.2
Beam	12'11"	Disp/LWL	198
Draft	7'10"	Blst/Disp	50%
Disp	16,800 lbs	Price	na
Ballast	8400 lbs		
Sail Area			
Sloop	789 sq ft		

Freeport 41

LOD	41'	Hull	FRP
LWL	32'6"	Deck	FRP
Beam	13'2"	Spar	Alum
Draft	5'	Fr. Water	188 gal
Disp	22,000 lbs	SA/Disp	16.6
Ballast	7000 lbs	Disp/LWL	286
Sail Aea		Blst/Disp	32%
Ketch	817 sq ft	Price	na
Mast Ht	51'		
Auxiliary	std		
Pathfinder	85 hp		
Diesel			
Fuel Cap	188 gal		

Newport 41 MKII

LOD	41'	Hull	FRP
LWL	32'3"	Deck	FRP
Beam	11'3"	Spar	Alum
Draft	6'3"	Headroom	6'3"
Disp	18,000 lbs	Fr. Water	75 gal
Ballast	8215 lbs	SA/Disp	17.5
Sail Area		Disp/LWL	239
Sloop	750 sq ft	Blst/Disp	46%
Auxiliary	std	Price	na
Diesel			
Fuel Cap	35 gal		

C&C YACHTS
55 Port Street East
Mississauga, Ontario
Canada L5G 4P3
(416) 274-7131

ISLANDER YACHTS
1922 Barranca Rd.
Irvine, CA 92714
(714) 549-8526

CAPITAL YACHTS INC.
25914 President Ave.
Harbor City, CA 90710
(213) 530-1311

Sceptre 41

Bristol 41 — 1

Oceanic Vision 41

OCEANIC VISION 41

AFT COCKPIT

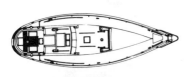

CENTER COCKPIT

LOD	41'	Hull
LWL	36'	Deck

LOD . . . . 41'
LWL . . . . 36'
Beam . . . . 12'8''
Draft . . . . 5'9''
Disp . . . . . 21,500 lbs
Ballast . . . . . 8000 lbs
Sail Area
  Sloop . . . . 805 sq ft
  Cutter . . . 805 sq ft
Mast Ht . . . . . . 58'6''
Auxiliary . . . . std
  Nissan . . . . . 55 hp
  Diesel

Hull . . . . FRP
Deck . . . . FRP
Spar . . . . Alum
Cockpit . . . . 8'
Headroom . . . . . 6'5''
Fr. Water . . . . 192 gal
SA/Disp 16.7
Disp/LWL 206
Blst/Disp 37%
Designer
    H. W. Driehuyzen
First Built 1982
No. Built 8
Price $138,000
    with sails

LOD . . . . 41'2''
LWL . . . . 33'4''
Beam . . . . 12'11''
Draft
  cb up . . . . 4'6''
  cb dn . . . . 10'
Disp . . . . 26,530 lbs
Ballast . . . 10,500 lbs
Sail Area
  Sloop . . . . 830 sq ft
Auxiliary . . . . std
  Westerbeke . . 40 hp
  Diesel
Fuel Cap . . . . . . 70 gal

Hull . . . . FRP
Deck . . . . . FRP/Balsa
Spar . . . . Alum
Pos Float . . . . . . yes
Headroom . . . . . 6'5''
Fr. Water . . . 140 gal
SA/Disp 14.9
Disp/LWL 319
Blst/Disp 40%
Designer . . Ted Hood
First Built 1980
No. Built 43
Price $160.590
    without sails

LOD . . . . 41'3''
LWL . . . . 34'6''
Beam . . . . 12'11''
Draft
  Shoal . . . . 5'9''
  Deep . . . . 6'6''
Disp . . . . 23,500 lbs
Ballast . . . . 9400 lbs
Sail Area
  Cutter . . . 854 sq ft
Auxiliary . . . . std
  Perkins . . . . . 52 hp
  Diesel
Fuel Cap . . . . . 180 gal

Hull . . . . FRP
Deck . . . . FRP
Spar . . . . Alum
Fr. Water . . . . 180 gal
SA/Disp 16.7
Disp/LWL 255
Blst/Disp 40%
Designer . Ted Brewer
Price $99,500
    with sails

SCEPTRE YACHTS LTD.
4720 Cowley Cresc.
Richmond, B.C.
Canada V7B 1C2
(604) 273-1308

BRISTOL YACHT CO.
Franklin St.
Bristol, RI 02809
(401) 253-5200

PAN—OCEANIC MARINE
619 NW 12th Ave.
Miami, FL 33136
(305) 324-0088

Out Island 41

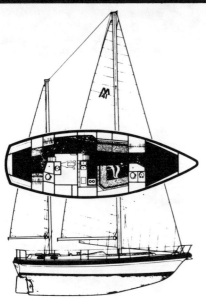

LOD	41'3"	Hull	FRP
LWL	34'	Deck	FRP
Beam	13'10"	Spar	Alum
Draft	4'2"	Fr. Water	200 gal
Disp	27,000 lbs	SA/Disp	15.6
Ballast	9000 lbs	Disp/LWL	306
Sail Area		Blst/Disp	33%
Ketch	878 sq ft	Price	na
Auxiliary	std		
Perkins	62 hp		
Diesel			
Fuel Cap	90 gal		

MORGAN YACHT INC.
7200 Bryan Dairy Rd.
Largo, FL 33543
(813) 544-6681

Faenoe 42

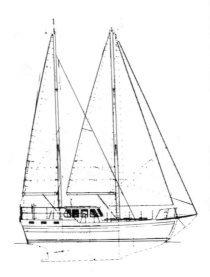

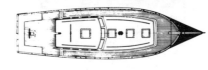

LOA	47'4"	Hull	FRP
LOD	41'4"	Deck	FRP
LWL	36'9"	Spar	Alum
Beam	12'5"	Fr. Water	246 gal
Draft	4'11"	SA/Disp	13.4
Disp	33,000 lbs	Disp/LWL	297
Ballast	8360 lbs	Blst/Disp	25%
Sail Area		Designer	
Schooner	861 sq ft		Erik Pedersen
Mast Ht	47'7"	Builder	
Auxiliary	std		Faenoe, Denmark
Diesel	72 hp	First Built	1976
Fuel Cap	250 gal	No. Built	10
		Price	$195,000 with sails

FAENOE YACHTYARDS LTD.
Havnen Skaerback
Fredericia, Denmark

Albin Nimbus

LOD	41'6"	Hull	FRP/Foam
LWL	34'2"	Deck	Teak
Beam	12'6"	Spar	Alum
Draft	5'10"	Fr. Water	120 gal
Disp	21,500 lbs	SA/Disp	18
Ballast	10,000 lbs	Disp/LWL	240
Sail Area		Blst/Disp	47%
Sloop	872 sq ft	Designer	
Mast Ht	58'		Kaufman & Ladd
Auxiliary	std	Price	$136,500 with sails
Pathfinder	50 hp		
Diesel			
Fuel Cap	60 gal		

ALBIN MARINE
Box 228
143 River Road
Cos Cob, CT 06807
(203) 661-4341

Cooper 416

LOD . . . . 41'6"	Hull . . . . FRP
LWL . . . . 32'6"	Deck . . . . FRP
Beam . . . . 14'	Spar . . . . Alum
Draft . . . . 6'7"	Cockpit . . . . 7'
Disp . . . 24,000 lbs	Headroom . . . . . 6'4"
Ballast . . . 10,500 lbs	Fr. Water . . . . 180 gal
Sail Area	SA/Disp 13.9
Sloop . . . . 723 sq ft	Disp/LWL 312
Auxiliary . . . . std	Blst/Disp 44%
Lehman . . . . 46 hp	Designer
Diesel	S. Huntingford
Fuel Cap . . . . . 100 gal	First Built 1979
	No. Built 31
	Price $104,500
	with sails

COOPER ENTERPRISES LTD.
1642 Langan Ave.
Port Coquituam, B.C.
Canada V3C 1K5
(604) 942-5945

Irwin 41 Ketch

LOD . . . . 41'8"	Hull . . . . FRP/Coremat
LWL . . . . 35'1"	Deck . . . . FRP
Beam . . . . 13'4"	Spar . . . . Alum
Draft	Fr. Water . . . . 160 gal
Shoal cb up . . 4'6"	SA/Disp 18
Shoal cb dn . 10'1"	Disp/LWL 258
Deep . . . . 6'6"	Blst/Disp 32%
Disp . . . . 25,000 lbs	Price $99,950
Ballast . . . . . 8000 lbs	with sails
Sail Area	
Ketch . . . . 960 sq ft	
Mast Ht . . . . 54'8"	
Auxiliary . . . . std	
Perkins . . . . . 62 hp	
Diesel	
Fuel Cap . . . . . 150 gal	

IRWIN YACHTS
13055 49th St. N.
Clearwater, FL 33520
(813) 577-4581

Vagabond 42

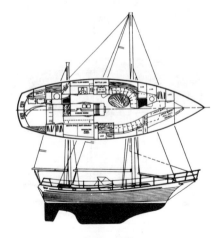

LOD . . . . 41'8"	Hull . . . . FRP
LWL . . . . 34'	Deck . . . . FRP
Beam . . . . 12'10"	Spar . . . . Alum
Draft . . . . 5'6"	Headroom . . . . . 6'2"
Disp . . . . 28,500 lbs	Fr. Water . . . . 140 gal
Ballast . . . . . 9200 lbs	SA/Disp 14.9
Sail Area	Disp/LWL 324
Ketch . . . . 871 sq ft	Blst/Disp 32%
Auxiliary . . . . std	Designer
Lehman . . . . 61 hp	George Stadel III
Diesel	Price $125,000
Fuel Cap . . . . . 100 gal	with sails

VAGABOND YACHT CORP.
1721 Pech, Suite 300
Houston, TX 77055
(713) 468-0511

Cascade 42

Passport 42

Tayana— VanCouver 42

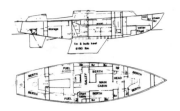

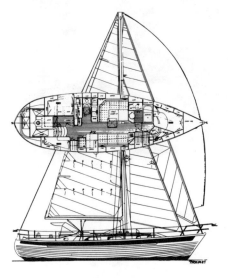

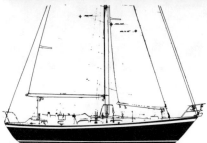

TAYANA V-42

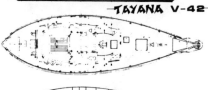

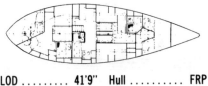

LOD .... 41'9"	Hull .... FRP	
LWL .... 34'	Deck ... FRP/Plywood	
Beam .... 11'8"	Spar .... Alum	
Draft .... 6'	Cockpit .... 6'6"	
Disp ..... 18,450 lbs	Headroom ..... 6'5"	
Ballast ..... 6180 lbs	Fr. Water ..... 70 gal	
Sail Area	SA/Disp 18.3	
Sloop .... 800 sq ft	Disp/LWL 210	
Mast Ht ...... 52'6"	Blst/Disp 33%	
Auxiliary .... std	Designer	
Perkins ..... 40 hp	Robert A. Smith	
Diesel	First Built 1964	
Fuel Cap ..... 75 gal	No. Built 100	
	Kit $60,000	

LOD .... 41'9"	Hull .... FRP
LWL .... 34'10"	Deck .... FRP
Beam .... 12'10"	Spar .... Alum
Draft .... 6'4"	Fr. Water ... 150 gal
Disp ..... 25,500 lbs	SA/Disp 13.6
Ballast .... na	Disp/LWL 269
Sail Area	Designer
Cutter ... 736 sq ft	Stan Huntingford
Auxiliary .... std	Price $108,000
	with sails

LOD .... 41'9"	Hull .... FRP
LWL .... 33'	Deck .... FRP
Beam .... 12'6"	Spar .... Alum
Draft .... 5'10"	Headroom ..... 6'6"
Disp ..... 29,147 lbs	Fr. Water .... 140 gal
Ballast ..... 9850 lbs	SA/Disp 15.9
Sail Area	Disp/LWL 362
Cutter ... 942 sq ft	Blst/Disp 34%
Auxiliary .... std	Designer
Perkins ..... 49 hp	Robert B. Harris
Diesel	Builder ..... Ta Yang
Fuel Cap ..... 120 gal	No. Built 76
	Price $105,900
	with sails

YACHT CONSTRUCTORS INC.
7030 N.E. 42nd Ave.
Portland, OR 97218
(503) 287-5794

PASSPORT YACHTS
2900 Westlake Ave. North
Seattle, WA 98109
(206) 282-0401

SOUTHERN OFFSHORE YACHTS
Box 6
Tarpon Springs, FL 33589
(813) 937-3188

Southern Offshore 42

LOD	41'10"	Hull	FRP
LWL	36'5"	Deck	FRP/Balsa
Beam	12'9"	Spar	Alum
Draft	5'10"	Headroom	6'4"
Disp	21,258 lbs	SA/Disp	16.7
Ballast	8700 lbs	Disp/LWL	197
Sail Area		Blst/Disp	41%
Sloop	800 sq ft	Designer	Robert Perry
Auxiliary	std	Builder	Angel Marine
Pathfinder	42 hp	Price	na
Diesel			

SOUTHERN OFFSHORE YACHTS
Box 6
Tarpon Springs, FL 33589
(813) 937-3188

Swan 42

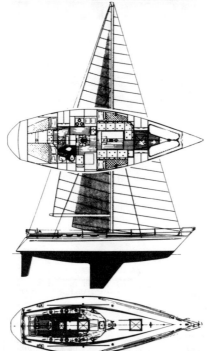

LOD	41'11"	Hull	FRP
LWL	33'11"	Deck	FRP
Beam	13'	Spar	Alum
Draft	7'11"	Disp/LWL	251
Disp	22000 lbs	Blst/Disp	42%
Ballast	9200 lbs	Designer	Ron Holland
Sail Area		Builder	
Sloop	na		Nautor, Finland
Auxiliary	std	Price	$152,000
Perkins	40 hp		with sails
Diesel			

NAUTOR EAST
55 America's Cup Avenue
Newport, RI 02840
(401) 846-8404

Walsted 42

LOD	41'11"	Hull	FRP
LWL	32'10"	Deck	FRP
Beam	12'10"	Spar	Alum
Draft		Cockpit	7'
Shoal cb up	5'	Headroom	6'5"
Shoal cb dn	na	Fr. Water	100 gal
Deep	7'1"	SA/Disp	16.6
Disp	22,000 lbs	Disp/LWL	277
Ballast	9500 lbs	Blst/Disp	43%
Sail Area		Designer	
Sloop	813 sq ft		Sparkman & Stephens
Mast Ht	61'	Builder	
Auxiliary	std		Walsted-Denmark
Perkins	50 hp	First Built	1983
Diesel		No. Built	1
Fuel Cap	50 gal	Price	na

SPARKMAN & STEPHENS
79 Madison Ave.
New York, NW 10016
(212) 689-3880

Baltic 42 DP

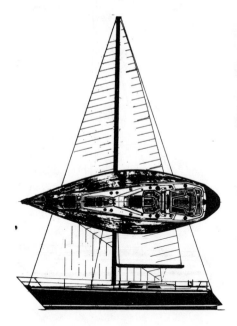

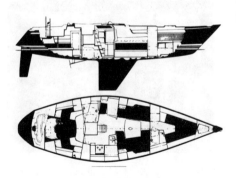

LOD	42'	Hull	FRP/Balsa
LWL	34'5"	Deck	FRP/Balsa
Beam	13'4"	Spar	Alum
Draft	7'11"	Fr. Water	60 gal
Disp	18,400 lbs	Disp/LWL	201
Ballast	8060 lbs	Blst/Disp	44%
Sail Area		Designer	
Sloop	na		Doug Peterson
Auxiliary	std	Builder	
Perkins	43 hp		Baltic Finland
Diesel		Price	na
Fuel Cap	45 gal		

Brewer 42

LOD	42'	Hull	FRP
LWL	32'8"	Deck	FRP
Beam	13'	Spar	Alum
Draft	5'	Fr. Water	300 gal
Disp	23,500 lbs	SA/Disp	17.1
Ballast	8000 lbs	Disp/LWL	300
Sail Area		Blst/Disp	34%
Ketch	875 sq ft	Designer	Ted Brewer
Auxiliary	std	First Built	1972
Lehman Ford	67 hp	Price	$99,600
Diesel			with sails
Fuel Cap	210 gal		

Formosa 42

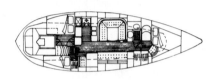

LOD	42'	Hull	FRP
LWL	34'10"	Deck	FRP
Beam	12'10"	Spar	Alum
Draft	6'4"	Disp/LWL	262
Disp	24,800 lbs	Blst/Disp	37%
Ballast	9260 lbs	Price	$71,550
Sail Area			with sails
Cutter	na		
Auxiliary	std		
Perkins	45 hp		
Diesel			

Golden Wave 42

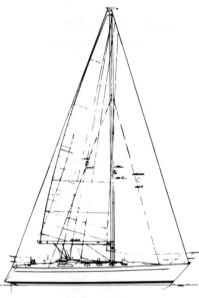

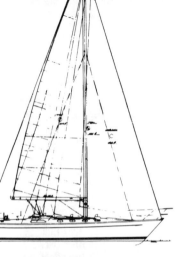

LOD	42'	Hull	FRP
LWL	34'4"	Deck	Teak
Beam	12'8"	Spar	Alum
Draft	6'2"	Fr. Water	120 gal
Disp	25,000 lbs	Disp/LWL	276
Ballast	na	Designer	Robert Perry
Sail Area		Builder	Cheoy Lee
Sloop	na	First Built	1980
Auxiliary	std	No. Built	20
Perkins	50 hp	Price	$157,000
Diesel			with sails
Fuel Cap	55 gal		

REX YACHT SALES
2152 S. E. 17th St.
Ft. Lauderdale, FL 33315
(305) 463-8810

Tartan 42

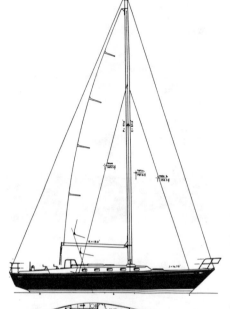

LOD	42'	Hull	FRP
LWL	32'	Deck	FRP
Beam	12'3"	Spar	Alum
Draft		Fr. Water	165 gal
Shoal	4'11"	SA/Disp	15.5
Deep	6'11"	Disp/LWL	300
Disp	22,000 lbs	Blst/Disp	42%
Ballast	9200 lbs	Designer	
Sail Area			Sparkman & Stephens
Cutter	759 sq ft	Price	na
Auxiliary	std		
Westerbeke	41 hp		
Diesel			
Fuel Cap	79 gal		

TARTAN MARINE CO.
320 River St.
Grand River, OH 44045
(216) 354-5671

Trintella 42

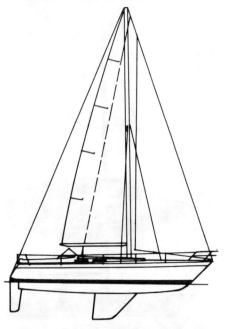

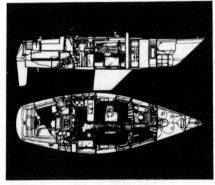

LOD	42'	Hull	FRP
LWL	34'9"	Deck	Teak
Beam	13'2"	Spar	Alum
Draft		Cockpit	8'
cb up	5'7"	Headroom	6'8"
cb dn	9'10"	Fr. Water	119 gal
Disp	20,160 lbs	SA/Disp	24.8
Ballast	8960 lbs	Disp/LWL	214
Sail Area		Blst/Disp	44%
Cutter	1150 sq ft	Designer	V/D Stadt
Sloop	1150 sq ft	Builder	
Mast Ht	55'		Jachtwerf Anne Wever
Auxiliary	std	First Built	1980
Volvo Penta	35 hp	No. Built	30
Diesel		1 Design	yes
		Price	$172,453
			with sails

ADAMS BLAIR & ASSOC.
Ste. 1111
2025 Pennsylvania Ave. NW
Washington, D.C. 20006
(202) 833-2696

Whitby 42

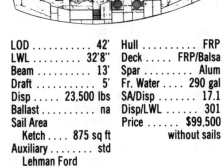

LOD . . . . 42'	Hull . . . . FRP
LWL . . . . 32'8''	Deck . . . . . FRP/Balsa
Beam . . . . 13'	Spar . . . . Alum
Draft . . . . 5'	Fr. Water . . . . 290 gal
Disp . . . . 23,500 lbs	SA/Disp 17.1
Ballast . . . . na	Disp/LWL 301
Sail Area	Price $99,500
Ketch . . 875 sq ft	without sails
Auxiliary . . . . std	
Lehman Ford	
Diesel	
Fuel Cap . . . . . 210 gal	

WHITBY BOAT WORKS LTD.
1710 Charles St.
Whitby, Ontario
Canada L1N 1C2
(416) 668-7755

Landfall 43

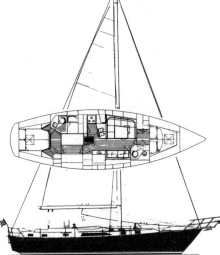

LOD . . . . 42'1''	Hull . . . . . . FRP/Balsa
LWL . . . . 34'5''	Deck . . . . . FRP/Balsa
Beam . . . . 12'7''	Spar . . . . Alum
Draft . . . . 5'6''	Headroom . . . . . 6'9''
Disp . . . . 24,600 lbs	Fr. Water . . . . 175 gal
Ballast . . . . 9080 lbs	SA/Disp 14.4
Sail Area	Disp/LWL 269
Sloop . . . . 761 sq ft	Blst/Disp . . . . . 37 %
Auxiliary . . . . std	Price $169,900
Westerbeke . . 52 hp	without sails
Diesel	
Fuel Cap . . . . . . 70 gal	

C&C YACHTS
55 Port Street East
Mississauga, Ontario
Canada L5G 4P3
(416) 274-7131

Pearson 424

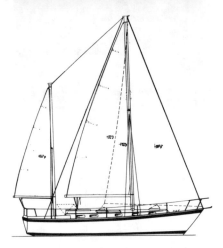

LOD . . . . 42'4''	Hull . . . . FRP
LWL . . . . 33'8''	Deck . . . . FRP
Beam . . . . 13'	Spar . . . . Alum
Draft . . . . 5'3''	Headroom . . . . . 6'4''
Disp . . . . 21,000 lbs	Fr. Water . . . . 170 gal
Ballast . . . . 7634 lbs	SA/Disp 15.2
Sail Area	Disp/LWL 246
Ketch . . . . 723 sq ft	Blst/Disp . . . . . 36 %
Mast Ht . . . . 48'10''	Designer . . . Bill Shaw
Auxiliary . . . . std	Price . . . . na
Diesel	
Fuel Cap . . . . . . 80 gal	

PEARSON YACHTS
West Shore Rd.
Portsmouth, RI 02871
(401) 683-0100

Oyster 43

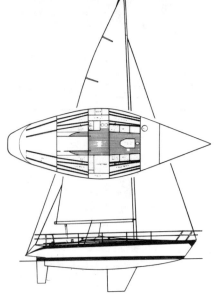

LOD	42'5"	Hull	FRP
LWL	34'	Deck	FRP
Beam	14'1"	Spar	Alum
Draft	7'6"	Fr. Water	80 gal
Disp	16,600 lbs	Disp/LWL	189
Ballast	8300 lbs	Blst/Disp	50%
Sail Area		Price	na
Sloop	na		
Auxiliary	na		
Volvo	36 hp		
Diesel			
Fuel Cap	30 gal		

OYSTER MARINE LTD.
9, East Hill,
Colchester, Essex,
England
0206 863090

Cascade 42 HS

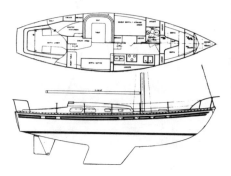

LOD	42'6"	Hull	FRP
LWL	34'	Deck	FRP/Plywood
Beam	12'	Spar	Alum
Draft	6'	Cockpit	7'
Disp	19,000 lbs	Headroom	6'5"
Ballast	6180 lbs	Fr. Water	170 gal
Sail Area		SA/Disp	18
Sloop	800 sq ft	Disp/LWL	216
Mast Ht	54'	Blst/Disp	33%
Auxiliary	std	Designer	
Perkins	40 hp		Robert A. Smith
Diesel		First Built	1964
Fuel Cap	150 gal	No. Built	100
		Kit	$70,000

YACHT CONSTRUCTORS INC.
7030 N.E. 42nd Ave.
Portland, OR 97218
(503) 287-5794

Slocum 43

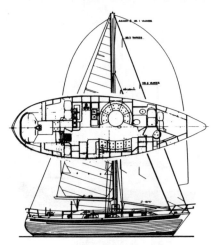

LOD	42'6"	Hull	FRP/Airex
LWL	35'8"	Deck	FRP/Balsa
Beam	12'11"	Spar	Alum
Draft	6'4"	Pos Float	yes
Disp	28,104 lbs	Cockpit	7'
Ballast	9000 lbs	Headroom	6'3"
Sail Area		Fr. Water	140 gal
Cutter	1028 sq ft	SA/Disp	17.8
Auxiliary	std	Disp/LWL	276
Perkins 410	50 hp	Blst/Disp	32%
Diesel		Designer	
Fuel Cap	180 gal		Stan Huntingford
		First Built	1982
		No. Built	26
		Price	$129,999
			with sails

CRUISING YACHTS INT'L.
12530 Olympia Dr.
Houston, TX 77077
(713) 497-6958

Young Sun 43

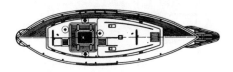

LOD .... 42'6"	Hull .... FRP
LWL .... 35'4"	Deck .... FRP
Beam .... 12'2"	Spar .... Alum
Draft .... 6'	Fr. Water .... 180 gal
Disp ..... 29,500 lbs	SA/Disp 16.1
Ballast ... 10,800 lbs	Disp/LWL 299
Sail Area	Blst/Disp 37%
Cutter ... 960 sq ft	Designer ... Ron Amy
Auxiliary .... std	Builder
Perkins ..... 51 hp	Young Sun, Taiwan
Diesel	Price $109,900
Fuel Cap ..... 150 gal	with sails

WONDERLAND INTERNATIONAL
P. O. Box 676
Syosset, NY 11791
(516) 689-8481

Contest 42

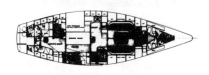

LOD .... 42'7"	Hull .... FRP
LWL .... 32'10"	Deck .... FRP
Beam .... 13'1"	Headroom ..... 6'5"
Draft .... 6'1"	Fr. Water .... 220 gal
Disp ..... 27,403 lbs	SA/Disp 15.1
Ballast ..... 9921 lbs	Disp/LWL 345
Sail Area	Blst/Disp 36%
Ketch .... 859 sq ft	Designer ... Dick Zaal
Mast Ht .... 56'	Builder
Auxiliary .... std	Conyplex, Holland
Volvo Penta . 52 hp	Price .... na
Diesel	
Fuel Cap ..... 94 gal	

HOLLAND YACHTS
Box 129
Solomons, MD 20688
(301) 326-3960

43 Traditional

LOD .... 42'7"	Hull .... FRP
LWL .... 36'10"	Deck ...... FRP/Teak
Beam .... 13'	Spar .... Alum
Draft .... 6'	Cockpit .... 8'
Disp .... 31,500 lbs	Headroom ..... 6'6"
Ballast ... 12,300 lbs	Fr. Water .... 208 gal
Sail Area	SA/Disp 15.1
Ketch .... 942 sq ft	Disp/LWL 281
Cutter ... 950 sq ft	Blst/Disp 39%
Mast Ht	Designer
Ketch .... 56'3"	Harwood S. Ives
Cutter .... 58'6"	First Built 1977
Auxiliary .... std	No. Built 80
Diesel	Price $139,000
Fuel Cap ..... 120 gal	with sails

HANS CHRISTIAN YACHTS
6201 Bayshore Walk
Long Beach, CA 90803
(213) 434-2076

Lancer 45

Rajo — Sailer 46

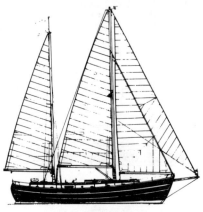

Cheoy Lee 43' Motorsailer

LOD	42'7"	Hull	FRP
LWL	35'3"	Deck	FRP
Beam	13'9"	Spar	Alum
Draft		Cockpit	6'6"
Shoal	4'11"	Headroom	6'
Deep	6'	Fr. Water	225 gal
Disp	21,000 lbs	SA/Disp	20.2
Ballast	7000 lbs	Disp/LWL	214
Sail Area		Blst/Disp	33%
Sloop	961 sq ft	Designer	Herb David
Mast Ht	60'	First Built	1980
Auxiliary	std	1 Design	yes
Perkins	85 hp	Price	$178,574
Diesel			with sails
Fuel Cap	104 gal		

LOA	47'7"	Hull	Steel
LOD	42'8"	Deck	Steel
LWL	39'	Spar	Alum
Beam	13'5"	Pos Float	yes
Draft	5'7"	Cockpit	7'4"
Disp	39,700 lbs	Headroom	6'6"
Ballast	13,230 lbs	Fr. Water	211 gal
Sail Area		SA/Disp	16.4
Ketch	1195 sq ft	Disp/LWL	299
Mast Ht	62'	Blst/Disp	33%
Auxiliary	std	Designer	M. Bekebrede
Ford	80 hp	First Built	1978
Diesel		No. Built	12
Fuel Cap	211 gal	Price	$190,000
			with sails

LOD	42'9"	Hull	FRP
LWL	na	Deck	Teak
Beam	13'2"	Spar	Alum
Draft	5'	Fr. Water	300 gal
Disp	34,000 lbs	Designer	Robert Perry
Ballast	na	First Built	1979
Sail Area		No. Built	7
Cutter	na	Price	$170,000
Ketch	na		with sails
Auxiliary	std		
Diesel			
Fuel Cap	600 gal		

LANCER YACHT CORP.
1939 Deere Ave.
Irvine, CA 92714
(714) 751-7220

RAJO — WATERSPORT BV
Werfweg 2 — 8243 PG Lelystad
Industrieterrein Noordersluis
Holland
(03200) 60929/60979

REX YACHT SALES
2152 S.E. 17th St.
Ft. Lauderdale, FL 33315
(305) 463-8810

44 Pilot House

Sou'wester 42

Worldcruiser 43 Pilothouse

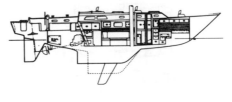

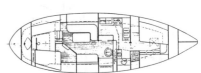

LOA . . . . 54'	Hull . . . . FRP
LOD . . . . 42'9"	Deck . . . . . FRP/Teak
LWL . . . . 37'6"	Spar . . . . Alum
Beam . . . . 14'6"	Cockpit . . . . 11'
Draft . . . . 5'8"	Headroom . . . . . 6'6"
Disp . . 44,000 lbs	Fr. Water . . 550 gal
Ballast . 14,000 lbs	SA/Disp 14.8
Sail Area	Disp/LWL 372
Ketch . . . 1150 sq ft	Blst/Disp 32%
Mast Ht . . . . 58'	Designer Harwood Ives
Auxiliary . . . . std	First Built 1979
Isuzu . . . . 130 hp	No. Built 12
Diesel	Price $179,000
Fuel Cap . . . . 450 gal	with sails

HANS CHRISTIAN YACHTS
6201 Bayshore Walk
Long Beach, CA 90803
(213) 434-2076

LOD . . . . 42'9"	Hull . . . . FRP
LWL . . . . 31'3"	Deck . . . . FRP
Beam . . . . 12'6"	Spar . . . . Alum
Draft	Cockpit . . . . . . 9'6"
cb up . . . . . . 4'9"	Headroom . . . . . . 6'
cb dn . . . . . . 8'10"	Fr. Water . . 175 gal
Disp . . . . 20,500 lbs	SA/Disp 17.5
Ballast . . . . 8500 lbs	Disp/LWL 299
Sail Area	Blst/Disp 41%
Sloop . . . . 818 sq ft	Designer
Mast Ht . . . . . . 58'4"	McCurdy & Rhodes
Auxiliary . . . . std	First Built 1981
Westerbeke . . 35 hp	No. Built 4
Diesel	Price $197,500
Fuel Cap . . . . . . 60 gal	without sails

HENRY R. HINCKLEY & CO.
Southwest Harbor, ME 04679
(207) 244-5531

LOA . . . . 46'	Hull . . . . FRP
LOD . . . . 42'11"	Deck . . . . FRP
LWL . . . . 33'4"	Spar . . . . Alum
Beam . . . . 13"	Cockpit . . . . 6'
Draft . . . . 5'9"	Headroom . . . . . 6'4"
Disp . . 31,500 lbs	Fr. Water . . 300+ gal
Ballast . . . 11,000 lbs	SA/Disp 17.1
Sail Area	Disp/LWL 380
Ketch . . . 1069 sq ft	Blst/Disp 35%
Mast Ht . . . . 62'	Designer Wm. Crealock
Auxiliary . . . . std	First Built 1978
Diesel . . . 60-80 hp	No. Built 2
	Kit . . . . available
	Price $200,000
	with sails

WORLDCRUISER YACHT CO.
1300 Logan St.
Costa Mesa, CA 92626
(714) 549-9331

Endeavour 43

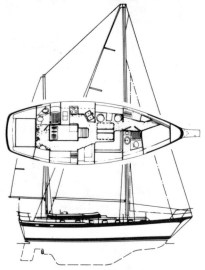

LOA	45'3"	Hull	FRP
LOD	43'	Deck	FRP
LWL	35'	Spar	Alum
Beam	14'	Headroom	6'7"
Draft	5'5"	Fr. Water	200 gal
Disp	33,000 lbs	SA/Disp	16.1
Ballast	12,000 lbs	Disp/LWL	343
Sail Area		Blst/Disp	36%
Ketch	1035 sq ft	Designer	
Cutter	1000 sq ft		Robert K. Johnson
Mast Ht	60'	Price	$129,900
Auxiliary	std		without sails
Perkins	62 hp		
Diesel			
Fuel Cap	153 gal		

ENDEAVOUR YACHT CORP.
11700 S. Belcher Rd.
Largo, FL 33543
(813) 541-3553

Oceanic 43

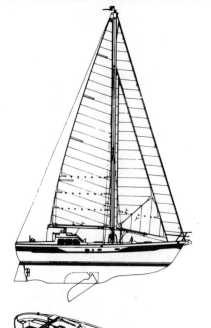

LOD	43'	Hull	FRP
LWL	36'4"	Deck	FRP
Beam	13'1"	Spar	Alum
Draft		Cockpit	8'
Shoal cb up	4'4"	Headroom	6'4"
Shoal cb dn	8'	Fr. Water	250 gal
Deep	5'7"	SA/Disp	16
Disp	27,500 lbs	Disp/LWL	255
Ballast	9000 lbs	Blst/Disp	33%
Sail Area		Designer	Ted Brewer
Cutter	912 sq ft	First Built	1980
Ketch	na	No. Built	10
Mast Ht	62'	Price	$114,500
Auxiliary	std		with sails
Perkins	52 hp		
Diesel			
Fuel Cap	180 gal		

PAN—OCEANIC MARINE
619 NW 12th Ave.
Miami, FL 33136
(305) 324-0088

Surprise 45

LOA	45'11"	Hull	FRP
LOD	43'	Deck	FRP
LWL	35'7"	Spar	Alum
Beam	13'5"	Headroom	6'4"
Draft	6'5"	Fr. Water	170 gal
Disp	26,400 lbs	SA/Disp	16.6
Ballast	11,023 lbs	Disp/LWL	262
Sail Area		Blst/Disp	42%
Ketch	919 sq ft	Designer	
Mast Ht	57'4"		Pieter Beeldsnijder
Auxiliary	std	Builder	Ta Yang
Puegeot	52 hp	First Built	1981
Diesel		Price	na
Fuel Cap	85 gal		

SOUTHERN OFFSHORE YACHTS
Box 6
Tarpon Springs, FL 33589
(813) 937-3188

CT 44

Tanton 43

Oyster 435

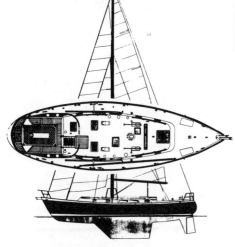

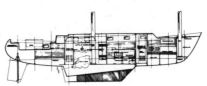

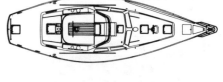

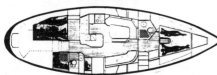

LOD .... 43'2"	Hull ..... FRP/Foam
LWL .... 37'7"	Deck ..... FRP/Foam
Beam .... 13'1"	Spar .... Alum
Draft .... 6'	Fr. Water .... 120 gal
Disp ..... 20,216 lbs	Disp/LWL 170
Ballast .... 9,267 lbs	Blst/Disp 46%
Sail Area	Designer .... Tanton
Cutter .... na	Builder
Auxiliary .... std	Ta Chio, Taiwan
Perkins	Price $109,500
Diesel	with sails
Fuel Cap ..... 100 gal	

LOD .... 43'2"	Hull .... FRP
LWL .... 37'7"	Deck .... FRP
Beam .... 13'1"	Spar ...... Carb Fib
Draft .... 4'10"	Fr. Water .. 120 gal
Disp .... 20,216 lbs	SA/Disp 17.1
Ballast .... 9000 lbs	Disp/LWL 170
Sail Area	Blst/Disp 45%
Cat ketch . 794 sq.ft	Price .... na
Auxiliary .... std	
Perkins ..... 50 hp	
Diesel	
Fuel Cap ...... 80 gal	

LOD .... 43'5"	Hull .... FRP
LWL .... 36'11"	Deck .... FRP
Beam .... 13'8"	Spar .... Alum
Draft	Fr. Water .... 288 gal
Shoal cb up .. 4'6"	SA/Disp 17
Shoal cb dn .. 8'9"	Disp/LWL 201
Deep .... 6'	Designer . Holman/Pye
Disp .... 22,600 lbs	Price .... na
Ballast .... na	
Sail Area	
Ketch .... 850 sq ft	
Sloop .... 825 sq ft	
Auxiliary .... std	
Volvo ..... 61 hp	
Diesel	

TA CHIAO USA INC.
17 Lakewood Lane
Seabrook, TX 77586
(713) 474-5967

OFFSHORE YACHTS
P. O. Box 6
Cos Cob, CT 06807
(203) 869-8054

OYSTER MARINE LTD.
9, East Hill,
Colchester, Essex,
England
0206 863090

Alden 44

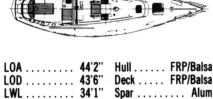

LOA	44'2"	Hull	FRP/Balsa
LOD	43'6"	Deck	FRP/Balsa
LWL	34'1"	Spar	Alum
Beam	12'6"	Cockpit	9'
Draft		Headroom	6'4"
cb up	4'11"	Fr. Water	160 gal
cb dn	8'9"	SA/Disp	20.7
Disp	24,300 lbs	Disp/LWL	274
Ballast	10,000 lbs	Blst/Disp	41%
Sail Area		Designer	
Sloop	1086 sq ft		John G. Alden
Mast Ht	59'	Builder	
Auxiliary	std		Tillotson-Pearson
Perkins	50 hp	First Built	1977
Diesel		No. Built	22
Fuel Cap	90 gal	Price	$203,000
			without sails

TILLOTSON—PEARSON INC.
Bend Boat Basin — Melville
Newport, RI 02840
(401) 683-3500

Nauticat 44

LOD	43'7"	Hull	FRP
LWL	38'8"	Deck	FRP/Teak
Beam	12'1"	Spar	Alum
Draft	6'	Fr. Water	200 gal
Disp	39,700 lbs	SA/Disp	14
Ballast	12,100 lbs	Disp/LWL	306
Sail Area		Blst/Disp	30%
Ketch	1017 sq ft	Price	na
Schooner	816 sq ft		
Mast Ht			
Ketch	54'11"		
Schooner	53'6"		
Auxiliary	std		
Ford	120 hp		
Diesel			
Fuel Cap	285 gal		

NAUTICAT INC.
Box 809, Tucker's Wharf
Marblehead, MA 01945
(617) 631-8491

Concept 44

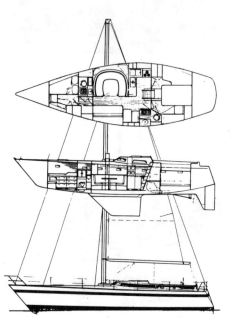

LOD	43'9"	Hull	FRP
LWL	37'1"	Deck	FRP
Beam	13'6"	Spar	Alum
Draft	6'6"	Fr. Water	214 gal
Disp	25,000 lbs	SA/Disp	17.3
Ballast	10,593 lbs	Disp/LWL	218
Sail Area		Blst/Disp	42%
Sloop	925 sq ft	Designer	Gary Mull
Auxiliary	std	Builder	
Pathfinder	42 hp		Hyundai, Korea
Diesel		Price	$137,000
Fuel Cap	86 gal		without sails

HYUNDAI CORP.
One Bridge Plaza North
Suite 600
Fort Lee, NJ 07024
(201) 592-7766

Mason 43

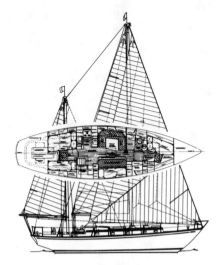

LOD .... 43'10"	Hull .... FRP
LWL .... 31'3"	Deck .... Teak
Beam .... 12'3"	Spar .... Alum
Draft	Cockpit .... 8'
Shoal ...... 5'9"	Headroom .... 6'2"
Deep .... 6'3"	Fr. Water .. 205 gal
Disp .... 25,000 lbs	SA/Disp 17.1
Ballast ..... 8400 lbs	Disp/LWL 366
Sail Area	Blst/Disp 34%
Ketch .... 916 sq ft	Designer ... Al Mason
Cutter ... 899 sq ft	Builder
Mast Ht	Ta-Shing Yacht
Ketch .... 58'	First Built 1979
Cutter ..... 59'2"	No. Built 56
Auxiliary .... std	Price $145,000
Perkins 4-108 50 hp	with sails
Diesel	
Fuel Cap ..... 105 gal	

PACIFIC ASIAN ENTERPRISES
Box FA
Dana Point, CA 92629-0937
(714) 496-4848

Nordic 44

LOD .... 43'10"	Hull .... FRP
LWL .... 35'5"	Deck ..... FRP/Balsa
Beam .... 12'11"	Spar .... Alum
Draft	Headroom ..... 6'4"
Shoal ...... 5'11"	Fr. Water .. 140 gal
Deep .... 7'	SA/Disp 17.7
Disp .... 24,000 lbs	Disp/LWL 241
Ballast ..... 9340 lbs	Blst/Disp 39%
Sail Area	Designer Robert Perry
Sloop ... 919 sq ft	Price $172,000
Auxiliary .... std	without sails
Universal ... 44 hp	
Diesel	
Fuel Cap ...... 76 gal	

NORDIC YACHTS INC.
Box 964
Bellingham, WA 98227
(206) 398-1090

Sea Wolf 44

LOA .... 49'10"	Hull .... FRP
LOD .... 43'10"	Deck ...... FRP/Teak
LWL .... 34'9"	Spar .... Wood
Beam .... 13'	Cockpit .... 5'8"
Draft .... 6'	Headroom ..... 6'4"
Disp ... 32,000 lbs	Fr. Water .. 240 gal
Ballast ... 10,000 lbs	SA/Disp 14.3
Sail Area	Disp/LWL 340
Ketch .... 900 sq ft	Blst/Disp 31%
Mast Ht ..... 56'10"	Designer
Auxiliary .... std	William Garden
Ford Lehman 80 hp	First Built 1977
Diesel	No. Built 141
Fuel Cap ..... 220 gal	1 Design .... yes
	Price $72,000
	with sails

HUDSON BOAT LTD.
3608 Coolheights Dr.
Rancho Palos Verdes, CA 90274
(213) 541-2993

Worldcruiser 44 Schooner

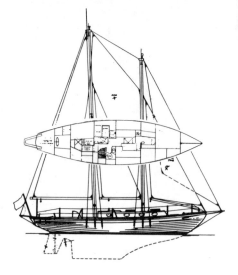

LOA	50'10"	Hull	FRP
LOD	43'10"	Deck	Teak
LWL	32'6"	Spar	Alum
Beam	11'	Cockpit	5'
Draft	6'2"	Headroom	6'2"
Disp	23,000 lbs	Fr. Water	100+ gal
Ballast	8500 lbs	SA/Disp	20
Sail Area		Disp/LWL	299
Schooner	1011 sq ft	Blst/Disp	37%
Mast Ht	52'	Designer	
Auxiliary	std		Bailey Taplin
Diesel	25 hp	First Built	1978
		No. Built	3
		Kit	available
		Price	$180,000
			with sails

WORLDCRUISER YACHT CO.
1300 Logan St.
Costa Mesa, CA 92626
(714) 549-9331

Cherubini 44'

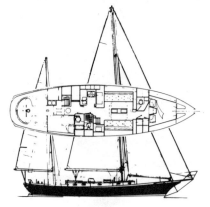

LOA	50'	Hull	FRP
LOD	44'	Deck	Wood Epoxy
LWL	40'	Spar	Alum
Beam	12'	Cockpit	6'6"
Draft	4'10"	Headroom	6'5"
Disp	28,000 lbs	Fr. Water	165 gal
Ballast	12,000 lbs	SA/Disp	19.7
Sail Area		Disp/LWL	195
Ketch	1133 sq ft	Blst/Disp	43%
Mast Ht	56'	Designer	
Auxiliary	std		John E. Cherubini
Westerbeke	50 hp	First Built	1976
Diesel		No. Built	30
Fuel Cap	75 gal	Kit	$80,000
		Price	$221,000
			with sails

CHERUBINI BOAT CO.
222 Wood St.
Burlington, NJ 08016
(609) 499-2200

Freedom 44

LOD	44'	Hull	FRP/Balsa
LWL	39'6"	Deck	FRP/Balsa
Beam	12'	Spar	Carbon Fiber
Draft	6'	Cockpit	9'6"
Disp	24,000 lbs	Headroom	6'4"
Ballast	6000 lbs	Fr. Water	200 gal
Sail Area		SA/Disp	16.1
Cat Ketch	836 sq ft	Disp/LWL	174
Mast	unstayed	Blst/Disp	25%
Auxiliary	std	Builder	
Perkins	50 hp		Tillotson-Pearson
Diesel		First Built	1981
Fuel Cap	107 gal	No. Built	16
		Price	$154,000
			without sails

FREEDOM YACHTS
49 America's Cup Ave.
Newport, RI 02840
(401) 847-7475

Pacific Passage 44

The PACIFIC PASSAGE 44 is a world class yacht built to meet the demands of the experienced yachtsman who occasionally makes a major ocean passage but spends most of his time sailing in coastal waters and anchored in protected coves and harbors. Her size, displacement, underbody design and sail plan will allow you to make major ocean passages safely, quickly and comfortably. Her structural integrity easily surpasses most production sailboats (our New Zealand design/production management team wouldn't have it any other way!) and the finest marine hardware and equipment is used for years of trouble-free service. The PACIFIC PASSAGE 44 will sail higher and faster than comparable cruising sailboats due to an advanced NACA foil section keel (modified fin with skeg), high-aspect sail plan, moderate displacement, and a relatively long waterline. The design, materials, construction and equipment meet or exceed Lloyd's rules for certification of FRP yachts, along with BIA, ABYC and U.S. Coast Guard requirements.

The interior of the PACIFIC PASSAGE 44 is spacious and beautifully finished in select Thai teak with custom cabinets, doors, gratings, etc. Our Thai craftsmen have produced an interior that represents the finest teak joiner work available today. The electrical system is carefully engineered meeting ABYC and BIA recommendations for color code and circuit protection, with marine grade tinned wire and terminals, master DC and AC circuit breaker panels, and a common ground buss (copper bar)/external ground plate/lightning protection/galvanic corrosion protection system. The interior is light and airy due to an abundance of opening ports, hatches and dorade vents along with extensive cabin lighting.

On deck, Barient winches are used (self-tailing sheet winches) along with American made spars (Kenyon) and rigging. Teak decks with teak inlay in the hatches and cockpit area along with teak cap rail and trim are beautifully set off by a beige cabin top (also cuts down on glare). Yacht Specialties steering (cable/pedestal) and Danforth Constellation Compass are also standard.

The PACIFIC PASSAGE 44 is truly a world class yacht utilizing the finest in materials, construction and equipment. You will be proud to entertain aboard this superb yacht or set sail for Fiji or Tahiti! By building her in our new plant in Thailand, we can deliver this outstanding yacht in Annapolis complete with working sails for only $129,000.

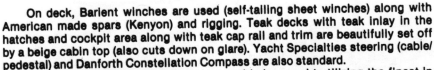

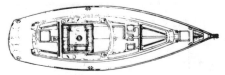

LOD	44'	Hull	FRP
LWL	37'	Deck	FRP/Teak
Beam	13'2"	Spar	Alum
Draft	5'6"	Cockpit	6'6"
Disp	26,300 lbs	Headroom	6'4"
Ballast	10,000 lbs	Fr. Water	150 gal
Sail Area		SA/Disp	15.6
Ketch	862 sq ft	Disp/LWL	232
Staysail Ketch		Blst/Disp	38%
	1016 sq ft	Designer	
Mast Ht	56'	Jack Hall, New Zealand	
Auxiliary	std	Builder	
BMW	45 hp	Royal Thai Yts., Thailand	
Diesel		First Built	1982
Fuel Cap	180 gal	No. Built	1
		Price	$129,000 with sails

ROYAL THAI YACHTS NA
Box 3565
Annapolis, MD 21403
(301) 946-8681

Norton 44

CANTING KEEL

LOD . . . . 44'	Hull . . . . Wood Epoxy
LWL . . . . 40'	Deck . . . Wood Epoxy
Beam . . . . 9'6''	Spar . . . . Alum
Draft	Cockpit . . . . 7'
lb up . . . . 3'6''	Headroom . . . . . 6'2''
lb dn . . . . 7'6''	Fr. Water . . . . 45 gal
Disp . . . . . . 8800 lbs	SA/Disp 34.7
Ballast . . . . . 2500 lbs	Disp/LWL 61
Sail Area	Blst/Disp 28%
Mast Ht . . . . 54'	David Hubbard
Mast . . . . . . unstayed	First Built 1982
Auxiliary . . . . std	No. Built 1
Universal . . . 21 hp	Kit $35,000
Diesel	Price $125,000
Fuel Cap . . . . . 40 gal	with sails

NORTON BOAT WORKS
Box 464
Green Lake, WI 54941
(414) 294-6813

Southerly 135

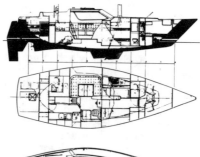

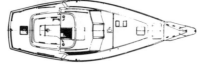

LOD . . . . 44'	Hull . . . . FRP
LWL . . . . 34'	Deck . . . . . FRP/Balsa
Beam . . . . . . 13'11''	Spar . . . . Alum
Draft	Cockpit . . . . 6'6''
Swing keel up . 2'6''	Headroom . . . . 6'
Swing keel dn . 7'8''	Fr. Water . . . . 150 gal
Disp . . . . . 23,000 lbs	SA/Disp 15.9
Ballast . . . . 9200 lbs	Disp/LWL 261
Sail Area	Blst/Disp 40%
Sloop . . . . 803 sq ft	Designer . . Dick Carter
Mast Ht . . . . . . 59'6''	Builder
Auxiliary . . . . std	Northshore, England
Perkins . . . . . 47 hp	First Built 1981
Diesel	No. Built 5
Fuel Cap . . . . 100 gal	1 Design . . . . . . yes
	Price . . . . na

PARKER YACHTS
South Freeport, ME 04078
(207) 865-6692

Stamas 44

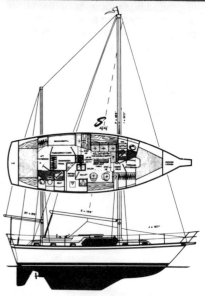

LOD . . . . 44'	Hull . . . . FRP
LWL . . . . 34'	Deck . . . . FRP
Beam . . . . 14'	Spar . . . . Alum
Draft . . . . 5'1''	Cockpit . . . . 8'
Disp . . . . 30,000 lbs	Headroom . . . . . 6'4''
Ballast . . 12,000 lbs	Fr. Water . . . 325 gal
Sail Area	SA/Disp 15
Ketch . . . 903 sq ft	Disp/LWL 341
Cutter . . . 903 sq ft	Blst/Disp 40%
Mast Ht . . . . 58'	Designer
Auxiliary . . . . std	Robert K. Johnson
Perkins . . . . 62 hp	First Built 1981
Diesel	No. Built 110
Fuel Cap . . . . 175 gal	Price $149,600
	without sails

STAMAS YACHTS INC.
300 Pampas Ave.
Tarpon Springs, FL 33589
(813) 937-4118

Transpac 44

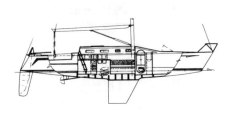

LOD	44'	Hull	FRP
LWL	38'4"	Deck	FRP
Beam	12'7"	Spar	Alum
Draft	7'	Headroom	6'3"
Disp	12,000 lbs	Fr. Water	80 gal
Ballast	6500 lbs	SA/Disp	26.6
Sail Area		Disp/LWL	95
Sloop	872 sq ft	Blst/Disp	54%
Auxiliary	std	Designer	Chuck Burns
Westerbeke	21 hp	Price	na
Diesel			
Fuel Cap	50 gal		

PYRAMID BOATWORKS
2429 Pratt Ave.
Hayward, CA 94544
(415) 489-8025

Trintella 45

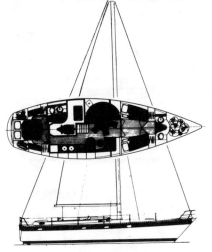

LOA	45'	Hull	FRP
LOD	44'	Deck	Teak
LWL	35'5"	Spar	Alum
Beam	13'5"	Cockpit	6'
Draft		Headroom	6'8"
cb up	6'5"	Fr. Water	211 gal
cb dn	7'2"	SA/Disp	21.4
Disp	29,000 lbs	Disp/LWL	291
Ballast	12,000 lbs	Blst/Disp	41%
Sail Area		Designer	V/D Stadt
Sloop	1260 sq ft	Builder	
Ketch	1200 sq ft	Jachtwerf Anne Wever	
Cutter	1260 sq ft	No. Built	4
Mast Ht.	56'	1 Design	yes
Auxiliary	std	Price	$308,660
Perkins	72 hp		with sails
Diesel			

ADAMS BLAIR & ASSOC.
Ste. 1111
2025 Pennsylvania Ave. NW
Washington, D.C. 20006
(202) 833-2696

Wellington 44

LOD	44'	Hull	FRP
LWL	37'3"	Deck	FRP/Balsa
Beam	13'6"	Spar	Alum
Draft		Pos Float	opt
cb up	4'3"	Cockpit	6'4"
cb dn	7'3"	Headroom	6'6"
Disp	28,000 lbs	Fr. Water	165 gal
Ballast	10,000 lbs	SA/Disp	16.8
Sail Area		Disp/LWL	242
Cutter	970 sq ft	Blst/Disp	36%
Mast Ht	61'	Designer	
Auxiliary	std		Bill Wellington
Lehman	61 hp	First Built	1978
Diesel		No. Built	8
Fuel Cap	165 gal	Kit	available
		Price	$149,000
			with sails

WELLINGTON BOATS INC.
11544 Normandy Blvd.
Jacksonville, FL 32221
(904) 781-1055

Lancer 45 Motorsailer

Little Harbor 44

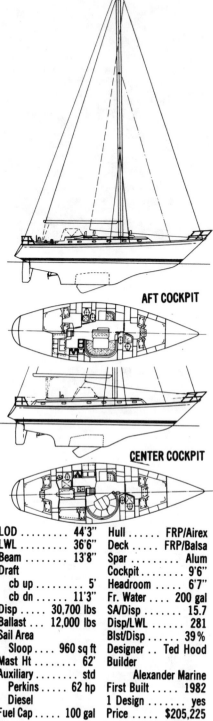

AFT COCKPIT

CENTER COCKPIT

Reliance 44

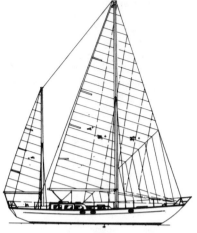

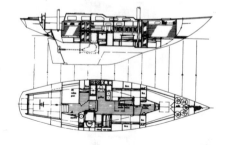

Lancer 45

LOD	44'2"	Hull	FRP
LWL	37'3"	Deck	FRP
Beam	13'9"	Spar	Alum
Draft		Cockpit	5'5"
Shoal	4'11"	Headroom	6'
Deep	6'	Fr. Water	225 gal
Disp	23,000 lbs	SA/Disp	17.7
Ballast	7000 lbs	Disp/LWL	199
Sail Area		Blst/Disp	30%
Sloop	896 sq ft	Designer	Herb David
Mast Ht	60'	First Built	1979
Auxiliary	std	1 Design	yes
Perkins twin 85 hp		Price	$214,920
Diesel			with sails
Fuel Cap	225 gal		

Little Harbor 44

LOD	44'3"	Hull	FRP/Airex
LWL	36'6"	Deck	FRP/Balsa
Beam	13'8"	Spar	Alum
Draft		Cockpit	9'6"
cb up	5'	Headroom	6'7"
cb dn	11'3"	Fr. Water	200 gal
Disp	30,700 lbs	SA/Disp	15.7
Ballast	12,000 lbs	Disp/LWL	281
Sail Area		Blst/Disp	39%
Sloop	960 sq ft	Designer	Ted Hood
Mast Ht	62'	Builder	
Auxiliary	std		Alexander Marine
Perkins	62 hp	First Built	1982
Diesel		1 Design	yes
Fuel Cap	100 gal	Price	$205,225
			without sails

Reliance 44

LOD	44'4"	Hull	FRP
LWL	31'5"	Deck	FRP
Beam	11'8"	Spar	Alum
Draft	6'2"	Cockpit	6'10"
Disp	28,000 lbs	Headroom	6'6"
Ballast	11,200 lbs	Fr. Water	100 gal
Sail Area		SA/Disp	15.7
Ketch	905 sq ft	Disp/LWL	403
Cutter	na	Blst/Disp	40%
Auxiliary	std	First Built	1974
Volvo	35 hp	No. Built	435
Diesel		Kit	available
Fuel Cap	60 gal	Price	na

LANCER YACHT CORP.
1939 Deere Ave.
Irvine, CA 92714
(714) 751-7220

LITTLE HARBOR CUSTOM YACHTS
Little Harbor Way
Marblehead, MA 01945
(617) 631-8840

RELIANCE SAILING CRAFT
Box 693, St. Laurent (Montreal)
Quebec, Canada H4L 4V9
(514) 695-2271

Liberty 45

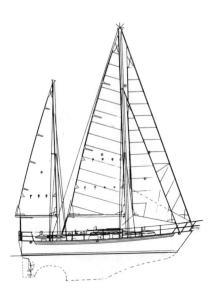

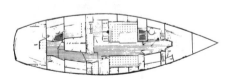

LOD	44'5"	Hull	FRP
LWL	39'7"	Deck	Teak
Beam	12'10"	Spar	Alum
Draft	6'6"	Headroom	6'3"
Disp	30,000 lbs	Fr. Water	125 gal
Ballast	10,250 lbs	SA/Disp	15.7
Sail Area		Disp/LWL	216
Ketch	950 sq ft	Blst/Disp	34%
Auxiliary	std	Builder	Taiwan
Ford Lehman 65 hp		Price	$110,000
Diesel			with sails
Fuel Cap	110 gal		

PASSPORT YACHTS
2900 Westlake Ave. North
Seattle, WA 98109
(206) 282-0401

Atlantic 45

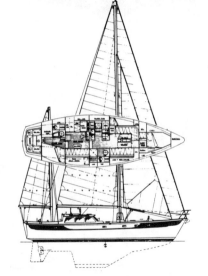

LOD	44'6"	Hull	Steel
LWL	36'8"	Deck	Steel/Teak
Beam	13'10"	Spar	Alum
Draft		Cockpit	10'6"
Shoal	6'	SA/Disp	15
Deep	6'10"	Disp/LWL	326
Disp	36,000 lbs	Designer	Ted Brewer
Ballast	na	Price	$132,000
Sail Area			with sails
Cutter	1021 sq ft		
Ketch	1077 sq ft		
Auxiliary	std		
Ford	60 hp		
Diesel			
Fuel Cap	150 gal		

KANTER YACHTS
P. O. Box 730, Port Stanly,
Ontario, Canada N0L 2A0
(519) 782-4231

Seguin 44

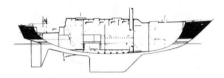

LOD	44'6"	Hull	FRP
LWL	33'6"	Deck	FRP
Beam	12'10"	Spar	Alum
Draft		Cockpit	8'6"
Shoal cb up	5'	Headroom	6'9"
Shoal cb dn	na	Fr. Water	150 gal
Deep	7'	SA/Disp	17.3
Disp	25,000 lbs	Disp/LWL	297
Ballast	11,000 lbs	Blst/Disp	44%
Sail Area		Designer	
Sloop	926 sq ft	Sparkman & Stephens	
Mast Ht	61'	Builder . Lyman Morse	
Auxiliary	std	First Built	1981
Perkins	50 hp	No. Built	6
Diesel		Price	na
Fuel Cap	60 gal		

SPARKMAN & STEPHENS
79 Madison Ave.
New York, NY 10016
(212) 689-3880

Norseman 447

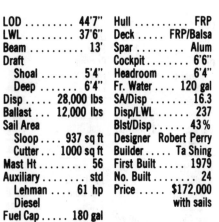

LOD . . . . 44'7"	Hull . . . . FRP
LWL . . . . 37'6"	Deck . . . . . FRP/Balsa
Beam . . . . 13'	Spar . . . . Alum
Draft	Cockpit . . . . 6'6"
Shoal . . . . . . 5'4"	Headroom . . . . . . 6'4"
Deep . . . . . . 6'4"	Fr. Water . . . . 120 gal
Disp . . . . 28,000 lbs	SA/Disp 16.3
Ballast . . . 12,000 lbs	Disp/LWL 237
Sail Area	Blst/Disp 43%
Sloop . . . . 937 sq ft	Designer Robert Perry
Cutter . . . 1000 sq ft	Builder . . . . . Ta Shing
Mast Ht 56	First Built 1979
Auxiliary . . . . std	No. Built 24
Lehman . . . . 61 hp	Price $172,000
Diesel	with sails
Fuel Cap . . . . . 180 gal	

NORSEMAN YACHTS
14025 Panay Way
Marina Del Rey, CA 90291
(213) 822-7141

Gulfstar 44

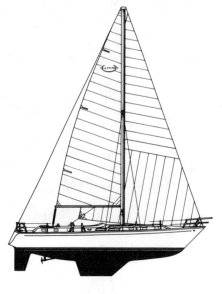

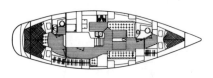

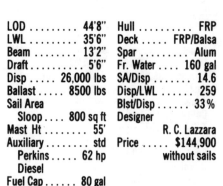

LOD . . . . 44'8"	Hull . . . . FRP
LWL . . . . 35'6"	Deck . . . . . FRP/Balsa
Beam . . . . 13'2"	Spar . . . . Alum
Draft . . . . 5'6"	Fr. Water . . . . 160 gal
Disp . . . . 26,000 lbs	SA/Disp 14.6
Ballast . . . . . 8500 lbs	Disp/LWL 259
Sail Area	Blst/Disp 33%
Sloop . . . . 800 sq ft	Designer
Mast Ht . . . . 55'	R. C. Lazzara
Auxiliary . . . . std	Price $144,900
Perkins . . . . . 62 hp	without sails
Diesel	
Fuel Cap . . . . . . 80 gal	

GULFSTAR INC.
6101 45th St. N.
St. Petersburg, FL 33714
(813) 527-7251

Morgan 45

LOD . . . . 45'	Hull . . . . FRP
LWL . . . . 36'9"	Deck . . . . FRP
Beam . . . . 13'5"	Spar . . . . Alum
Draft	Fr. Water . . . . 200 gal
cb up . . . . 5'	SA/Disp 18.8
cb dn . . . . . . 7'5"	Disp/LWL 202
Disp . . . . 22,500 lbs	Price . . . . na
Ballast . . . . na	
Sail Area	
Sloop . . . . 938 sq ft	
Auxiliary . . . . std	
Pathfinder	
Diesel	
Fuel Cap . . . . . 100 gal	

MORGAN YACHT INC.
7200 Bryan Dairy Rd.
Largo, FL 33543
(813) 544-6681

Seamaster 45

Whitby 45 Mark II

Gale Force 45

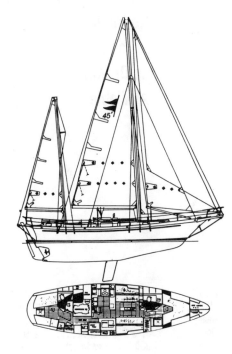

LOA	45'2"	Hull	FRP
LOD	45'	Deck	FRP
LWL	34'6"	Spar	Alum
Beam	13'3"	Cockpit	6'
Draft	5'6"	Headroom	6'3"
Disp	26,000 lbs	Fr. Water	250 gal
Ballast	9100 lbs	SA/Disp	16.4
		Disp/LWL	283
Sail Area		Blst/Disp	35 %
Ketch	900 sq ft	Designer	
Mast Ht	51'		Bruce Roberts
Auxiliary	std	First Built	1977
Perkins	60 hp	No. Built	22
Diesel		Kit	$30,000
Fuel Cap	200 gal	Price	$138,000
			with sails

SEAMASTER YACHTS
2238 SW 34th St.
Ft. Lauderdale, FL 33312
(305) 761-9035

LOD	45'	Hull	FRP/Balsa
LWL	32'	Deck	FRP/Balsa
Beam	12'	Spar	Alum
Draft	6'	SA/Disp	16.2
Disp	23,500 lbs	Disp/LWL	320
Ballast	na	Price	$127,820
Sail Area			without sails
Sloop	832 sq ft		
Sloop (tall)	915 sq ft		
Auxiliary	std		
Perkins			
Diesel			

WHITBY BOAT WORKS LTD.
1710 Charles St.
Whitby, Ontario
Canada L1N 1C2
(416) 668-7755

LOA	52'	Hull	FRP/Airex
LOD	45'1"	Deck	FRP
LWL	39'10"	Spar	Alum
Beam	12'2"	SA/Disp	14.8
Draft		Disp/LWL	219
cb up	5'	Blst/Disp	33 %
cb dn	8'	Price	$280,000
Disp	31,000 lbs		with sails
Ballast	10,200 lbs		
Sail Area			
Ketch	914 sq ft		
Auxiliary	std		
Westerbeke	85 hp		
Diesel			

KAISER YACHTS
1122 E. 7th St.
Wilmington, DE 19801

Cape Dory 45

No Photo
or
Line Drawing
Available

LOD . . . . 45'2"	Hull . . . . FRP
LWL . . . . 33'6"	Deck . . . . FRP/Balsa
Beam . . . . 13'	Spar . . . . Alum
Draft . . . . 6'3"	Cockpit . . . . 9'3"
Disp . . . . 24,000 lbs	Headroom . . . . 6'9"
Ballast . . . . 9400 lbs	Fr. Water . . . 200 gal
Sail Area	SA/Disp 18
Ketch . . . . 936 sq ft	Disp/LWL 284
Cutter . . . 882 sq ft	Blst/Disp 39%
Mast Ht . . . . 57'	Designer . . Carl Alberg
Auxiliary . . . . std	First Built 1983
Westerbeke . . 52 hp	No. Built 2
Diesel	1 Design . . . . yes
Fuel Cap . . . . 100 gal	Price . . . . na

CAPE DORY YACHTS INC.
160 Middleboro Ave.
E. Taunton, MA 02718
(617) 823-6776

Westide

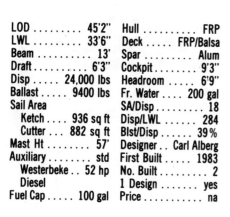

WESTIDE - 45 ★
AFT CABIN KETCH
Beautiful Outside and
"See-Out" Inside

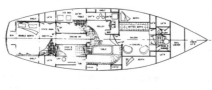

LOD . . . . 45'2"	Hull . . . . FRP
LWL . . . . 34'6"	Deck . . . . FRP
Beam . . . . 13'4"	Spar . . . . Wood
Draft . . . . 5'6"	Fr. Water . . . 170 gal
Disp . . . . 32,000 lbs	SA/Disp 12.8
Ballast . . . . 8500 lbs	Disp/LWL 347
Sail Area	Blst/Disp 27%
Ketch . . . . 809 sq ft	Price . . . . na
Auxiliary . . . . std	
Diesel	
Fuel Cap . . . . . 170 gal	

EAST WEST YACHTS
Box 9953
Marina Del Rey, CA 90291
(213) 822-1300

Bristol 45.5

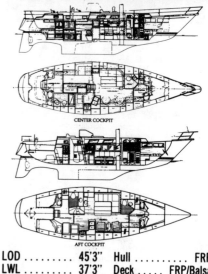

CENTER COCKPIT

AFT COCKPIT

LOD . . . . 45'3"	Hull . . . . FRP
LWL . . . . 37'3"	Deck . . . . FRP/Balsa
Beam . . . . 13'3"	Spar . . . . Alum
Draft	Pos Float . . . . yes
cb up . . . . . 4'11"	Headroom . . . . 6'6"
cb dn . . . . . . 11'	Fr. Water . . . . 170 gal
Disp . . . . 34,660 lbs	SA/Disp 16.9
Ballast . . . 15,000 lbs	Disp/LWL 305
Sail Area	Blst/Disp 43%
Sloop . . . 1125 sq ft	Designer . . Ted Hood
Ketch . . . 1033 sq ft	First Built 1979
Auxiliary . . . . std	No. Built 24
Westerbeke . . 58 hp	Price $202,931
Diesel	without sails
Fuel Cap . . . . . 140 gal	

BRISTOL YACHT CO.
Franklin St.
Bristol, RI 02809
(401) 253-5200

Irwin 46

LOD	45'6"	Hull	FRP/Coremat
LWL	37'7"	Deck	FRP
Beam	13'6"	Spar	Alum
Draft		Fr. Water	190 gal
Shoal cb up	4'8"	SA/Disp	15.5
Shoal cb dn	10'11"	Disp/LWL	277
Deep	6'1"	Blst/Disp	36%
Disp	33,000 lbs	Price	$132,590
Ballast	12,000 lbs		with sails
Sail Area			
Ketch	998 sq ft		
Mast Ht	58'		
Auxiliary	std		
Perkins			
Diesel			
Fuel Cap	190 gal		

IRWIN YACHTS
13055 49th St. N.
Clearwater, FL 33520
(813) 577-4581

Island Trader 46 Trawl'r Sailer

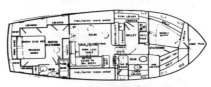
Galley Down Interior

Galley Up Interior

LOD	45'6"	Hull	FRP
LWL	39'9"	Deck	Teak
Beam	15'2"	Spar	Wood
Draft	5'6"	Cockpit	13'4"
Disp	48,360 lbs	Headroom	6'9"
Ballast	8500 lbs	Fr. Water	450 gal
Sail Area		SA/Disp	7.8
Ketch	647 sq ft	Disp/LWL	343
Mast Ht	45'9"	Blst/Disp	18%
Auxiliary	std	1 Design	yes
Lehman/Ford	120 hp	Price	$135,900
Diesel			with sails
Fuel Cap	450 gal		

MARINE TRADING INTERNATIONAL
Box 1232
Point Pleasant Beach, NJ 08742
(201) 899-6800

ALC 46

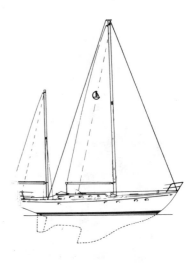

LOD	45'7"	Hull	FRP
LWL	33'	Deck	Teak
Beam	12'3"	Spar	Alum
Draft		Cockpit	8'
Shoal	5'6"	Headroom	6'5"
Deep	6'9"	Fr. Water	160 gal
Disp	25,000 lbs	SA/Disp	16.6
Ballast	10,000 lbs	Disp/LWL	311
Sail Area		Blst/Disp	40%
Ketch	888 sq ft	Designer	Luders
Sloop	na	Builder	
Mast Ht	60'		Lecomte, Holland
Auxiliary	std	First Built	1974
Westerbeke	40 hp	Price	$275,000
Diesel			with sails
Fuel Cap	80 gal		

A. LECOMTE CO.
P. O. Box 406
New Rochelle, NY 10802

Passage 458

Y.E.S. 46

Oceanic 46

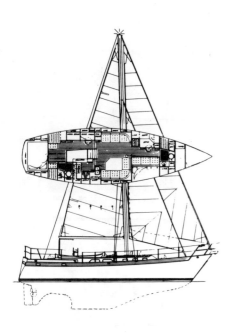

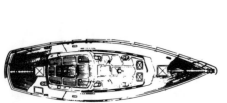

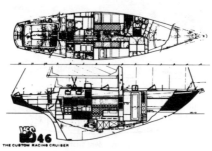

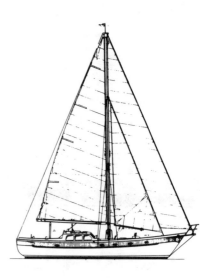

LOD	45'8"	Hull	FRP
LWL	40'4"	Deck	FRP
Beam	12'8"	Spar	Alum
Draft	6'4"	Cockpit	6'2"
Disp	31,000 lbs	Headroom	6'4"
Ballast	10,000 lbs	Fr. Water	225 gal
Sail Area		SA/Disp	17.4
Cutter	1075 sq ft	Disp/LWL	211
Ketch	1021 sq ft	Blst/Disp	32%
Mast Ht		Designer	Peter Doone
Cutter	58'	Builder	
Ketch	56'		Shin Fa Industry
Auxiliary	std	First Built	1982
Perkins	73 hp	No. Built	15
Diesel		Price	$130,000
Fuel Cap	160 gal		with sails

PASSPORT YACHTS
2900 Westlake Ave. North
Seattle, WA 98109
(206) 282-0401

LOD	45'8"	Hull	FRP
LWL	32'	Deck	FRP
Beam	11'	Spar	Alum
Draft	6'3"	Cockpit	8'4"
Disp	29,800 lbs	Headroom	6'10"
Ballast	12,000 lbs	Fr. Water	225 gal
Sail Area		SA/Disp	14.7
Sloop	883 sq ft	Disp/LWL	406
Yawl	982 sq ft	Blst/Disp	40%
Mast Ht	55'3"	Designer	
Auxiliary	opt		Morgan/Miller
Diesel	52 hp	First Built	1975
Fuel Cap	100 gal	No. Built	220
		Kit	$19,900
		Price	$115,000
			with sails

YACHT ENGINEERING SPECIALTIES
130 16th Ave. North
St. Petersburg, FL 33704
(813) 821-6076

LOD	45'10"	Hull	FRP
LWL	36'6"	Deck	FRP
Beam	13'6"	Spar	Alum
Draft	5'10"	Cockpit	10'
Disp	33,500 lbs	Headroom	6'7"
Ballast	11,500 lbs	Fr. Water	300 gal
Sail Area		SA/Disp	16.8
Cutter	1093 sq ft	Disp/LWL	308
Ketch	na	Blst/Disp	34%
Mast Ht	59'	Designer	Ted Brewer
Auxiliary	std	First Built	1979
Perkins	62 hp	No. Built	19
Diesel		Price	$132,500
Fuel Cap	240 gal		with sails

PAN—OCEANIC MARINE
619 NW 12th Ave.
Miami, FL 33136
(305) 324-0088

Comet 14

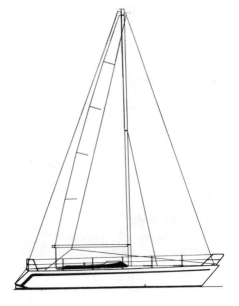

LOD	45'11"	Hull	FRP
LWL	39'7"	Deck	FRP/Balsa
Beam	14'1"	Spar	Alum
Draft		Fr. Water	225 gal
Shoal	5'3"	Disp/LWL	187
Deep	7'3"	Blst/Disp	33%
Disp	26,000 lbs	Designer	Groupe Finot
Ballast	8600 lbs	Builder	Comar Italy
Sail Area		Price	na
Sloop	na		
Auxiliary	std		
Diesel	50 hp		
Fuel Cap	75 gal		

COMAR USA
149 Shaw Ave.
Irvington, NJ 07111

Oyster 46

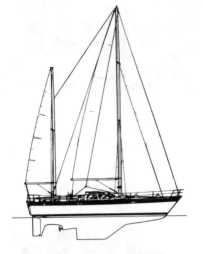

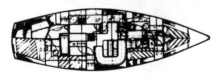

LOD	46'2"	Hull	FRP
LWL	39'7"	Deck	FRP
Beam	14'	Spar	Alum
Draft	6'6"	Fr. Water	222 gal
Disp	32,000 lbs	SA/Disp	12.9
Ballast	12,900 lbs	Disp/LWL	230
Sail Area		Blst/Disp	40%
Ketch	815 sq ft	Designer	Holman/Pye
Auxiliary	std	Price	na
Diesel			
Fuel Cap	222 gal		

OYSTER MARINE LTD.
9, East Hill,
Colchester, Essex,
England
0206 863090

Faenoe 47

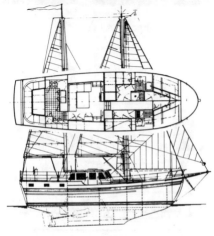

LOA	52'10"	Hull	FRP
LOD	46'3"	Deck	FRP
LWL	41'	Spar	Alum
Beam	13'9"	Fr. Water	370 gal
Draft	5'11"	SA/Disp	14.8
Disp	39,600 lbs	Disp/LWL	257
Ballast	11,000 lbs	Blst/Disp	28%
Sail Area		Designer	
Schooner	1076 sq ft		Erik Pedersen
Mast Ht	54'	Builder	
Auxiliary	std		Faenoe, Denmark
Diesel	125 hp	First Built	1975
Fuel Cap	528 gal	No. Built	12
		Price	$265,000
			with sails

FAENOE YACHTYARDS LTD.
Havnen Skaerback
Fredericia, Denmark

Morgan 46

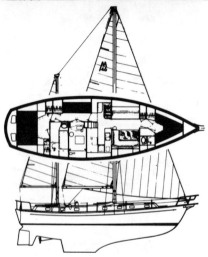

LOD	46'6"	Hull	FRP
LWL	39'3"	Deck	FRP
Beam	13'6"	Spar	Alum
Draft		Fr. Water	195 gal
Shoal	5'3"	SA/Disp	15.1
Deep	6'	Disp/LWL	221
Disp	30,000 lbs	Blst/Disp	28%
Ballast	8400 lbs	Price	na

Sail Area
   Sloop . . . . . 912 sq ft
   Ketch . . . . 876 sq ft
Mast Ht
   Sloop . . . . . . 60'4"
   Ketch . . . . . . 56'6"
Auxiliary . . . . std
   Perkins . . . . . 62 hp
   Diesel
Fuel Cap . . . . . 175 gal

MORGAN YACHT INC.
7200 Bryan Dairy Rd.
Largo, FL 33543
(813) 544-6681

Valiant 47

LOD	46'6"	Hull	FRP
LWL	40'8"	Deck	FRP
Beam	13'10"	Spar	Alum
Draft	6'	Fr. Water	180 gal
Disp	30,000 lbs	SA/Disp	16.2
Ballast	10,891 lbs	Disp/LWL	199

Sail Area | Blst/Disp 36%
   Cutter . . . 980 sq ft | Designer Robert Perry
Auxiliary . . . . std | Price $280,000
   Westerbeke | with sails
   Diesel
Fuel Cap . . . . . 100 gal

VALIANT YACHTS CORP.
2000 Westlake Ave. North
Seattle, WA 98109
(206) 284-7943

Rittun Perry 47

LOD	46'7"	Hull	FRP
LWL	36'8"	Deck	FRP
Beam	13'6"	Spar	Alum
Draft	6'4"	Fr. Water	300 gal
Disp	30,400 lbs	SA/Disp	14.5
Ballast	12,000 lbs	Disp/LWL	275

Sail Area | Blst/Disp 39%
   Cutter . . . 884 sq ft | Designer Robert Perry
   Ketch . . . . 973 sq ft | Builder
Auxiliary . . . . std | Rittun Marine, Taiwan
   Lehman Ford 80 hp | Price $79,500
   Diesel | with sails
Fuel Cap . . . . . 200 gal

LITTON MARINE INC.
P. O. Box 600931
North Miami Beach, FL 33160
(305) 944-1556

Vagabond Voyager 47

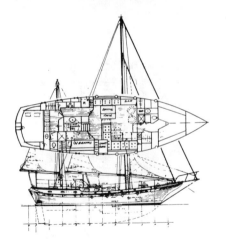

LOD	. . . . 52'	Hull	. . . . FRP
LOD	. . . . 46'7"	Deck	. . . . FRP
LWL	. . . . 36'	Spar	. . . . Wood
Beam	. . . . 13'5"	Headroom	. . . . . 6'4"
Draft	. . . . 5'3"	Fr. Water	. . . . 200 gal
Disp	. . . . . 44,800 lbs	SA/Disp	. . . . . . 14.2
Ballast	. . . 12,000 lbs	Disp/LWL	 429
Sail Area		Blst/Disp	. . . . . 27%
Ketch	. . . 1120 sq ft	Designer	
Auxiliary	. . . . std		William Garden
Ford	. . . . . . 80 hp	Builder	. . . Blue Water
Diesel		Price	. . . . . $150,000
Fuel Cap	. . . . . 200 gal		with sails

SOUTHERN OFFSHORE YACHTS
Box 6
Tarpon Springs, FL 33589
(813) 937-3188

Durbeck 46

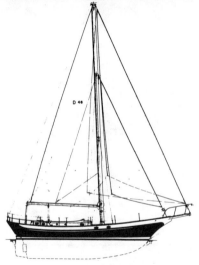

LOA	. . . . 54'	Hull	. . . . FRP
LOD	. . . . 46'9"	Deck	. . . . . FRP/Foam
LWL	. . . . 35'8"	Spar	. . . . Alum
Beam	. . . . 13'8"	Cockpit	. . . . 6'
Draft	. . . . 5'2"	Headroom	. . . . . 6'2"
Disp	. . . . 37,375 lbs	Fr. Water	. . . 160 gal
Ballast	. . . 12,000 lbs	SA/Disp	. . . . . . 18.7
Sail Area		Disp/LWL	 367
Ketch	. . . 1307 sq ft	Blst/Disp	. . . . . 32%
Cutter	. . . 1246 sq ft	First Built	 1972
Schooner	. . . . . na	No. Built	 27
Mast Ht		Price	. . . . . $345,000
Ketch	. . . . . 56'5"		with sails
Cutter	. . . . . 65'5"		
Auxiliary	. . . . std		
Perkins	. . . . . 85 hp		
Diesel			
Fuel Cap	. . . . . 160 gal		

DURBECK'S INC.
4504 28th St.
Bradenton, FL 33507
(813) 755-8155

Stevens Custom 47

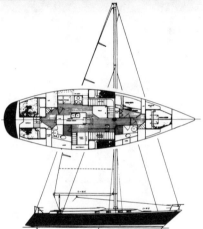

LOD	. . . . 46'10"	Hull	. . . . FRP
LWL	. . . . 37'9"	Deck	. . . . FRP
Beam	. . . . 14'3"	Spar	. . . . Alum
Draft	. . . . 6'	Cockpit	. . . . 8'
Disp	. . . . 32,000 lbs	Headroom	. . . . . 6'4"
Ballast	. . . 14,500 lbs	Fr. Water	. . . 250 gal
Sail Area		SA/Disp	. . . . . . 16.7
Cutter	. . . 1051 sq ft	Disp/LWL	 266
Sloop	. . . . na	Blst/Disp	. . . . . 45%
Mast Ht	. . . . 65'	Designer	
Auxiliary	. . . . std		Sparkman & Stephens
Universal	. . . 50 hp	First Built	 1981
Diesel		No. Built	 35
Fuel Cap	. . . . . 100 gal	1 Design	. . . . . . yes
		Price	. . . . . $225,000
			with sails

STEVENS YACHTS OF ANNAPOLIS
P. O. Box 129
Stevensville, MD 21666
(301) 269-0810

CT 47

CT-47 CUTTER OR KETCH
(Center or Aft Cockpit)

LOD . . . . 46'11"	Hull . . . . FRP
LWL . . . . 37'6"	Deck . . . . FRP
Beam . . . . 13'2"	Spar . . . . Alum
Draft . . . . 6'	Fr. Water . . . . 160 gal
Disp . . . 29,395 lbs	Disp/LWL 249
Ballast . . . 12,000 lbs	Blst/Disp 41%
Sail Area	Designer Kaufman/Ladd
Cutter . . . . na	Builder
Ketch . . . . na	Ta Chiao, Taiwan
Auxiliary . . . . std	Price $128,500
Perkins	with sails
Diesel	
Fuel Cap . . . . . 150 gal	

TA CHIAO USA INC.
17 Lakewood Lane
Seabrook, TX 77586
(713) 474-5967

Wellington 47

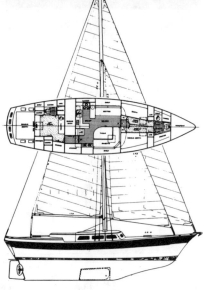

LOD . . . . 46'11"	Hull . . . . FRP
LWL . . . . 38'8"	Deck . . . . . FRP/Balsa
Beam . . . . 13'6"	Spar . . . . Alum
Draft	Pos Float . . . . opt
cb up . . . . . . 4'10"	Cockpit . . . . 6'4"
cb dn . . . . 8'4"	Headroom . . . . . . 6'6"
Disp . . . . 45,000 lbs	Fr. Water . . . . 470 gal
Ballast . . . 11,000 lbs	SA/Disp 14
Sail Area	Disp/LWL 347
Cutter . . . 1110 sq ft	Blst/Disp 24%
Ketch . . . 1146 sq ft	Designer
Mast Ht . . . . 61'	John G. Alden
Auxiliary . . . . std	First Built 1969
Lehman . . . 80 hp	No. Built 29
Diesel	Kit . . . . available
Fuel Cap . . . . . 440 gal	Price $192,000
	without sails

WELLINGTON BOATS INC.
11544 Normandy Blvd.
Jacksonville, FL 32221
(904) 781-1055

Swan 46

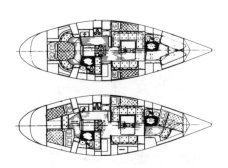

LOD . . . . 47'1"	Hull . . . . FRP
LWL . . . . 37'11"	Deck . . . . FRP
Beam . . . . 14'6"	Spar . . . . Alum
Draft	Disp/LWL 256
Deep . . . . 8'2"	Blst/Disp 36%
Shoal cb up . . 5'7"	Designer German Frers
Shoal cb dn . . 9'6"	Builder
Disp . . . . . 31,300 lbs	Nautor, Finland
Ballast . . . 11,400 lbs	First Built 1983
Sail Area	Price . . . . na
Sloop . . . . na	
Auxiliary . . . . std	
Perkins . . . . . 58 hp	
Diesel	

NAUTOR EAST
55 America's Cup Avenue
Newport, RI 02840
(401) 846-8404

Cygnet 48

LOD	47'3"	Hull	FRP/Airex
LWL	36'	Deck	FRP/Klegecell
Beam	13'6"	Spar	Alum
Draft		Cockpit	8'
cb up	4'8"	Headroom	6'4"
cb dn	8'	Fr. Water	320 gal
Disp	42,000 lbs	SA/Disp	14.2
Ballast	15,000 lbs	Disp/LWL	402
Sail Area		Blst/Disp	36%
Cutter	1070 sq ft	Designer	
Ketch	1050 sq ft		Al Mason/Bruce Kelley
Auxiliary	std	First Built	1982
Diesel	80 hp	No. Built	44
Fuel Cap	180 gal	Kit	$18,500
		Price	$250,000
			without sails

HIDDEN HARBOR BOATWORKS
2029 Whitfield Park Ave.
Sarasota, FL 33580
(813) 775-7533

Islander 48

LOD	47'6"	Hull	FRP
LWL	37'	Deck	FRP
Beam	13'10"	Spar	Alum
Draft	5'10"	Fr. Water	255 gal
Disp	19,125 lbs	SA/Disp	22.3
Ballast	11,000 lbs	Disp/LWL	168
Sail Area		Blst/Disp	58%
Cutter	997 sq ft	Price	na
Mast Ht	61'		
Auxiliary	std		
Pathfinder	82 hp		
Diesel			
Fuel Cap	100 gal		

ISLANDER YACHTS
1922 Barranca Rd.
Irvine, CA 92714
(714) 549-8526

Landfall 48

LOD	47'6"	Hull	FRP/Balsa
LWL	38'3"	Deck	FRP/Balsa
Beam	14'	Spar	Alum
Draft	6'	Fr. Water	375 gal
Disp	35,600 lbs	SA/Disp	14.2
Ballast	16,000 lbs	Disp/LWL	283
Sail Area		Blst/Disp	45%
Sloop	960 sq ft	Price	na
Mast Ht	61'		
Auxiliary	std		
Perkins	85 hp		
Diesel			
Fuel Cap	160 gal		

C&C YACHTS
55 Port Street East
Mississauga, Ontario
Canada L5G 4P3
(416) 274-7131

Maple Leaf 48

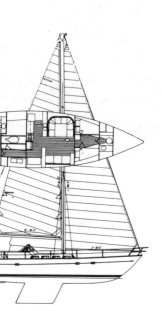

LOD	47'8"	Hull	FRP
LWL	40'6"	Deck	FRP
Beam	14'6"	Spar	Alum
Draft		Pos Float	opt
Deep	6'6"	Cockpit	6'9"
Shoal cb up	5'6"	Headroom	6'6"
Shoal cb dn	9'6"	Fr. Water	350 gal
Disp	34,000 lbs	SA/Disp	14.2
Ballast	9500 lbs	Disp/LWL	228
Sail Area		Blst/Disp	28%
Sloop	933 sq ft	Designer	
Cutter	1000 sq ft		S. Huntingford
Auxiliary	std	First Built	1972
Ford Lehman	85 hp	No. Built	46
Diesel		Price	$185,000
Fuel Cap	350 gal		with sails

Nicholson 48

LOD	47'8"	Hull	FRP
LWL	33'4"	Deck	FRP
Beam	12'11"	Spar	Alum
Draft	5'6"	Fr. Water	180 gal
Disp	28,000 lbs	SA/Disp	18.3
Ballast	10,000 lbs	Disp/LWL	337
Sail Area		Blst/Disp	36%
Ketch	1052 sq ft	Builder	England
Auxiliary	std	Price	$218,400
Perkins	62 hp		with sails
Diesel			
Fuel Cap	85 gal		

Golden Wave 48

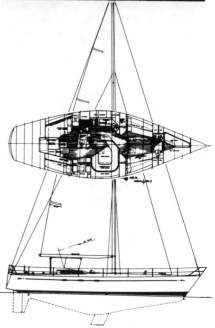

LOD	47'10"	Hull	FRP
LWL	40'8"	Deck	Teak
Beam	15'11"	Spar	Alum
Draft		Fr. Water	210 gal
Shoal cb up	4'8"	Disp/LWL	226
Shoal cb dn	11'7"	Designer	
Deep	6'6"		Britton Chance
Disp	34,000 lbs	Builder	Cheoy Lee
Ballast	na	First Built	1981
Sail Area		No. Built	5
Sloop	na	Price	$210,000
Ketch	na		with sails
Auxiliary	std		
Perkins	80 hp		
Diesel			
Fuel Cap	80 gal		

Hans Christian 48

Everyone who has voyaged in small craft (and all of us in the Hans Christian family) has a dream ship. The **Hans Christian 48** represents the experience gained in many years building the Hans Christians, an expression of everything our group has learned in design, building and working with hundreds of owners, many coming off long voyages.

Our general goals were clear: to produce a small, fast ship that can go anywhere safely, with striking beauty, for the aesthetic character of the ship is as important to us as its practical qualities. Fortunately, our designer Scott Sprague has ideas of beauty coinciding with ours and with the heritage of the Hans Christians developed and refined in our yards over a 10-year period of production.

We gave our designer specific goals:

• Give the ship weatherly and downwind ability for safe, fast passage making with a light easy helm under all conditions, both under power and sail. Take the lessons learned from the Hans Christian 33 with oversized rudder surfaces placed way aft, cutaway forward and lots of lateral plane.

• Give her easy sections for comfort at sea similar to those used by some European boats in competition in the North Sea and English Channel—boats famous for their easy motion at sea without the snap recovery from a roll so typical of some IOR designs in a seaway.

• Give her sections forward that will not pound allowing passages to weather against steep seas—conditions encountered beating north to the westerlies out of Honolulu close-hauled to West Coast ports.

• Give her very high ultimate stability with generous reserve buoyancy of at least 7,500 pounds with all tanks full.

• Give her flawless lines with the purity of the best Danish traditional double-enders exemplified so well in our 38T.

• Finally, give her that indefinable quality that makes a classic little ship (and the pride in ownership) characterized by great designs in the 1930s by Alden, the Herreshoff-designed *Ticonderoga,* some of Atkins best, even the Hannas, and above all, the marvelous Lilli Danske of K. Aage Nielsen of Boston.

Only the yard can translate concepts and lines into quality and reliability using the world's best materials and highest levels of skills and experience. We chose the German Hansa Yacht Und Schiffsbau G.M.B.H. for many reasons. Foremost is our delight in the flawless Hans Christian 33 built by the same yard, perfection which assures the owner a ship that can safely survive the demands of offshore work under any conditions. We wanted awareness of problems likely to occur many years after the yacht is delivered—problems anticipated and understood and eliminated.

The 48 will be available in many versions . . . cutter with performance keel or long keel, with or without bowsprit, shoal draft version (4'6"), center cockpit or aft cockpit version, ketch on all versions.

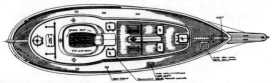

LOD	47'10"	Hull	FRP
LWL	41'3"	Deck	FRP/Teak
Beam	14'3"	Spar	Alum
Draft		Cockpit	11'
Shoal	4'6"	Headroom	6'6"
Deep	6'6"	Fr. Water	200 gal
Disp	44,000 lbs	SA/Disp	17.3
Ballast	14,700 lbs	Disp/LWL	280
Sail Area		Blst/Disp	33%
Cutter	1350 sq ft	Designer	
Ketch	1387 sq ft		Scott Sprague
Mast Ht		First Built	1983
Cutter	60'	Price	$200,000
Ketch	55'		with sails
Auxiliary	std		
Diesel	90 hp		
Fuel Cap	150 gal		

HANS CHRISTIAN YACHTS
6201 Bayshore Walk
Long Beach, CA 90803
(213) 434-2076

Swan 47

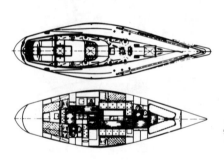

LOD .... 47'10"	Hull .... FRP
LWL .... 36'3"	Deck .... FRP
Beam .... 13'9"	Spar .... Alum
Draft	Disp/LWL 303
Deep .... 7'10"	Blst/Disp 48%
Shoal cb up . 5'11"	Designer
Shoal cb dn .. 9'6"	Sparkman & Stephens
Disp	Builder
Deep ... 32,400 lbs	Nautor, Finland
Shoal .. 34,170 lbs	Price .... na
Ballast	
Deep ... 15,500 lbs	
Shoal .. 17,200 lbs	
Sail Area	
Sloop .... na	
Auxiliary .... std	
Volvo ..... 61 hp	
Diesel	

NAUTOR EAST
55 America's Cup Avenue
Newport, RI 02840
(401) 846-8404

Sunward 48

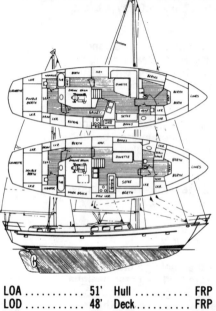

LOA .... 51'	Hull .... FRP
LOD .... 48'	Deck .... FRP
LWL .... 38'	Spar .... Alum
Beam .... 14'3"	Cockpit .... 7'
Draft .... 5'7"	Headroom ..... 6'1"
Disp ..... 48,000 lbs	Fr. Water .... 400 gal
Ballast ... 16,500 lbs	SA/Disp 14.5
Sail Area	Disp/LWL 391
Ketch ... 1200 sq ft	Blst/Disp 34%
Cutter ... 1100 sq ft	Designer
Mast Ht	Sparkman & Stephens
Ketch .... 62'	First Built 1976
Cutter .... 62'	No. Built 14
Auxiliary .... std	Kit .... available
Perkins ..... 85 hp	Price $275,000
Diesel	with sails
Fuel Cap ..... 400 gal	

SUNWARD YACHT CORP.
8118 Market St.
Wilmington, NC 28405
(919) 686-7532

Contest 48

LOD .... 48'3"	Hull .... FRP
LWL .... 37'7"	Deck .... FRP
Beam .... 14'2"	SA/Disp 18.1
Draft .... 6'5"	Disp/LWL 318
Disp ..... 37,881 lbs	Blst/Disp 32%
Ballast ... 12,179 lbs	Designer ... Dick Zaal
Sail Area	Builder
Ketch ... 1277 sq ft	Conyplex, Holland
Auxiliary .... std	Price .... na
Volvo Penta . 75 hp	
Diesel	

HOLLAND YACHTS
Box 129
Solomons, MD 20688
(301) 326-3960

Chapman 48

LOD . . . . 48'4"	Hull . . . . FRP
LWL . . . . 40'6"	Deck . . . . FRP
Beam . . . . . . 13'10"	Spar . . . . Alum
Draft . . . . 6'9"	Headroom . . . . . 6'6"
Disp . . . . . 29,500 lbs	Fr. Water . . . . 240 gal
Ballast . . . 10,600 lbs	SA/Disp 19.1
Sail Area	Disp/LWL 198
Cutter. . . . 1140 sq ft	Blst/Disp 36%
Ketch . . . 2290 sq ft	Designer
Schooner 1250 sq ft	Raymond H. Richards
Auxiliary . . . . std	First Built 1982
Perkins . . . . . 85 hp	Kit $27,000
Diesel	Price $224,500
Fuel Cap . . . . . 130 gal	with sails

CHAPMAN YACHT CORP.
5201 Argosy Drive
Huntington Beach, CA 92649
(714) 891-3428

Garrett 50

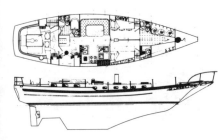

LOA . . . . 53'	Hull . . . . Wood Epoxy
LOD . . . . 48'6"	Deck . . . Wood Epoxy
LWL . . . . 38'6"	Spar . . . . Alum
Beam . . . . 13'7"	Cockpit . . . . 7'
Draft . . . . 6'	Headroom . . . . . 6'4"
Disp . . . . 30,000 lbs	Fr. Water . . . 295 gal
Ballast . . . 12,500 lbs	SA/Disp 17.6
Sail Area	Disp/LWL 234
Cutter . . . 1060 sq ft	Blst/Disp 42%
Ketch . . . 1300 sq ft	Designer
Mast Ht	Dennis Garrett
Cutter . . . . 59'	First Built 1981
Ketch . . . . . . 55'	No. Built 1
Auxiliary . . . . std	Price $170,000
Perkins . . . . . 85 hp	with sails
Diesel	
Fuel Cap . . . . 185 gal	

DISEÑO Y CONSTRUCCION NAVAL S
Apartado 33
San Pedro De Montes De Oca
Costa Rica, 1000

Cherubini 48 Schooner

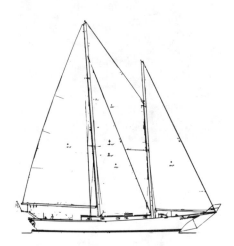

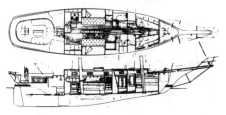

LOA . . . . 60'	Hull . . . . FRP
LOD . . . . 48'9"	Deck . . . Wood Epoxy
LWL . . . . 44'	Spar . . . . Alum
Beam . . . . 13'	Cockpit . . . . 6'6"
Draft . . . . 5'	Headroom . . . . . 6'6"
Disp . . . . 37,500 lbs	Fr. Water . . . . 200 gal
Ballast . . . 17,000 lbs	SA/Disp 17.2
Sail Area	Disp/LWL 196
Stsl Scnr 1204 sq ft	Blst/Disp 45%
Mast Ht . . . . 60'	Designer
Auxiliary . . . . std	John Cherubini
Westerbeke . . 75 hp	First Built 1982
Diesel	No. Built 1
Fuel Cap . . . . . 100 gal	Kit $100,000
	Price $350,000
	with sails

CHERUBINI BOAT CO.
222 Wood St.
Burlington, NJ 08016
(609) 499-2200

Dickerson 50

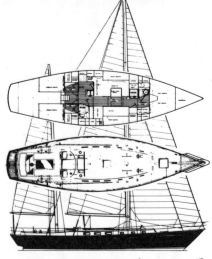

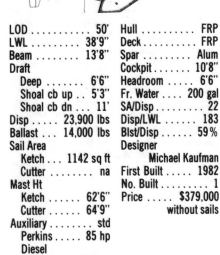

LOD	50'	Hull	FRP
LWL	38'9"	Deck	FRP
Beam	13'8"	Spar	Alum
Draft		Cockpit	10'8"
Deep	6'6"	Headroom	6'6"
Shoal cb up	5'3"	Fr. Water	200 gal
Shoal cb dn	11'	SA/Disp	22
Disp	23,900 lbs	Disp/LWL	183
Ballast	14,000 lbs	Blst/Disp	59%
Sail Area		Designer	
Ketch	1142 sq ft		Michael Kaufman
Cutter	na	First Built	1982
Mast Ht		No. Built	1
Ketch	62'6"	Price	$379,000
Cutter	64'9"		without sails
Auxiliary	std		
Perkins	85 hp		
Diesel			
Fuel Cap	135 gal		

DICKERSON BOATBUILDERS
Route 2 Box 92
Trappe, MD 21673
(301) 822-8556

Sailmaster 50

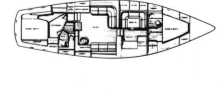

LOD	50'	Hull	FRP/Balsa
LWL	41'	Deck	FRP/Balsa
Beam	14'6"	Spar	Alum
Draft	5'6"	Fr. Water	350 gal
Disp	41,000 lbs	SA/Disp	12
Ballast	11,900 lbs	Disp/LWL	265
Sail Area		Blst/Disp	29%
Sloop	890 sq ft	Designer	Dick Lazzara
Ketch	945 sq ft	Price	$198,000
Auxiliary	std		without sails
Perkins	135 hp		
Diesel			
Fuel Cap	200 gal		

GULFSTAR INC.
6101 45th St. N.
St. Petersburg, FL 33714
(813) 527-7251

Santa Cruz 50

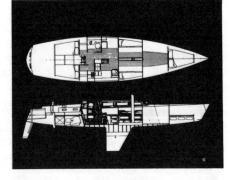

LOD	50'	Hull	FRP
LWL	46'6"	Deck	FRP
Beam	12'	Spar	Alum
Draft	8'	Fr. Water	150 gal
Disp	16,000 lbs	SA/Disp	26.5
Ballast	8000 lbs	Disp/LWL	71
Sail Area		Blst/Disp	50%
Sloop	1050 sq ft	Designer	Bill Lee
Auxiliary	std	Price	$185,000
Pathfinder	42 hp		without sails
Diesel			
Fuel Cap	60 gal		

BILL LEE YACHTS INC.
3700-B Hilltop Road
Soquel, CA 95073
(408) 475-9627

Worldcruiser 50 Schooner

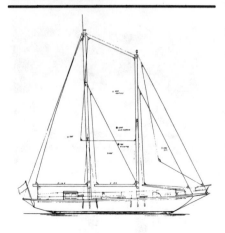

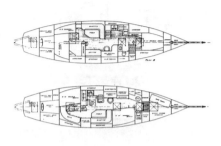

LOA .... 55'8"	Hull .... FRP
LOD .... 50'	Deck ..... FRP/Teak
LWL .... 34'4"	Spar .... Alum
Beam .... 13'	Cockpit .... 5'
Draft .... 6'8"	Headroom ..... 6'2"
Disp ..... 32,000 lbs	Fr. Water .. 200+ gal
Ballast ... 13,000 lbs	SA/Disp 22.1
Sail Area	Disp/LWL 353
Schooner 1395 sq ft	Blst/Disp 41%
Mast Ht .... 60'	Designer
Auxiliary .... std	Bailey Taplin
Diesel ..... 60 hp	First Built 1981
	No. Built 4
	Kit .... available
	Price $250,000
	with sails

WORLDCRUISER YACHT CO.
1300 Logan St.
Costa Mesa, CA 92626
(714) 549-9331

FD-12 Meter

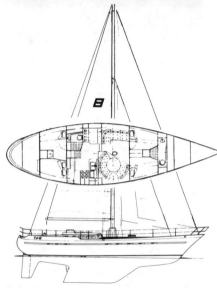

LOA .... 54'	Hull ..... FRP/Foam
LOD .... 50'4"	Deck ..... FRP/Foam
LWL .... 42'	Spar .... Alum
Beam .... 14'3"	Pos Float ...... opt
Draft .... 6'6"	Cockpit ..... 8'6"
Disp ..... 35,175 lbs	Headroom ..... 6'6"
Ballast ... 14,350 lbs	Fr. Water .... 250 gal
Sail Area	SA/Disp 17.1
Cutter .. 1146 sq ft	Disp/LWL 211
Sloop ... 1146 sq ft	Blst/Disp 41%
Mast Ht .... 66'	Designer Eva Hollmann
Auxiliary .... std	/Willem Eickholt
Lehman ..... 61 hp	First Built 1977
Diesel	No. Built 24
Fuel Cap ..... 250 gal	Kit .... available
	Price $189,500
	with sails

WILLEM EICKHOLT & ASSOC.
Hamlin Pier-Suite B
2727 Fairview E.
Seattle, WA 98102
(206) 329-7373

Maple Leaf 50

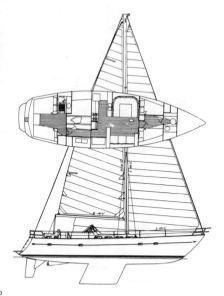

LOD .... 50'4"	Hull .... FRP
LWL .... 42'	Deck .... FRP
Beam .... 14'6"	Spar .... Alum
Draft	Pos Float ...... opt
Deep ...... 6'6"	Cockpit ...... 6'9"
Shoal cb up .. 5'6"	Headroom ..... 6'6"
Shoal cb dn .. 9'6"	Fr. Water .... 400 gal
Disp ..... 35,000 lbs	SA/Disp 14.5
Ballast ... 10,000 lbs	Disp/LWL 210
Sail Area	Blst/Disp 29%
Sloop .... 970 sq ft	Designer
Cutter ... 1040 sq ft	S. Huntingford
Auxiliary ...... std	First Built 1982
Diesel	No. Built 1
Fuel Cap ..... 400 gal	Price $190,000
	with sails

COOPER ENTERPRISES LTD.
1642 Langan Ave.
Port Coquituam, B.C.
Canada V3C 1K5
(604) 942-5945

Banner 51

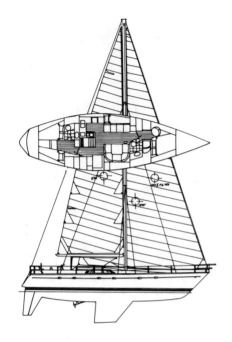

Cooper 508

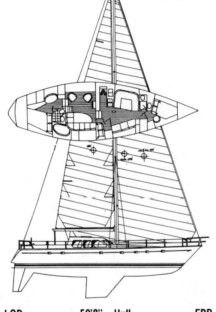

Sou'wester 50

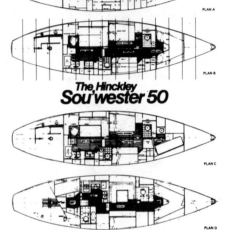

The Hinckley
Sou'wester 50

LOD . . . . 50'8"	Hull . . . . FRP
LWL . . . . 44'	Deck . . . . FRP
Beam . . . . 15'	Spar . . . . Alum
Draft . . . . 8'	Cockpit . . . . 10'
Disp . . . . . 37,000 lbs	Headroom . . . . . 6'6"
Ballast . . . 16,500 lbs	Fr. Water . . . . 190 gal
Sail Area	SA/Disp 18.7
Sloop . . . 1299 sq ft	Disp/LWL 193
Auxiliary . . . . std	Blst/Disp 45%
Lehman . . . . 60 hp	Designer
Diesel	S. Huntingford
Fuel Cap . . . . . 100 gal	First Built 1983
	Price $195,000
	with sails

LOD . . . . 50'8"	Hull . . . . FRP
LWL . . . . 44'	Deck . . . . FRP
Beam . . . . 15'	Spar . . . . Alum
Draft . . . . 8'	Cockpit . . . . 10'
Disp . . . . . 38,500 lbs	Headroom . . . . . 6'6"
Ballast . . . 16,500 lbs	Fr. Water . . . . 185 gal
Sail Area	SA/Disp 17.4
Sloop . . . 1239 sq ft	Disp/LWL 201
Auxiliary . . . . std	Blst/Disp 43%
Lehman . . . . 85 hp	Designer
Diesel	S. Huntingford
Fuel Cap . . . . . 185 gal	First Built 1981
	No. Built 5
	Price $210,000
	with sails

LOD . . . . 50'8"	Hull . . . . FRP
LWL . . . . 36'5"	Deck . . . . FRP
Beam . . . . 13'	Spar . . . . Alum
Draft	Fr. Water . . . . 280 gal
cb up . . . . . . 5'9"	SA/Disp 15.4
cb dn . . . . 10'	Disp/LWL 338
Disp . . . . . 36,600 lbs	Designer
Ballast . . . . na	Henry R. Hinckley
Sail Area	Price $328,500
Yawl . . . 1060 sq ft	without sails
Auxiliary . . . . std	
Lehman Ford 120 hp	
Diesel	
Fuel Cap . . . . . 300 gal	

COOPER ENTERPRISES LTD.
1642 Langan Ave.
Port Coquituam, B.C.
Canada V3C 1K5
(604) 942-5945

COOPER ENTERPRISES LTD.
1642 Langan Ave.
Port Coquituam, B.C.
Canada V3C 1K5
(604) 942-5945

HENRY R. HINCKLEY & CO.
Southwest Harbor, ME 04679
(207) 244-5531

Durbeck 50

LOA	59'	Hull	FRP
LOD	50'9"	Deck	FRP/Foam
LWL	39'8"	Spar	Alum
Beam	13'10"	Cockpit	6'
Draft	5'2"	Headroom	6'2"
Disp	46,450 lbs	Fr. Water	200 gal
Ballast	16,000 lbs	SA/Disp	16.8
Sail Area		Disp/LWL	332
Ketch	1356 sq ft	Blst/Disp	34%
Cutter	1328 sq ft	First Built	1981
Schooner	na	No. Built	2
Mast Ht	65'6"	Price	$397,000
Auxiliary	std		with sails
Perkins	85 hp		
Diesel			
Fuel Cap	200 gal		

DURBECK'S INC.
4504 28th St.
Bradenton, FL 33507
(813) 755-8155

Little Harbor 50

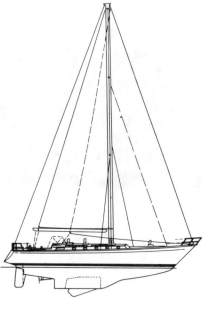

LOD	50'9"	Hull	FRP/Airex
LWL	42'4"	Deck	FRP/Balsa
Beam	15'1"	Spar	Alum
Draft		Cockpit	10'
cb up	5'6"	Headroom	6'8"
cb dn	12'	Fr. Water	330 gal
Disp	43,500 lbs	SA/Disp	16.2
Ballast	18,000 lbs	Disp/LWL	255
Sail Area		Blst/Disp	41%
Sloop	1249 sq ft	Designer	Ted Hood
Mast Ht	70'	Builder	
Auxiliary	std		Alexander Marine
Westerbeke	100 hp	First Built	1982
Diesel		No. Built	2
Fuel Cap	175 gal	1 Design	yes
		Price	$328,500
			without sails

**LITTLE HARBOR
CUSTOM YACHTS**
Little Harbor Way
Marblehead, MA 01945
(617) 631-8840

Force 50

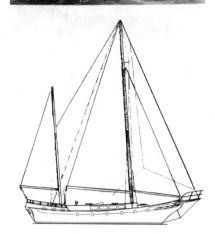

LOA	58'10"	Hull	FRP
LOD	50'10"	Deck	FRP/Teak
LWL	40'	Spar	Wood
Beam	14'2"	Cockpit	6'
Draft	6'	headroom	6'5"
Disp	52,000 lbs	Fr. Water	350 gal
Ballast	15,000 lbs	SA/Disp	14.4
Sail Area		Disp/LWL	362
Ketch	1254 sq ft	Blst/Disp	29%
Mast Ht	60'6"	Designer	
Auxiliary	std		William Garden
Ford Lehman	80 hp	First Built	1977
Diesel		No. Built	114
Fuel Cap	350 gal	1 Design	yes
		Price	$99,800
			with sails

HUDSON BOAT LTD.
3608 Coolheights Dr.
Rancho Palos Verdes, CA 90274
(213) 541-2993

Island Trader 51   Shannon 50   Baltic 51

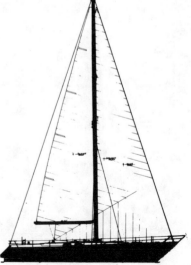

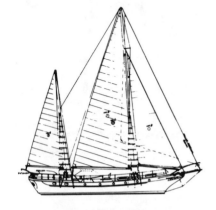

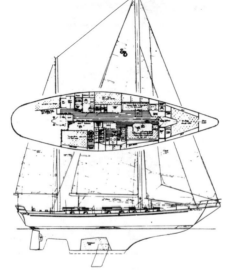

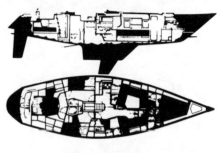

Pilothouse Interior

Center Cockpit Interior

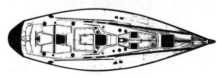

Island Trader 51

LOD	50'10"	Hull	FRP
LWL	39'7"	Deck	Teak
Beam	14'1"	Spar	Wood
Draft	6'2"	Pos Float	yes
Disp	52,100 lbs	SA/Disp	14.3
Ballast	12,000 lbs	Disp/LWL	375
Sail Area		Blst/Disp	23%
Ketch	1250 sq ft	1 Design	yes
Auxiliary	std	Price	$134,900
			with sails

MARINE TRADING INTERNATIONAL
Box 1232
Point Pleasant Beach, NJ 08742
(201) 899-6800

Shannon 50

LOA	55'	Hull	FRP/Airex
LOD	50'11"	Deck	FRP/Balsa
LWL	42'9"	Spar	Alum
Beam	14'3"	Cockpit	12'
Draft		Headroom	6'8"
cb up	5'8"	Fr. Water	300 gal
cb dn	9'9"	SA/Disp	17.1
Disp	39,000 lbs	Disp/LWL	223
Ballast	15,000 lbs	Blst/Disp	38%
Sail Area		Designer	
Ketch	1227 sq ft		Schultz & Assoc.
Schooner	1326 sq ft	First Built	1981
Mast Ht	62'	No. Built	8
Auxiliary	std	Price	$387,500
Perkins	85 hp		with sails
Diesel			
Fuel Cap	150 gal		

SHANNON BOAT CO. INC.
19 Broad Common Rd.
Bristol, RI 02809
(401) 253-2441

Baltic 51

LOD	51'	Hull	FRP/Balsa
LWL	40'11"	Deck	FRP/Balsa
Beam	15'3"	Spar	Alum
Draft	9'	Fr. Water	1188 gal
Disp	34,390 lbs	Disp/LWL	224
Ballast	13,536 lbs	Blst/Disp	39%
Sail Area		Designer	
Sloop	na		C&C Design Group
Auxiliary	std	Builder	
Volvo	61 hp		Baltic Finland
Diesel		Price	na
Fuel Cap	528 gal		

BALTIC YACHTS NORTH AMERICA
Box 832
Tucker's Wharf
Marblehead, MA 01945
(617) 639-0590

Magic Class

Passport 51

Nauticat 52

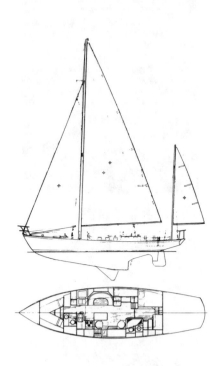

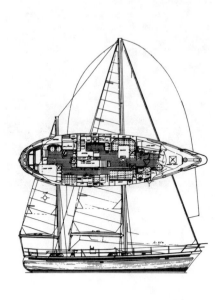

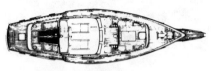

LOD . . . . 51'	Hull Epoxy wood fiber
LWL . . . . 38'6"	Deck Epoxy wood fiber
Beam . . . . 13'6"	Spar . . . . Wood
Draft	SA/Disp 19.7
cb up . . . . 5'6"	Disp/LWL 268
cb dn . . . . 11'	Price . . . . na
Disp . . . . . 34,300 lbs	
Ballast . . . . na	
Sail Area	
Yawl . . . . 1300 sq ft	

LOD . . . . 51'1"	Hull . . . . FRP
LWL . . . . 43'3"	Deck . . . . FRP
Beam . . . . 14'5"	Spar . . . . Alum
Draft . . . . 7'2"	Fr. Water . . . . 275 gal
Disp . . . . . 38,000 lbs	SA/Disp 17
Ballast . . . . na	Disp/LWL 210
Sail Area	Designer
Ketch . . . 1203 sq ft	Stan Huntingford
Cutter . . . . na	Price $185,000
Auxiliary . . . . std	with sails

LOD . . . . 51'2"	Hull . . . . FRP
LWL . . . . 39'7"	Deck . . . . FRP
Beam . . . . 15'	Spar . . . . Alum
Draft . . . . 7'2"	Fr. Water . . . . 530 gal
Disp . . . . . 54,000 lbs	SA/Disp 18.4
Ballast . . . 15,200 lbs	Disp/LWL 388
Sail Area	Blst/Disp 28%
Ketch . . . 1647 sq ft	Builder
Auxiliary . . . . std	Siltala Yachts oy Finland
Ford . . . . . 121 hp	Price . . . . na
Diesel	
Fuel Cap . . . . . 530 gal	

SANFORD BOAT CO. INC.
Pleasant St.
Nantucket, MA 02554
(617) 228-4108

PASSPORT YACHTS
2900 Westlake Ave. North
Seattle, WA 98109
(206) 282-0401

NAUTICAT INC.
Box 809, Tucker's Wharf
Marblehead, MA 01945
(617) 631-8491

Swan 51

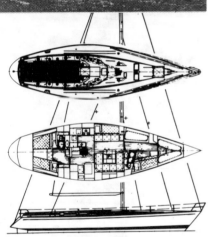

LOD	51'3"	Hull	FRP
LWL	42'5"	Deck	FRP
Beam	14'9"	Spar	Alum
Draft		Disp/LWL	231
Deep	8'11"	Blst/Disp	42%
Shoal cb up	5'11"	Designer	German Frers
Shoal cb dn	9'11"	Builder	
Disp	39,600 lbs		Nautor, Finland
Ballast	16,500 lbs	Price	$301,500
Sail Area			with sails
Sloop	na		
Auxiliary	std		
Perkins	73 hp		
Diesel			

NAUTOR EAST
55 America's Cup Avenue
Newport, RI 02840
(401) 846-8404

Farrington 52

FARRINGTON 52 The ultimate live-aboard for those desiring TRUE INDEPENDENCE.

LOD	52'	Hull	FRP/Airex
LWL	41'	Deck	FRP/Airex
Beam	13'11"	Spar	Alum
Draft		Headroom	6'6"
Shoal	5'6"	Fr. Water	450 gal
Deep	6'6"	SA/Disp	21.2
Disp	50,000 lbs	Disp/LWL	323
Ballast	19,600 lbs	Blst/Disp	39%
Sail Area		Designer	
Schooner	1800 sq ft		W. I. B. Crealock
Auxiliary	std	Price	$350,000
Mercedes Benz			with sails
Diesel	130 hp		
Fuel Cap	550 gal		

FARRINGTON MARINE INC.
1548 Quivira Way
San Diego, CA 92109
(619) 223-1937

Irwin 52

LOA	56'	Hull	FRP/Coremat
LOD	52'	Deck	FRP
LWL	44'	Spar	Alum
Beam	15'4"	Fr. Water	375 gal
Draft		SA/Disp	17.6
Shoal	5'6"	Disp/LWL	244
Deep	7'1"	Blst/Disp	35%
Disp	46,500 lbs	Price	$194,950
Ballast			with sails
Shoal	16,100 lbs		
Deep	19,350 lbs		
Sail Area			
Ketch	1425 sq ft		
Mast Ht	67'		
Auxiliary	std		
Perkins	85 hp		
Diesel			
Fuel Cap	260 gal		

IRWIN YACHTS
13055 49th St. N.
Clearwater, FL 33520
(813) 577-4581

Rajo — Sailer 53

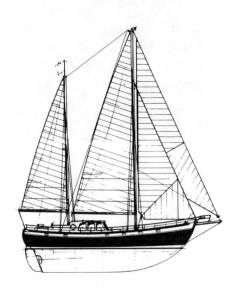

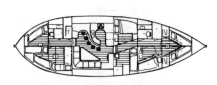

LOA .... 60'11"	Hull .... Steel
LOD .... 53'	Deck .... Steel
LWL .... 48'	Spar .... Alum
Beam .... 16'5"	Pos Float ...... yes
Draft .... 6'10"	Cockpit .... 7'
Disp ..... 63,000 lbs	Headroom ...... 6'6"
Ballast ... 20,000 lbs	Fr. Water .... 528 gal
Sail Area	SA/Disp 19.4
Ketch ... 1921 sq ft	Disp/LWL 254
Mast Ht .... 70'	Blst/Disp 32%
Auxiliary .... std	Designer M. Bekebrede
Volvo ..... 144 hp	First Built 1983
Diesel	Price $365,000
Fuel Cap ..... 528 gal	with sails

RAJO — WATERSPORT BV
Werfweb 2 — 8243 PG Lelystad
Industrieterrein Noordersluis
Holland
(03200) 60929/60979

Trintella 53

LOA .... 54'	Hull .... FRP
LOD .... 53'	Deck .... Teak
LWL .... 43'4"	Spar .... Alum
Beam .... 15'5"	Cockpit .... 7'
Draft	Headroom ...... 7'
cb up ...... 5'7"	Fr. Water .... 330 gal
cb dn ...... 9'10"	SA/Disp 18.4
Disp .... 50,600 lbs	Disp/LWL 277
Ballast ... 15,432 lbs	Blst/Disp 30%
Sail Area	Designer ... V/D Stadt
Sloop ... 1573 sq ft	Builder
Ketch ... 1509 sq ft	Jachtwerf Anne Wever
Cutter ... 1573 sq ft	First Built 1982
Mast Ht .... 62'	No. Built 7
Auxiliary .... std	1 Design .... yes
Perkins .... 124 hp	Price $381,433
Diesel	with sails
Fuel cap ..... 211 gal	

ADAMS BLAIR & ASSOC.
Ste. 1111
2025 Pennsylvania Ave. NW
Washington, D.C. 20006
(202) 833-2696

CT 54

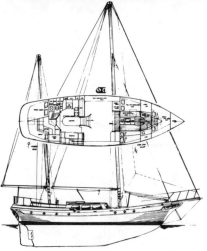

LOA .... 62'	Hull .... FRP
LOD .... 53'7"	Deck ..... FRP/Balsa
LWL .... 42'6"	Spar .. Alum or Wood
Beam .... 15'1"	Cockpit .... 11'
Draft	Headroom ...... 6'8"
Shoal ...... 6'6"	Fr. Water .... 200 gal
Deep ...... 6'8"	SA/Disp 16.4
Disp .... 54,000 lbs	Disp/LWL 314
Ballast ... 16,500 lbs	Blst/Disp 31%
Sail Area	Designer
Ketch ... 1465 sq ft	Robert H. Perry
Mast Ht .... 68'	Builder
Auxiliary .... std	Ta Chiao, Taiwan
Lehman-Ford 120 hp	First Built 1973
Diesel	No. Built 76
Fuel Cap ..... 200 gal	Price $182,000
	with sails

TA CHIAO USA INC.
17 Lakewood Lane
Seabrook, TX 77586
(713) 474-5967

Pearson 530

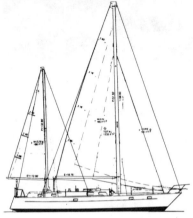

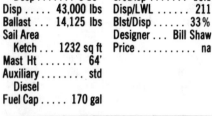

LOD	53'7"	Hull	FRP
LWL	45'	Deck	FRP
Beam	14'11"	Spar	Alum
Draft		Cockpit	7'4"
Shoal cb up	5'9"	Headroom	6'4"
Shoal cb dn	na	Fr. Water	280 gal
Deep	6'10"	SA/Disp	16.1
Disp	43,000 lbs	Disp/LWL	211
Ballast	14,125 lbs	Blst/Disp	33%
Sail Area		Designer	Bill Shaw
Ketch	1232 sq ft	Price	na
Mast Ht	64'		
Auxiliary	std		
Diesel			
Fuel Cap	170 gal		

PEARSON YACHTS
West Shore Rd.
Portsmouth, RI 02871
(401) 683-0100

Mason 53

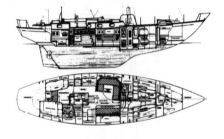

LOD	53'9"	Hull	FRP
LWL	39'8"	Deck	Teak
Beam	14'5"	Spar	Alum
Draft		Cockpit	8'6"
Shoal	5'9"	headroom	6'2"
Deep	6'8"	Fr. Water	340 gal
Disp	38,600 lbs	SA/Disp	18.9
Ballast	10,360 lbs	Disp/LWL	276
Sail Area		Blst/Disp	27%
Ketch	1352 sq ft	Designer	Al Mason
Cutter	1223 sq ft	Builder	
Mast Ht			Ta-Shing Yacht
Ketch	64'	First Built	1982
Cutter	65'5"	No. Built	5
Auxiliary	std	Price	$325,000
Perkins	85 hp		with sails
Diesel			
Fuel Cap	204 gal		

PACIFIC ASIAN ENTERPRISES
Box FA
Dana Point, CA 92629-0937
(714) 496-4848

Hunter 54

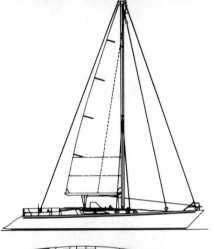

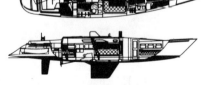

LOD	53'10"	Hull	FRP
LWL	43'6"	Deck	FRP
Beam	11'4"	Spar	Alum
Draft	6'	Headroom	6'4"
Disp	20,500 lbs	Fr. Water	120 gal
Ballast	8200 lbs	SA/Disp	19.5
Sail Area		Disp/LWL	111
Cutter	912 sq ft	Blst/Disp	40%
Mast Ht	59'2"	Designer	
Auxiliary	std		Cherubini/Steck
Universal	50 hp	Price	na
Diesel			
Fuel Cap	75 gal		

HUNTER MARINE
Box 1030, Hwy 441
Aluchua, FL 32601
(904) 462-3077

Maple Leaf 54

Wellington 57

Southern Offshore 55

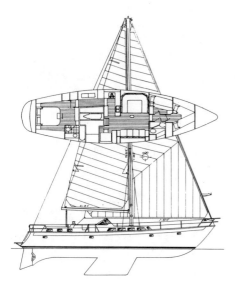

Maple Leaf 54

LOD	54'5"	Hull	FRP
LWL	47'4"	Deck	FRP
Beam	14'9"	Spar	Alum
Draft		Pos Float	opt
Deep	7'2"	Cockpit	6'9"
Shoal cb up	5'6"	Headroom	6'6"
Shoal cb dn	9'6"	Fr. Water	550 gal
Disp	42,000 lbs	SA/Disp	13.6
Ballast	11,500 lbs	Disp/LWL	176
Sail Area		Blst/Disp	27%
Sloop	1030 sq ft	Designer	
Cutter	1090 sq ft		S. Huntingford
Auxiliary	std	First Built	1979
Lehman	120 hp	No. Built	12
Diesel		Price	$225,000
Fuel Cap	550 gal		with sails

Wellington 57

LOA	57'	Hull	FRP
LOD	54'6"	Deck	FRP/Balsa
LWL	50'	Spar	Alum
Beam	14'6"	Pos Float	opt
Draft		Headroom	6'6"
Shoal	4'3"	Fr. Water	500 gal
Deep	4'3"	SA/Disp	9.4
Disp	50,000 lbs	Disp/LWL	179
Ballast	6000 lbs	Blst/Disp	12%
Sail Area		Designer	
Cutter	800 sq ft		Bill Wellington
Ketch	800 sq ft	First Built	1983
Mast Ht	54'	No. Built	1
Auxiliary	std	Kit	available
Lehman	120 hp	Price	$250,000
Diesel			without sails
Fuel Cap	500 gal		

Southern Offshore 55

LOD	55'	Hull	FRP
LWL	45'11"	Deck	FRP
Beam	16'1"	Spar	Alum
Draft		Headroom	6'4"
Shoal cb up	5'3"	SA/Disp	19.7
Shoal cb dn	9'10"	Disp/LWL	223
Deep	6'6"	Blst/Disp	35%
Disp	48,400 lbs	Designer	
Ballast			Pieter Beeldsnijder
Shoal	16,940 lbs	Builder	Ta Yang
Deep	17,600 lbs	First Built	1982
Sail Area		No. Built	1
Cutter	1635 sq ft	Price	$218,250
Schooner	1022 sq ft		with sails
Auxiliary	std		
Perkins or Ford			
Diesel	120 hp		

COOPER ENTERPRISES LTD.

1642 Langan Ave.
Port Coquituam, B.C.
Canada V3C 1K5
(604) 942-5945

WELLINGTON BOATS INC.

11544 Normandy Blvd.
Jacksonville, FL 32221
(904) 781-1055

SOUTHERN OFFSHORE YACHTS

Box 6
Tarpon Springs, FL 33589
(813) 937-3188

Nautical 56

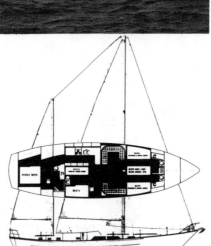

LOD	55'9"	Hull	FRP
LWL	43'4"	Deck	FRP
Beam	15'7"	Spar	Alum
Draft	5'6'	Fr. Water	500 gal
Disp	50,000 lbs	SA/Disp	14.2
Ballast	12,000 lbs	Disp/LWL	274
Sail Area		Blst/Disp	24%
Ketch	1205 sq ft	Designer	
Auxiliary	std		Seaton/Warren
Lehman Ford 120 hp		Price	$332,900
Diesel			without sails
Fuel Cap	200 gal		

NAUTICAL DEVELOPMENT CORP.
2055 34th Way
Largo, FL 33541
(813) 531-4674

Stevens Custom 56

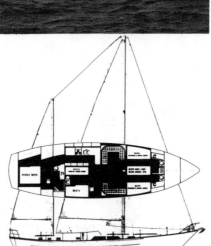

LOD	55'9"	Hull	FRP
LWL	45'4"	Deck	FRP
Beam	15'7"	Spar	Alum
Draft	5'6"	Cockpit	9'
Disp	51,000 lbs	Headroom	7'
Ballast	14,000 lbs	Fr. Water	500 gal
Sail Area		SA/Disp	14
Ketch	1205 sq ft	Disp/LWL	244
Mast Ht	65'	Blst/Disp	27%
Auxiliary	std	Designer	
Lehman Ford 120 hp			Seaton/Warren
Diesel		Builder	Nautical
Fuel Cap	200 gal		Development Corp.
		First Built	1979
		No. Built	10
		Price	$405,000
			with sails

STEVENS YACHTS OF ANNAPOLIS
P. O. Box 129
Stevensville, MD 21666
(301) 269-0810

Maple Leaf 56

LOD	56'4"	Hull	FRP
LWL	48'	Deck	FRP
Beam	14'9"	Spar	Alum
Draft		Pos Float	opt
Deep	6'	Cockpit	8'6"
Shoal cb up	5'6"	Headroom	6'6"
Shoal cb dn	9'6"	Fr. Water	550 gal
Disp		SA/Disp	13.5
Deep	46,000 lbs	Disp/LWL	185
Shoal	44,000 lbs	Blst/Disp	28%
Ballast		Designer	
Deep	13,000 lbs		S. Huntingford
Shoal	12,000 lbs	First Built	1981
Sail Area		No. Built	3
Sloop	1080 sq ft	Price	$230,000
Cutter	1160 sq ft		with sails
Ketch	1230 sq ft		
Auxiliary	std		
Lehman	120 hp		
Diesel			
Fuel Cap	550 gal		

COOPER ENTERPRISES LTD.
1642 Langan Ave.
Port Coquituam, B.C.
Canada V3C 1K5
(604) 942-5945

Little Harbor 57

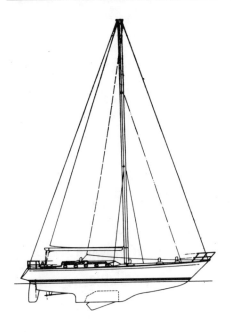

Swan 57

Nicholson 58

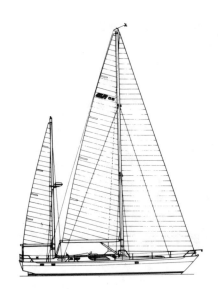

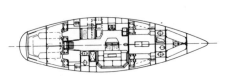

LOD	56'8"	Hull	FRP/Airex
LWL	47'3"	Deck	FRP/Balsa
Beam	15'10"	Spar	Alum
Draft		Fr. Water	430 gal
cb up	5'9"	SA/Disp	19
cb dn	11'9"	Disp/LWL	228
Disp	54,000 lbs	Blst/Disp	41%
Ballast	22,000 lbs	Designer	Ted Hood
Sail Area		1 Design	yes
Sloop	1700 sq ft	Price	$425,000
Auxiliary	std		
Diesel			
Fuel Cap	300 gal		

LOD	57'5"	Hull	FRP
LWL	45'10"	Deck	FRP
Beam	15'10"	Spar	Alum
Draft		SA/Disp	16.9
Deep	9'1"	Disp/LWL	229
Shoal cb up	6'5"	Blst/Disp	38%
Shoal cb dn	10'2"	Designer	
Disp			Sparkman & Stephens
Deep	49,500 lbs	Builder	
Shoal	51,500 lbs		Nautor, Finland
Ballast		Price	na
Deep	18,900 lbs		
Shoal	20,900 lbs		
Sail Area			
Sloop	1426 sq ft		
Auxiliary	std		
Perkins	73 hp		
Diesel			

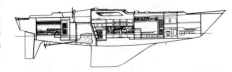

LOD	57'7"	Hull	FRP
LWL	46'8"	Deck	FRP
Beam	15'7"	Spar	Alum
Draft	8'6"	Builder	England
Disp	na	Price	$386,400
Ballast	na		with sails
Sail Area			
Ketch	na		
Auxiliary	std		

Little Harbor 58

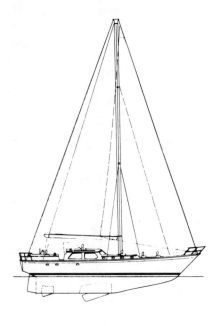

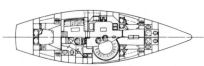

LOD . . . . 57'8"	Hull . . . . . FRP/Airex
LWL . . . . 47'9"	Deck . . . . FRP/Balsa
Beam . . . . 16'9"	Spar . . . . Alum
Draft	Fr. Water . . . . 450 gal
cb up . . . . . . 5'6"	SA/Disp 15.1
cb dn . . . . na	Disp/LWL 292
Disp . . . . 71,400 lbs	Blst/Disp 38%
Ballast . . . 27,000 lbs	Designer . . Ted Hood
Sail Area	1 Design . . . . yes
Sloop . . . 1625 sq ft	Price $635,000
Auxiliary . . . . std	
Diesel	
Fuel Cap . . . . . 500 gal	

LITTLE HARBOR
CUSTOM YACHTS
Little Harbor Way
Marblehead, MA 01945
(617) 631-8840

Sou'wester 59

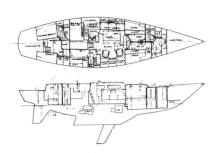

LOD . . . . 58'7"	Hull . . . . FRP
LWL . . . . 44'2"	Deck . . . . FRP
Beam . . . . 15'6"	Spar . . . . Alum
Draft	Headroom . . . . . . 6'
cb up . . . . . . 6'1"	Fr. Water . . . . 450 gal
cb dn . . . . . 12'2"	SA/Disp 15.9
Disp . . . . 62,000 lbs	Disp/LWL 321
Ballast . . . 23,200 lbs	Blst/Disp 37%
Sail Area	Designer
Ketch . . . 1556 sq ft	McCurdy & Rhodes
Mast Ht . . . . . . 72'3"	First Built 1982
Auxiliary . . . . std	No. Built 1
Perkins . . . 115 hp	Price $515,000
Diesel	without sails
Fuel Cap . . . . . 300 gal	

HENRY R. HINCKLEY & CO.
Southwest Harbor, ME 04679
(207) 244-5531

Force 50 Plus 8

No Photo
or
Line Drawing
Available

LOA . . . . 63'10"	Hull . . . . FRP
LOD . . . . 58'10"	Deck . . . . . FRP/Teak
LWL . . . . 48'	Spar . . . . Wood
Beam . . . . 16'	Cockpit . . . . 6'6"
Draft . . . . 6'4"	Headroom . . . . . 6'6"
Disp . . 59,500 lbs	Fr. Water . . . . 600 gal
Ballast . . . 19,500 lbs	SA/Disp 15.5
Sail Area	Disp/LWL 240
Ketch . . . 1475 sq ft	Blst/Disp 33%
Cutter . . . 1475 sq ft	Designer Robert Perry
Mast Ht . . . . . . 69'6"	First Built 1983
Auxiliary . . . . std	1 Design . . . . yes
Perkins . . . 130 hp	Price $165,500
Diesel	with sails
Fuel Cap . . . . 500 gal	

HUDSON BOAT LTD.
3608 Coolheights Dr.
Rancho Palos Verdes, CA 90274
(213) 541-2993

Nautical 60

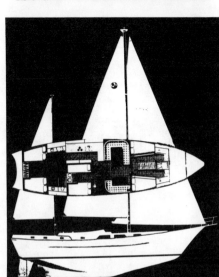

LOD . . . . 59'6"	Hull . . . . FRP
LWL . . . . 43'6"	Deck . . . . FRP
Beam . . . . 15'7"	Spar . . . . Alum
Draft . . . . 5'6"	Fr. Water . . . . 500 gal
Disp . . . . 52,000 lbs	SA/Disp 14.4
Ballast . . . 12,500 lbs	Disp/LWL 282
Sail Area	Blst/Disp 24%
Ketch . . . 1250 sq ft	Designer Roger Warren
Auxiliary . . . . std	Price $352,900
Lehman Ford 120 hp	without sails
Diesel	
Fuel Cap . . . . . 200 gal	

NAUTICAL DEVELOPMENT CORP.
2055 34th Way
Largo, FL 33541
(813) 531-4674

Morgan 60

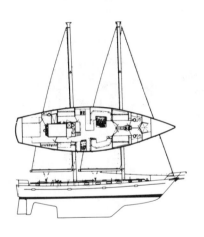

LOD . . . . 59'11"	Hull . . . . FRP
LWL . . . . 50'	Deck . . . . FRP
Beam . . . . . . 15'10"	Spar . . . . Alum
Draft . . . . 5'10"	Fr. Water . . . . 500 gal
Disp . . . . 60,000 lbs	SA/Disp 14.6
Ballast . . . 18,400 lbs	Disp/LWL 214
Sail Area	Blst/Disp 31%
Schooner 1400 sq ft	Price . . . . na
Mast Ht . . . . . 64'	
Auxiliary . . . . std	
Perkins . . . . 130 hp	
Diesel	
Fuel Cap . . . . . 340 gal	

MORGAN YACHT INC.
7200 Bryan Dairy Rd.
Largo, FL 33543
(813) 544-6681

Gulfstar 60

LOD . . . . 60'6"	Hull . . . . . FRP/Balsa
LWL . . . . 48'4"	Deck . . . . . FRP/Balsa
Beam . . . . 16'	Spar . . . . Alum
Draft	Fr. Water . . . . 345 gal
Deep . . . . 9'	SA/Disp 17.2
Shoal cb up . . . . 6'	Blst/Disp 35%
Shoal cb dn . 12'6"	Designer Dick Lazzara
Disp . . . . 55,400 lbs	Price $450,000
Ballast . . . 19,650 lbs	without sails
Sail Area	
Sloop . . . 1566 sq ft	
Ketch . . . 1675 sq ft	
Auxiliary . . . . std	
Perkins . . . . 135 hp	
Diesel	
Fuel Cap . . . . . 230 gal	

GULFSTAR INC.
6101 45th St. N
St. Petersburg, FL 33714
(813) 527-7251

Little Harbor 62

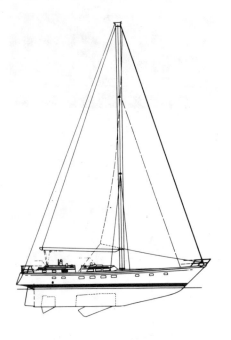

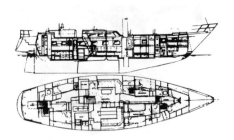

LOD	61'7"	Hull	FRP/Airex
LWL	50'	Deck	FRP/Balsa
Beam	16'4"	Spar	Alum
Draft		Cockpit	11'
cb up	5'11"	Headroom	6'8"
cb dn	13'9"	Fr. Water	800 gal
Disp	88,000 lbs	SA/Disp	15
Ballast	31,000 lbs	Disp/LWL	314
Sail Area		Blst/Disp	35%
Sloop	1850 sq ft	Designer	Ted Hood
Mast Ht	84'	Builder	Lhien Wha
Auxiliary	std	First Built	1980
Perkins	185 hp	No. Built	7
Diesel		1 Design	yes
Fuel Cap	600 gal	Price	$595,000
			without sails

Sailmaster 62

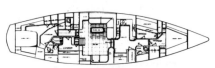

LOD	62'10"	Hull	FRP/Balsa
LWL	52'	Deck	FRP/Balsa
Beam	16'2"	Spar	Alum
Draft	6'7"	Fr. Water	400 gal
Disp	68,500 lbs	Disp/LWL	217
Ballast	20,500 lbs	Blst/Disp	30%
Sail Area		Designer	Dick Lazzara
Sloop	na	Price	$500,000
Auxiliary	std		without sails
Perkins	135 hp		
Diesel			
Fuel Cap	360 gal		

Wellington 63

LOA	68'8"	Hull	FRP/Airex
LOD	63'2"	Deck	FRP/Balsa
LWL	54'	Spar	Alum
Beam	17'	Cockpit	7'6"
Draft		Headroom	6'6"
cb up	5'9"	Fr. Water	600 gal
cb dn	13'	SA/Disp	17.1
Disp	75,000 lbs	Disp/LWL	213
Ballast	21,000 lbs	Blst/Disp	28%
Sail Area		Designer	
Cutter	1900 sq ft		Bill Wellington
Ketch	1675 sq ft	Builder	
Mast Ht			Wellington Boat Co.
Cutter	83'	First Built	1982
Ketch	65'	No. Built	1
Auxiliary	std	Price	$657,000
Caterpillar	210 hp		with sails
Diesel			
Fuel Cap	1000 gal		

Cheoy Lee 63'

Mason 63

Hinckley 64

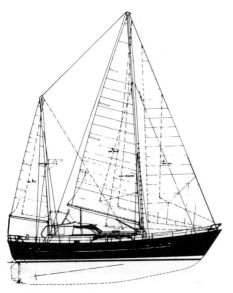

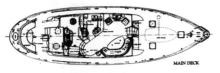

MAIN DECK

CABIN PLAN

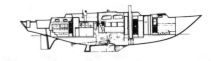

Cheoy Lee 63'

LOD	63'4"	Hull	FRP
LWL	54'2"	Deck	Teak
Beam	18'6"	Spar	Alum
Draft	6'6"	Fr. Water	950 gal
Disp	98,500 lbs	SA/Disp	11
Ballast	31,000 lbs	Disp/LWL	277
Sail Area		Blst/Disp	31%
Ketch	1466 sq ft	Designer Steve Seaton
Auxiliary	std	First Built	1982
Caterpillar	225 hp	No. Built	5
Diesel		Price	$617,000
Fuel Cap	1450 gal		with sails

Mason 63

LOD	63'7"	Hull	FRP
LWL	46'8"	Deck	Teak
Beam	16'6"	Spar	Alum
Draft	7'	Cockpit	13'6"
Disp	64,400 lbs	Headroom	6'2"
Ballast	15,000 lbs	Fr. Water	700 gal
Sail Area		SA/Disp	16.3
Ketch	1632 sq ft	Disp/LWL	283
Mast Ht	70'10"	Blst/Disp	23%
Auxiliary	std	Designer	Al Mason
Detroit		Builder	
Diesel			Ta-Shing Yacht
Fuel Cap	448 gal	First Built	1981
		No. Built	5
		Price	$525,000
			with sails

Hinckley 64

LOD	64'8"	Hull	FRP
LWL	50'	Deck	FRP
Beam	15'11"	Spar	Alum
Draft		SA/Disp	13.6
cb up	5'9"	Disp/LWL	232
cb dn	12'4"	Designer	
Disp	65,000 lbs		Henry R. Hinckley
Ballast	na	First Built	1978
Sail Area		No. Built	4
Ketch	1378 sq ft	Price	$625,000
Auxiliary	std		without sails
2 Lehman	120 hp		
Diesel			

Irwin 65

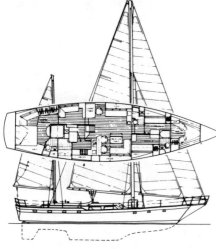

LOA	72'	Hull	FRP/Coremat
LOD	64'8"	Deck	FRP
LWL	54'	Spar	Alum
Beam	17'4"	Fr. Water	900 gal
Draft		SA/Disp	18.1
Shoal	5'9"	Disp/LWL	222
Deep	8'6"	Blst/Disp	29%
Disp	78,500 lbs	Price	$374,950
Ballast	23,000 lbs		with sails
Sail Area			
Ketch	2076 sq ft		
Mast Ht	81'6"		
Auxiliary	std		
Perkins			
Diesel			
Fuel Cap	620 gal		

IRWIN YACHTS
13055 49th St. N.
Clearwater, FL 33520
(813) 577-4581

CT 65

LOA	71'	Hull	FRP
LOD	64'10"	Deck	FRP/Balsa
LWL	50'10"	Spar	Alum
Beam	17'6"	Cockpit	14'
Draft		Headroom	6'6"
Shoal	6'10"	Fr. Water	700 gal
Deep	7'	SA/Disp	15.6
Disp	77,383 lbs	Disp/LWL	263
Ballast	26,000 lbs	Blst/Disp	34%
Sail Area		Designer	
Ketch	1774 sq ft		Robert H. Perry
Mast Ht	72'	Builder	
Auxiliary	std		Ta Chiao, Taiwan
Perkins	200 hp	First Built	1981
Diesel		No. Built	2
Fuel Cap	700 gal	Price	$385,000
			with sails

TA CHIAO USA INC.
17 Lakewood Lane
Seabrook, TX 77586
(713) 474-5967

MacGregor 65

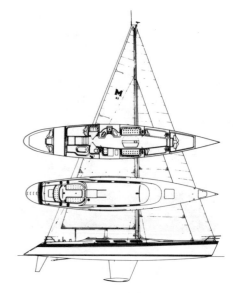

LOD	65'	Hull	FRP
LWL	63'	Deck	FRP
Beam	12'	Spar	alum
Draft	8'6"	Pos Float	yes
Disp	20,000 lbs	Cockpit	12'
Ballast	9000 lbs	Headroom	7'
Sail Area		Fr. Water	100 gal
Cutter	1632 sq ft	SA/Disp	35.4
Mast Ht	76'	Disp/LWL	35
Auxiliary	std	Blst/Disp	45%
Pathfinder	85 hp	Designer	
Diesel			R. N. MacGregor
Fuel Cap	100 gal	First Built	1982
		No. Built	1
		1 Design	yes
		Price	$110,000
			with sails

MacGREGOR
1631 Placentia
Costa Mesa, CA 92627
(714) 642-6830

Lancer 65 Motorsailer

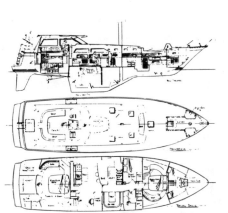

LOD	65'4"	Hull	FRP
LWL	55'	Deck	FRP
Beam	17'11"	Spar	Alum
Draft		Cockpit	15'6"
Shoal	5'8"	Headroom	6'
Deep	6'11"	Fr. Water	500 gal
Disp	55,000 lbs	SA/Disp	21.2
Ballast	14,000 lbs	Disp/LWL	147
Sail Area		Blst/Disp	25%
Sloop	1917 sq ft	Designer	Herb David
Mast Ht	87'	First Built	1982
Auxiliary	std	1 Design	yes
Perkins	130 hp	Price	$472,139
Diesel			with sails
Fuel Cap	1000 gal		

LANCER YACHT CORP.
1939 Deere Ave.
Irvine, CA 92714
(714) 751-7220

Swan 651

LOD	65'6"	Hull	FRP
LWL	55'1"	Deck	FRP
Beam	17'5"	Spar	Alum
Draft		Disp/LWL	200
Deep	11'6"	Blst/Disp	42%
Shoal cb up	7'2"	Designer	German Frers
Shoal cb dn	13'1"	Builder	
Disp	75,000 lbs		Nautor, Finland
Ballast	31,700 lbs	Price	na
Sail Area			
Sloop	na		
Ketch	na		
Auxiliary	std		
Diesel	115 hp		

NAUTOR EAST
55 America's Cup Avenue
Newport, RI 02840
(401) 846-8404

Huntingford 65

LOD	65'7"	Hull	FRP
LWL	55'7"	Deck	FRP
Beam	17'4"	Spar	Alum
Draft	7'5"	SA/Disp	17.1
Disp	75,000 lbs	Disp/LWL	194
Ballast	26,000 lbs	Blst/Disp	35%
Sail Area		Designer	
Ketch	1896 sq ft		Stan Huntingford
Auxiliary	std	First Built	1980
Diesel		No. Built	1
		Kit	$150,000
		Price	$650,000
			with sails

MARKOS YACHTS LTD.
#3: 1210 Pipeline Rd.
Coquitlam, B.C. Canada V3B 4S1
(604) 464-7533

Little Harbor 75

**Luxury Cruising Yachts
and
Bermuda Race Winners!**

The Little Harbor 75 was first to finish in the MHA division of the 1982 Bermuda Race. Ted Hood's 52' luxury cruising yacht was overall winner of the 1968 Bermuda Race. Like all Hood designed yachts, the Little Harbor 75 is a shoal draft, moderate displacement, keel/centerboarder with all the sailing performance, load carrying ability, ease of handling and seakindliness that are the hallmark of Ted's designs. And the cruising amenities and finishing touches that belong in a yacht of this size.

See the Little Harbor 75 or any of the Little Harbor Yachts from 38 to 100 feet. Let us prove to you that luxury cruising can be fast, safe and easy.

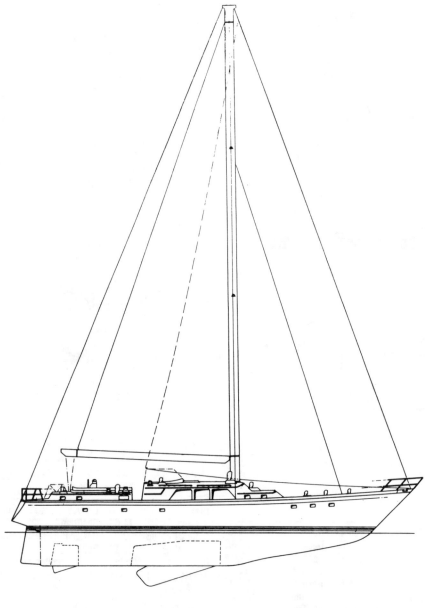

LOD .... 74'4"	Hull ...... FRP/Airex
LWL .... 64'	Deck ..... FRP/Balsa
Beam .... 18'5"	Spar .... Alum
Draft	Cockpit .... 11'
cb up .... 6'6"	Headroom ..... 6'8"
cb dn .... 13'	Fr. Water .... 700 gal
Disp .... 127,500 lbs	SA/Disp 16
Ballast ... 56,000 lbs	Disp/LWL 217
Sail Area	Blst/Disp 44%
Sloop ... 2540 sq ft	Designer .. Ted Hood
Mast Ht .... 96'6"	Builder ... Lhien Wha
Auxiliary .... std	First Built 1980
Perkins .... 185 hp	No. Built 4
Diesel	1 Design .... yes
Fuel Cap ..... 750 gal	Price $1,100,000
	without sails

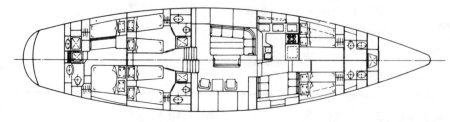

LITTLE HARBOR
CUSTOM YACHTS
Little Harbor Way
Marblehead, MA 01945
(617) 631-8840

Swan 76

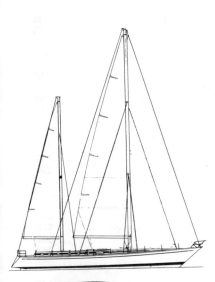

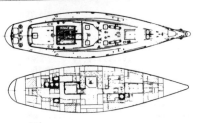

LOD	76'4"	Hull	FRP
LWL	61'4"	Deck	FRP
Beam	19'	Spar	Alum
Draft		Disp/LWL	190
Deep	12'	Blst/Disp	24%
Shoal cb up	7'6"	Designer	
Shoal cb dn	15'6"		Sparkman & Stephens
Disp	98,700 lbs	Builder	
Ballast			Nautor, Finland
Deep	24,000 lbs	Price	na
Shoal	28,000 lbs		
Sail Area			
Ketch	na		
Auxiliary	std		
Mercedes	200 hp		
Diesel			

NAUTOR EAST
55 America's Cup Avenue
Newport, RI 02840
(401) 846-8404

Baltic 80

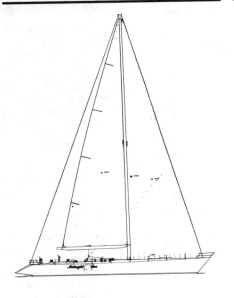

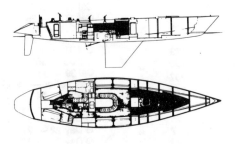

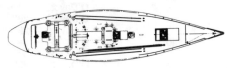

LOD	79'8"	Hull	FRP/Balsa
LWL	69'4"	Deck	FRP/Balsa
Beam	19'	Spar	Alum
Draft	12'7"	Fr. Water	140 gal
Disp	75,178 lbs	Disp/LWL	100
Ballast	48,500 lbs	Blst/Disp	65%
Sail Area		Designer	
Sloop	na		Doug Peterson
Auxiliary	std	Builder	
Perkins	185 hp		Baltic Finland
Diesel		Price	na
Fuel Cap	140 gal		

BALTIC YACHTS NORTH AMERICA
Box 832
Tucker's Wharf
Marblehead, MA 01945
(617) 639-0590

Little Harbor 100

LOD	99'9"	Hull	FRP/Airex
LWL	82'	Deck	FRP/Balsa
Beam	26'5"	Spar	Alum
Draft		Fr. Water	1200 gal
cb up	7'9"	SA/Disp	15.5
cb dn	na	Disp/LWL	256
Disp	317,000 lbs	Blst/Disp	36%
Ballast	115,000 lbs	Designer	Ted Hood
Sail Area		1 Design	yes
Sloop	4500 sq ft	Price	na
Auxiliary	std		
Diesel			
Fuel Cap	1000 gal		

LITTLE HARBOR CUSTOM YACHTS
Little Harbor Way
Marblehead, MA 01945
(617) 631-8840

MANUFACTURER INDEX

MANUFACTURER INDEX

MANUFACTURER INDEX

MANUFACTURER INDEX

MANUFACTURER INDEX

MANUFACTURER INDEX

MANUFACTURER INDEX

MANUFACTURER INDEX

BOAT INDEX

BOAT INDEX

BOAT INDEX

BOAT INDEX

BOAT INDEX

BOAT INDEX

BOAT INDEX

BOAT INDEX

To obtain additional copies of the Sailboat Buyers' Guide, contact your local bookstore, or order from:

Sea Shore Publications
211 S. Sea Shore Avenue
Long Beach, MS 39560
(601) 864-4573

Send $12.95 per copy or provide Master Card or Visa card number and expiration date.